IGMacdonald

March 1960

ALGEBRAIC CURVES

ALGEBRAIC CURVES

BY

J. G. SEMPLE

PROFESSOR OF MATHEMATICS
KING'S COLLEGE, LONDON

AND

G. T. KNEEBONE

LECTURER IN MATHEMATICS
BEDFORD COLLEGE, LONDON

OXFORD
AT THE CLARENDON PRESS
1959

Oxford University Press, Amen House, London E.C.4

GLASGOW NEW YORK TORONTO MELBOURNE WELLINGTON
BOMBAY CALCUTTA MADRAS KARACHI KUALA LUMPUR
CAPE TOWN IBADAN NAIROBI ACCRA

PRINTED IN GREAT BRITAIN

PREFACE

EVERY author of a book on algebraic geometry must be conscious that this subject is one to which mathematicians have been powerfully drawn over a very long period of time; and a number of reasons for this enduring influence of algebraic geometry come readily to mind. Most obviously, the subject makes a strong appeal to the imagination in that it not only illuminates properties of geometrical figures that we are able to draw and visualize but also extends the range of geometrical thinking far beyond the bounds of intuition; and one can think about it and understand it in a much deeper sense than that of granting formal assent to its conclusions. Algebraic geometry, moreover, has shown itself again and again to be immensely fertile, giving rise to profound and far-reaching investigations of the most general character, while at the same time suggesting innumerable particular problems and leading to a wealth of special results of great elegance and attractiveness. One of its chief virtues indeed, for many who study it, is that so many of its general theorems are not merely stepping-stones to other general theorems but have also a wide field of application to special problems that are of interest in themselves. It is with such considerations very much in mind that we have written the present volume on algebraic curves, hoping that it will serve as an introduction, no less in spirit than in substance, to the general study of algebraic geometry.

Our book is designed specifically to provide its readers (especially university students in their final undergraduate or early postgraduate years) with a rigorous and reasonably self-contained account of the basic theory of algebraic curves; and in order to emphasize the motivation and the geometrical significance of the formal development, we have made full use throughout of the traditional language of geometry. For the sake of the increased unity and simplicity thereby achieved, we have chosen to develop the formal theory by purely algebraic means, in conformity with the general mathematical tendency of the present time; but the reader is also made aware of the alternative older approach by way of the theory of algebraic functions of a complex variable and their Riemann surfaces, and he will be able to supplement our account by referring to books such as those of Hensel and Landsberg and Severi-Löffler. To illustrate the wide range of applications and special developments that arise from the general theory, and also to help the reader to understand this theory fully, we have appended to each chapter a copious set of notes and exercises, and we regard these as being in many ways quite as important as the main text itself.

We have not presupposed any very extensive knowledge of algebra on the part of the reader, but we have nevertheless tried to avoid too frequent derivation of algebraic results from first principles. Our first concern has been not to obscure the main development of the geometrical argument by interpolation of detailed proofs of purely algebraic results that have to be used but which may not be familiar to the reader. All the necessary algebraic references have accordingly been gathered together in Appendix A at the end of the book, and reference is made in the text to the appropriate sections of this appendix. In Appendix B we have given a detailed constructive proof of the fundamental Theorem of Puiseux, since this theorem, the main application of which is to algebraic geometry, is not discussed in the standard textbooks of algebra.

As regards the scope of our book, we have carried the main development of the theory of algebraic curves as far as the Riemann–Roch Theorem; and we have also included two chapters on rather more special topics. Chapter IX, 'The Coordinates of a Curve', deals with Cayley forms, and is intended as an introduction to the general theory of Cayley forms of varieties and the concept of an algebraic system of varieties. Chapter XI, 'Local Geometry in S_2', is concerned with the basic theory, so peculiarly geometrical, of infinitely near points in the plane.

Finally, in acknowledging our indebtedness to other mathematicians we must mention first of all three particular books from which we have drawn much inspiration. First among these is van der Waerden's *Einführung in die algebraische Geometrie*, which has shown the way to a basic redevelopment of the foundations of algebraic geometry, and to which we ourselves are indebted in general and in detail at places too numerous to specify. Secondly, we have profited much from the pioneering work of R. J. Walker, whose *Algebraic Curves* was the first textbook on this particular subject in which the modern algebraic point of view was consistently adhered to. Our borrowings from Walker are very numerous, as the reader will see, but we are most of all indebted to him for the methods that we have used in proving what we have now called the Unirational Transformation Theorem (p. 164) and for the constructive proof of Puiseux's Theorem (p. 340). Finally, we must acknowledge a substantial debt to Hodge and Pedoe's masterly *Methods of Algebraic Geometry*, in particular for the account in volume I of the basic algebra, a most valuable complement to van der Waerden's earlier *Moderne Algebra*.

Our sincere thanks are due to a number of geometers who have given us generous assistance. Dr. D. B. Scott (King's College, London) has read almost all the text in typescript and has offered valuable criticisms and suggestions. Dr. D. Kirby (Leeds) has made a substantial contribution to Chapter XI and has checked most of the details of that chapter. Dr. J. E. Reeve (Reading) has made invaluable contributions to the Notes and Exercises, particularly to those appended to Chapters II, VIII, IX, and XI. Dr. A. J. Tyrrell (King's College, London) has read through all the proofs, corrected many errors of detail in the Notes and Exercises and elsewhere, and shared the work of preparing the index.

Finally, we would like to express our most sincere thanks to the Clarendon Press, both for the very high standard of their printing and also for the patience and courtesy of their officers.

J. G. S.

G. T. K.

March 1959

CONTENTS

CONTENTS   xiii

CHAPTER I

PLANE ALGEBRAIC CURVES

1. Preliminary

GEOMETRY is the study of spatial relations, and in its most elementary form it is conceived as a systematic investigation into the properties of figures subsisting in the space familiar to common sense. As mathematical insight grows, however, the 'space' that constitutes the geometer's ultimate object of study is seen to be an ideal object—an intellectual construct that reveals itself to be essentially different from any possible object of naïve intuition. Nevertheless, even the most abstract geometrical thinking must retain some link, however attenuated, with spatial intuition, for otherwise it would be misleading to call it geometrical; and it is an historical fact that, throughout the long development of mathematics, geometers have again and again arisen who have given a fresh impulse to formal mathematics by going back once more for inspiration to the primitive geometrical sense. We may think, in this connexion, of Riemann, Grassmann, Klein, and Hilbert. A particularly instructive example of a branch of geometry which, although now completely freed from dependence on intuition, still remains properly geometrical is abstract projective geometry. In this subject we develop, in the form of a strict deductive theory, the properties of a certain axiomatically defined system $S_r(K)$—namely, projective space of r dimensions over a ground field K—and in so doing we build up a logical structure which we value primarily for its aesthetic qualities. But this same system, abstract though it is, has a bearing on the much more concrete geometry of figures which can be exhibited with pencil and paper, since the formal structure that it analyses may possibly inhere in a comparatively intuitive body of knowledge. So it comes about, for instance, that knowledge of the typical properties of quadric primals and rational normal curves in S_r increases our understanding of the properties of the curves known to elementary geometry as conic sections.

In this book, which comprises an introductory account of the properties of algebraic curves, we shall be concerned exclusively with what has come to be known as algebraic geometry. In

B

studying this subject, it is important to understand in what sense
it is algebraic and in what sense geometrical. This will become
clearer as the construction of the system proceeds, but a few
remarks by way of introduction may serve to fix the initial orientation of outlook.

The traditional view of algebraic geometry is that it is the
geometrical theory of algebraic equations, and this description goes
at least some way towards explaining the nature of the subject. Our
fundamental concern in algebraic geometry is indeed with properties of polynomials in a set of r variables $X_1,..., X_r$ (or forms in $r+1$
variables $x_0, x_1,..., x_r$) over a ground field K. But our inquiries are
inspired throughout—and, as we feel it, enlightened—by the use
of a suggestive geometrical language and nomenclature, and by the
geometrical way of thinking which this language and nomenclature
encourage. Every result in algebraic geometry must be expressible,
if we so desire, as a statement of a theorem in a special domain of
pure algebra, but its main interest, and the motivation for its
discovery, will often derive almost exclusively from geometrical
ideas and from the simplicity of its description in geometrical
terms.

It will be appreciated that, for the kind of development which we
propose, the choice of the ground field K is of very great importance.
The classical choices, that of the complex numbers and, to a less
extent, that of the real numbers, are the ones to which, above all
others, the geometrical approach comes most naturally and
suggestively. Indeed, in so far as the same general plan is followed
with other choices of ground field, the weaker inspiration of the
geometrical outlook tends to come mostly by analogy with these
classical cases. We shall confine ourselves, therefore, exclusively to
the main case, adopting the following convention.

CONVENTION. *In the absence of explicit statement to the contrary,
it will always be understood that the ground field K is the field of all
complex numbers.*

Adoption of this convention is a less severe limitation than it may
at first sight appear to be. The crucial characteristics of the field
of complex numbers are that it is (i) algebraically closed and (ii) of
characteristic zero; and since we very seldom use any properties of
the ground field beyond these two, almost the whole of our theory
will be valid for any ground field with the two properties in question.

2. The projective plane $S_2(K)$

We now turn to the consideration of geometry in the projective plane $S_2(K)$ over the ground field of the complex numbers.

S_2 possesses infinitely many allowable coordinate representations $\mathscr{R}$, and in any one of these every point can be represented by three homogeneous coordinates ξ_0, ξ_1, ξ_2. These coordinates can be any elements of K (not all zero) and any two proportional triads represent the same point. It will be convenient, as a rule, to reserve the notation (x_0, x_1, x_2) for the coordinate-triad either of an undetermined point or of an indeterminate point,† and similarly to use (u_0, u_1, u_2) for the coordinate-triad of an undetermined or indeterminate line.

We shall frequently adopt the device of representing a triad of homogeneous coordinates (or an $(r+1)$-ad when we are concerned with points in S_r) by a single symbol, using the bold-face letter corresponding to the ordinary letter used for the separate coordinates. Thus, for example, $\boldsymbol{\xi}$ will denote (ξ_0, ξ_1, ξ_2), and the symbol $f(x_0, x_1, x_2)$ for a form will often be abbreviated to $f(\mathbf{x})$. On the few occasions when we require to reserve bold-face letters more specifically for matrices, as in representing a linear transformation by a matrix equation, this will be made clear in the text.

If $\mathscr{R}$ is any allowable representation of $S_2(K)$, the transformation from $\mathscr{R}$ to any other allowable representation $\bar{\mathscr{R}}$ may be written as a matrix equation

$$\bar{\mathbf{x}} = \mathbf{A}\mathbf{x},$$

in which the square matrix $\mathbf{A}$ is non-singular; and conversely, every such equation yields an allowable representation $\bar{\mathscr{R}}$. A property of a set of points in S_2 is said to be *projective* if it can be expressed algebraically in a manner that is invariant with respect to transformation from one allowable representation to another.

With each allowable representation $\mathscr{R}$ we shall associate an *allowable affine representation* $\mathscr{R}_A$ of S_2. This is the representation

---

† In elementary geometry one thinks in terms of fixed and variable points. At the present level of rigour we need to replace the vague notion of a variable number by the more precise algebraic concept of an *indeterminate*, i.e. a mere symbol, about which nothing is postulated beyond the fact that it can be manipulated in accordance with the formal rules which apply to the elements of the field K. Instead of variable points, therefore, we shall now have 'indeterminate points', represented by triads of indeterminates (x_0, x_1, x_2). These are not points of $S_2(K)$, but they become such points whenever particular elements of K, not all zero, are substituted for the three indeterminates. They may be treated as ideal points (or point-schemata) adjoined to the space $S_2(K)$, or as actual points of an extended space $S_2(K(x_0, x_1, x_2))$. This will be made clearer in Chapter III, § 1.

of all those points of S_2 which do not lie on the line $x_0 = 0$ by pairs of non-homogeneous coordinates (X, Y) given by $X = x_1/x_0$, $Y = x_2/x_0$. The point with affine coordinates $(0, 0)$ will be called the *origin* and the lines $x_0 = 0$, $x_1 = 0$, and $x_2 = 0$ will be called the *line at infinity*, the *Y-axis*, and the *X-axis* respectively for the system $\mathscr{R}_A$, all these familiar terms now being used in a purely formal sense. The 'points at infinity' on the X-axis and the Y-axis will be denoted by X_∞ and Y_∞.

A polynomial $F(X, Y)$ in the indeterminates X and Y, with coefficients in K, will be called a *K-polynomial* in X and Y; and a homogeneous polynomial $f(x_0, x_1, x_2)$ with coefficients in K will be called a *K-form*.

Any point (ξ_0, ξ_1, ξ_2) of S_2 which is such that $f(\xi_0, \xi_1, \xi_2) = 0$ will be called a *zero* of the form $f(x_0, x_1, x_2)$; and similarly any point with affine coordinates (Ξ, H) such that $F(\Xi, H) = 0$ will be called a zero of the polynomial $F(X, Y)$.

We shall use the customary notation of square brackets for ring-adjunction and round brackets for field-adjunction. Thus $K[z_1, ..., z_r]$ will denote the ring of all K-polynomials in a set of r indeterminates $z_1, ..., z_r$, while $K(z_1, ..., z_r)$ will denote the set of all rational functions over K (i.e. quotients of K-polynomials) in $z_1, ..., z_r$.

3. Algebraic curves in S_2

We find it convenient, before defining plane algebraic curves in general, to define first the basic concept of irreducible plane algebraic curve.

DEFINITION. An *irreducible algebraic curve* C in S_2 is the aggregate of all the points of S_2 whose coordinate triads, in some fixed allowable representation $\mathscr{R}$, are zeros of some particular irreducible K-form $f(x_0, x_1, x_2)$ of positive degree. The degree of $f(x_0, x_1, x_2)$ is called the *order* of C.

EXERCISE. Establish the legitimacy of the above definition by showing that, if a given set of points forms the aggregate of zeros of an irreducible K-form in one representation $\mathscr{R}$, then it does so in every representation, and that all the K-forms that correspond in this way to the same set of points are of the same degree.

We shall tacitly assume, wherever appropriate, that a definite representation $\mathscr{R}$ of S_2 has been chosen, and that all the discussion is in terms of this frame of reference.

THEOREM 1. *If C is an irreducible algebraic curve, there are infinitely many points of S_2 which belong to C and also infinitely many points of S_2 which do not belong to C.*

Proof. C may be represented by an irreducible equation $f(x_0, x_1, x_2) = 0$, and we may suppose for definiteness that x_0 actually occurs in the form $f(\mathbf{x}) \equiv f(x_0, x_1, x_2)$. Then we have

$$f(\mathbf{x}) = a_0(x_1, x_2)x_0^r + \dots + a_r(x_1, x_2), \quad r \geqslant 1, \quad a_0(x_1, x_2) \neq 0;$$

and if we give to x_1 and x_2 arbitrary values x_1' and x_2' such that $a_0(x_1', x_2') \neq 0$, we can determine at least one value x_0' of x_0 such that $f(\mathbf{x}') = 0$ and infinitely many values such that $f(\mathbf{x}') \neq 0$.

THEOREM 2. *If C is an irreducible algebraic curve, with irreducible equation $f(x_0, x_1, x_2) = 0$, and $g(x_0, x_1, x_2)$ is any K-form which takes the value zero at infinitely many points of C, then $f(x_0, x_1, x_2)$ is a factor of $g(x_0, x_1, x_2)$ in the ring $K[x_0, x_1, x_2]$.*

Proof. If we change from the original representation $\mathscr{R}$ to a different representation $\bar{\mathscr{R}}$ of S_2 by expressing x_0, x_1, x_2 in terms of three linearly independent linear combinations $\bar{x}_0, \bar{x}_1, \bar{x}_2$ of themselves, the equation of C is transformed into an equation $\bar{f}(\bar{\mathbf{x}}) = 0$, where $\bar{f}(\bar{\mathbf{x}})$ is again irreducible, and the form $g(\mathbf{x})$ goes over into a form $\bar{g}(\bar{\mathbf{x}})$ which takes the value zero at infinitely many points of C, given in terms of the representation $\bar{\mathscr{R}}$. Plainly, also, $f(\mathbf{x})$ is a factor of $g(\mathbf{x})$ in $K[x_0, x_1, x_2]$ if and only if $\bar{f}(\bar{\mathbf{x}})$ is a factor of $\bar{g}(\bar{\mathbf{x}})$ in $K[\bar{x}_0, \bar{x}_1, \bar{x}_2]$. It follows that we may use any representation that we please in proving the theorem; and we shall accordingly suppose the representation $\mathscr{R}$ to be selected in such a way that neither of the reference points $X_1 = (0, 1, 0)$ and $X_2 = (0, 0, 1)$ is a zero of $f(\mathbf{x})$ or of $g(\mathbf{x})$. Such a choice of $\mathscr{R}$ may easily be shown to be possible by the kind of argument already used in proving Theorem 1.

The effect of the restriction on $\mathscr{R}$ is that both x_1 and x_2 actually occur to their maximum possible degrees in $f(\mathbf{x})$ and $g(\mathbf{x})$; and this means that we can form the x_1-resultant $R_1(x_0, x_2)$ and the x_2-resultant $R_2(x_0, x_1)$ of these polynomials. $R_1(x_0, x_2)$ is then identically zero if and only if $f(\mathbf{x})$ and $g(\mathbf{x})$ have a common factor involving x_1, and therefore, by the irreducibility of $f(\mathbf{x})$, if and only if $f(\mathbf{x})$ is a factor of $g(\mathbf{x})$ in $K[x_0, x_1, x_2]$.

Suppose $f(\mathbf{x})$ is not a factor of $g(\mathbf{x})$. Then, by what we have proved, $R_1(x_0, x_2)$ is not identically zero, nor, for similar reasons, is

$R_2(x_0, x_1)$. Any common zero of $f(\mathbf{x})$ and $g(\mathbf{x})$ must satisfy the two equations
$$R_1(x_0, x_2) = 0, \quad R_2(x_0, x_1) = 0,$$
which represent finite sets of lines issuing from X_1 and X_2 respectively. Since, by hypothesis, there are infinitely many such common zeros, while two distinct lines meet in only one point, it follows that the two sets of lines have a common member $X_1 X_2$, i.e. $x_0 = 0$. But then $f(\mathbf{x})$ and $g(\mathbf{x})$ both have x_0 as a factor, in contradiction to the hypothesis that neither X_1 nor X_2 is a zero of either form. It follows that $f(\mathbf{x})$ must be a factor of $g(\mathbf{x})$; and the theorem is proved.

COROLLARY. *If two irreducible equations $f(x_0, x_1, x_2) = 0$ and $g(x_0, x_1, x_2) = 0$ represent the same irreducible curve, then the forms $f(x_0, x_1, x_2)$ and $g(x_0, x_1, x_2)$ are identical to within a factor in K.*

Having established the above fundamental theorem on irreducible curves, we now extend the definition of algebraic curve to the general case.

DEFINITION. An *algebraic curve* C of S_2 is any finite set $(C_1, ..., C_s)$ of irreducible algebraic curves of S_2, each curve C_i of the set having associated with it a positive integer r_i, called its *multiplicity* as a component of C. If C_i is given by an irreducible equation $f_i(x_0, x_1, x_2) = 0$, then the *equation*† of C is

$$f(x_0, x_1, x_2) \equiv \prod_{i=1}^{s} (f_i(x_0, x_1, x_2))^{r_i} = 0.$$

Every homogeneous equation $f(x_0, x_1, x_2) = 0$ determines a well-defined algebraic curve, for the polynomial $f(x_0, x_1, x_2)$ has a unique resolution into irreducible factors, and these factors are of necessity also homogeneous. The truth of the last assertion may be inferred from the fact that from any factorization

$$f(x_0, x_1, x_2) = \prod_{i=1}^{s} (f_i(x_0, x_1, x_2))^{r_i}$$

we can obtain an identity

$$t^n \prod_{i=1}^{s} (f_i(x_0, x_1, x_2))^{r_i} = \prod_{i=1}^{s} (f_i(tx_0, tx_1, tx_2))^{r_i}.$$

Since factorization in $K[x_0, x_1, x_2][t]$ is unique, we may conclude from this last identity that each $f_i(tx_0, tx_1, tx_2)$ is of the form $t^{\lambda_i} f_i(x_0, x_1, x_2)$, i.e. that the polynomials $f_i(x_0, x_1, x_2)$ are forms.

† Strictly speaking, 'an equation of C', for there is an arbitrary factor in K; but we do not wish to be pedantic in such matters.

The outcome of the definitions that we have laid down is that (in any allowable representation $\mathscr{R}$ of S_2) every homogeneous equation $f(x_0, x_1, x_2) = 0$, of positive degree, defines a unique algebraic curve C, and every algebraic curve is definable in this way. From now on, except where the contrary is expressly stated, all the curves that we consider will be algebraic, and the adjective 'algebraic' will as a rule be omitted from all but the most formal statements.

The *order* of a curve C is the degree n of the equation of C (a projective invariant) and it is expressed in terms of the orders of the components of C by the equation $n = \sum_{i=1}^{s} r_i n_i$.

A point P of S_2 is said to be a point of C if it satisfies the equation of C, and this is the case if and only if P is a point of some component of C. Since no account is taken, in the theory of sets, of multiplicity of occurrence, the set of points on a curve which is not required to be irreducible is not by itself sufficient to characterize the curve.

THEOREM 3. *If all (or even if some infinite set) of the points of an irreducible curve C_0 lie on (i.e. are points of) a curve C, then C_0 is a component of C.*

Proof. Theorem 3 is an immediate consequence of Theorem 2.

A point which belongs to each of two curves C and C' will be called a *common point* or an *intersection* of C and C'. It follows from Theorem 3 that any two curves which have more than a finite number of intersections have a common component.

4.1. Intersections of a curve with a line

Let C be a curve of order n, with equation $f(\mathbf{x}) \equiv f(x_0, x_1, x_2) = 0$, and let L be a given line. We can represent the line parametrically by taking two fixed points $\mathbf{a}$ and $\mathbf{b}$ on it as base points, so that a general point P on it is given by $\lambda\mathbf{a} + \mu\mathbf{b}$, i.e. by the triad of co-ordinates $(\lambda a_0 + \mu b_0, \lambda a_1 + \mu b_1, \lambda a_2 + \mu b_2)$. We can take (λ, μ) as a pair of homogeneous parameters for P, which we may then denote by $P_{\lambda,\mu}$, as a point of the range with L as axis. The intersections of L and C are those points $P_{\lambda,\mu}$ for which the parameters satisfy the equation

$$J(\lambda, \mu) \equiv f(\lambda a_0 + \mu b_0, \lambda a_1 + \mu b_1, \lambda a_2 + \mu b_2) = 0. \qquad (1)$$

If this equation is identically satisfied, then every point of L lies on C, and therefore, by Theorem 3, L is a component of C. If the equation is not identically satisfied, it is a homogeneous equation, of degree n, in λ and μ; and this fact gives us at once a geometrical result:

If C is a curve of order n, any line L which is not a component of C intersects C in at most n points.

If $\bar{\lambda}$ and $\bar{\mu}$ are elements of K, not both zero, such that $(\bar{\lambda}, \bar{\mu})$ is an r-fold root of equation (1), i.e. if $\lambda\bar{\mu} - \mu\bar{\lambda}$ is a factor of $J(\lambda, \mu)$ of multiplicity r, we shall say that the point $P_{\bar{\lambda}, \bar{\mu}}$ is an *r-fold intersection*, or an *intersection of multiplicity r*, of L with C. We shall also on occasion find it convenient to say, somewhat illogically, that *L has r coincident intersections with C at the point $P_{\bar{\lambda}, \bar{\mu}}$*, or that *L meets C r times* at this point, all such forms of statement being understood as meaning precisely the same thing. In view of these explanations, the fact that equation (1) is of degree n in λ and μ may be expressed in the following geometrical form.

THEOREM 4. *Provided only that intersections are counted to their correct multiplicities, any curve of order n is met by any line which is not a component of it in n points.*

The simplicity of Theorem 4 results, of course, from the fact that we have, in this particular case, a very simple and direct interpretation of multiplicity of intersection. The general problem of defining a corresponding characteristic for the points of intersection of any two curves whatever in S_2 proves to be much more difficult, and it ranks as one of the main problems that have to be considered in the theory of plane algebraic curves. For its complete and satisfactory solution methods are required, as we shall see in later chapters, that are very much more powerful than the elementary methods we are at present using and indeed are revolutionary by comparison with them.

Reverting to our discussion of the intersections of the curve C with the line L, we now expand equation (1) in the form

$$J(\lambda, \mu) \equiv A_0\lambda^n + A_1\lambda^{n-1}\mu + \dots + A_n\mu^n = 0, \qquad (2)$$

where, in particular, $A_0 = f(a_0, a_1, a_2)$ and A_1 is the expression

$$b_0\frac{\partial f(\mathbf{a})}{\partial a_0} + b_1\frac{\partial f(\mathbf{a})}{\partial a_1} + b_2\frac{\partial f(\mathbf{a})}{\partial a_2}, \qquad (3)$$

derived from A_0 by a process of polarization.

The point $\mathbf{a}$ is an intersection of L with C if equation (2) in (λ, μ) has $(1, 0)$ as a root, i.e. if $f(\mathbf{a}) = 0$; and, if this first condition is satisfied, the further condition that L should meet C in at least two coincident points at **a** is $A_1 = 0$. There are then two cases to be distinguished.

(i) If the coefficients of b_0, b_1, b_2 in (3) are not all zero, then **b** must lie on the line with equation

$$x_0 \frac{\partial f(\mathbf{a})}{\partial a_0} + x_1 \frac{\partial f(\mathbf{a})}{\partial a_1} + x_2 \frac{\partial f(\mathbf{a})}{\partial a_2} = 0. \tag{4}$$

This line passes through the point **a**, by virtue of Euler's Theorem on homogeneous functions, and it is evidently the only line through **a** which has at least two coincident intersections with C there. We say in this case that the point **a** is a *simple point* of C, and that the line with equation (4) is the *tangent line* (or tangent) to C at **a**. The line is also said to *touch* C at **a**.

(ii) If $$\frac{\partial f(\mathbf{a})}{\partial a_0} = \frac{\partial f(\mathbf{a})}{\partial a_1} = \frac{\partial f(\mathbf{a})}{\partial a_2} = 0,$$

then every line through **a** has at least two coincident intersections with C at **a**, if it is not actually a component of C. We say in this case that **a** is a *singular point* of C.

DEFINITION. A point P of a curve C is said to be a *singular* (or *multiple*) *point* of C if every line through P has at least two coincident intersections with C there.

THEOREM 5. *The singular points of the curve C with equation $f(x_0, x_1, x_2) = 0$, if there are any, are the common zeros of the three derivatives $\partial f(\mathbf{x})/\partial x_i$ $(i = 0, 1, 2)$. A point P of C is simple for C if and only if C has a unique tangent line at P, i.e. a unique line which meets it more than once at P.*

Proof. The essential steps in the proof have already been given. It follows from Euler's Theorem that any common zero of the three partial derivatives of $f(\mathbf{x})$ is a point of C.

COROLLARY. *Every point of a multiple component of a curve C is a singular point of C.*

THEOREM 6. *If C is a curve of order n with no multiple component, and P is any point of S_2 which does not lie on C, then all but possibly a finite number of the lines through P meet C in n distinct points.*

Proof. Let us choose a representation $\mathscr{R}$ of S_2 in such a way that the line $x_0 = 0$ is not a component of C and P is the point $(0, 0, 1)$.

Since P is not on C, we may assume that the coefficient of x_2^n in the equation $f(x_0, x_1, x_2) = 0$ of C is unity. If, in the affine representation $\mathscr{R}_A$ associated with $\mathscr{R}$, the equation of C is

$$F(X, Y) \equiv f(1, X, Y) = 0,$$

the irreducible factors of $f(x_0, x_1, x_2)$ correspond exactly to the irreducible factors of $F(X, Y)$; and all the zeros of $f(x_0, x_1, x_2)$, with the exception of at most n, lying on the line $x_0 = 0$, correspond to zeros of $F(X, Y)$.

Every line L through P, other than the line $x_0 = 0$, has an affine equation of the form $X = X_0$; and the points in which L meets C are those points for which X has the value X_0 and Y has a value which satisfies the equation $F(X_0, Y) = 0$. But this equation is of the form

$$Y^n + A_1(X_0)Y^{n-1} + \ldots + A_n(X_0) = 0 \qquad (A_i(X) \in K[X]),$$

and it has n distinct roots except when its discriminant $D(X_0)$ is zero. Now the Y-resultant $D(X)$ of $F(X, Y)$ and $F_Y(X, Y)$ is only (identically) zero if F and F_Y have a common factor in $K[X][Y]$, and F consequently has a repeated factor in $K[X][Y]$. This is certainly not the case, since C has no multiple component; and the equation $D(X) = 0$ accordingly determines a finite set of numbers X_0 such that $D(X_0) = 0$. For every value of X_0 which does not belong to this finite set, the line $X = X_0$ meets C in n distinct points, and Theorem 6 is thus established.

COROLLARY. *The singular points, if there are any, of a curve C with no multiple component, are finite in number.*

EXERCISES. (i) Show that, in terms of affine coordinates (X, Y), a (finite) point is singular for the curve $F(X, Y) = 0$ if and only if it satisfies the equations $F(X, Y) = F_X(X, Y) = F_Y(X, Y) = 0$. Show also that the equation of the tangent to the curve at a (finite) simple point (X_0, Y_0) is

$$(X - X_0)F_X(X_0, Y_0) + (Y - Y_0)F_Y(X_0, Y_0) = 0.$$

(ii) Find a value of λ such that the cubic curve $(x_0 + x_1 + x_2)^3 = \lambda x_0 x_1 x_2$ has one singular point; and, with this value of λ, find the singular point.

4.2. Multiple points of a curve

We now return to our earlier equation (2) (p. 8)

$$J(\lambda, \mu) \equiv A_0 \lambda^n + A_1 \lambda^{n-1}\mu + \ldots + A_n \mu^n = 0,$$

the roots $(\lambda_1, \mu_1), \ldots, (\lambda_n, \mu_n)$ of which determine the n intersections, distinct or coincident, of the curve C with the line L defined by two points $\mathbf{a}$ and $\mathbf{b}$. The values of the coefficients A_i in (2) are given by

$$A_i = \frac{1}{i!}\left(b_0\frac{\partial}{\partial a_0}+b_1\frac{\partial}{\partial a_1}+b_2\frac{\partial}{\partial a_2}\right)^i f(a_0, a_1, a_2)$$

$$= \frac{1}{(n-i)!}\left(a_0\frac{\partial}{\partial b_0}+a_1\frac{\partial}{\partial b_1}+a_2\frac{\partial}{\partial b_2}\right)^{n-i} f(b_0, b_1, b_2). \qquad (5)$$

Let the point $\mathbf{a}$ be fixed. Then the coefficient A_i is zero for all choices of $\mathbf{b}$ if and only if all the derivatives of $f(\mathbf{x})$ of the ith order are zero at $\mathbf{a}$. But this implies, by Euler's Theorem, that all the derivatives of $f(\mathbf{x})$ of order less than i, and also $f(\mathbf{x})$ itself, are zero at $\mathbf{a}$. In other words, if A_i is zero for all positions of $\mathbf{b}$, then so also are $A_{i-1}, ..., A_0$. We see therefore that, in the case in question, $\mathbf{a}$ is a point of C, and every line through $\mathbf{a}$ has at least $i+1$ coincident intersections with C at $\mathbf{a}$. If, in addition, there is at least one line through $\mathbf{a}$ that has precisely $i+1$ coincident intersections with C there, we say that $\mathbf{a}$ is an $(i+1)$-*fold point* or a *point of multiplicity* $i+1$ of C. We can accordingly formulate the following theorem, already established by the preceding analysis.

THEOREM 7. *If C is a curve of order n, represented by an equation $f(x_0, x_1, x_2) = 0$, then a point $\mathbf{a}$ is an s-fold point of C ($s = 2, 3, ..., n$) if and only if all the derivatives of $f(x_0, x_1, x_2)$ of order $s-1$ are zero at $\mathbf{a}$, while one at least of the derivatives of order s is not zero at $\mathbf{a}$.*

If $\mathbf{a}$ is an s-fold point of C, so that $A_0 = A_1 = ... = A_{s-1} = 0$ for all $\mathbf{b}$, while $A_s \neq 0$ for some $\mathbf{b}$, we see that the points $\mathbf{b}$ whose joins to $\mathbf{a}$ have at least $s+1$ intersections with C at $\mathbf{a}$ make up a set of s lines through $\mathbf{a}$, namely the set of lines (not necessarily all distinct) given by the equation

$$\left(x_0\frac{\partial}{\partial a_0}+x_1\frac{\partial}{\partial a_1}+x_2\frac{\partial}{\partial a_2}\right)^s f(a_0, a_1, a_2) = 0.$$

We call the s lines which are jointly represented by this equation the *nodal tangents* of C at $\mathbf{a}$; and thus C has, at any s-fold point, precisely s nodal tangents, some of which may possibly be coincident. The distinction between multiple points with all the nodal tangents distinct and multiple points with at least two of the nodal tangents coincident is of great importance in the theory of plane algebraic curves, and we give a name to the non-special type of multiple point as follows.

DEFINITION. An s-fold point of a plane algebraic curve is said to be *ordinary* if and only if the s nodal tangents at the point are all distinct.

When we have occasion to examine in greater detail the local behaviour of a curve C in relation to a particular multiple point O, we naturally adopt a coordinate representation $\mathscr{R}$ in which the relevant equations take a simple form. The usual way of doing this is to arrange for O to be the reference point $(1, 0, 0)$. The resulting specialization of the equations may be summarized in the following terms.

The reference point X_0 is an s-fold point for a curve C of order n if and only if the equation of C reduces to the form

$$x_0^{n-s}u_s + x_0^{n-s-1}u_{s+1} + \ldots + u_n = 0,$$

where u_i is a K-form of degree i in x_1 and x_2, and $u_s \neq 0$. When this is so, the joint equation of the s nodal tangents to C at X_0 is $u_s = 0$.

A particular case of special interest is that of an irreducible curve C of order n with an $(n-1)$-fold point at X_0, its equation being of the form

$$x_0 u_{n-1}(x_1, x_2) + u_n(x_1, x_2) = 0.$$

Such a curve necessarily admits of a *rational parametric representation*, which we derive as follows. Consider a linear equation $\mu x_1 - \lambda x_2 = 0$, in which λ and μ are indeterminates. This represents an 'indeterminate line' (cf. p. 3, note) which meets C in $n-1$ points at X_0 and one further point. The coordinates of this nth point may be found by solving the equations of the curve and the line simultaneously; and when we do this we arrive at the desired parametric form

$$\frac{x_0}{-u_n(\lambda, \mu)} = \frac{x_1}{\lambda u_{n-1}(\lambda, \mu)} = \frac{x_2}{\mu u_{n-1}(\lambda, \mu)}.$$

The equations just given associate with every pair of values of λ and μ a definite point of C, depending upon the ratio $\lambda : \mu$. All the roots (λ', μ') of the equation $u_{n-1}(\lambda, \mu) = 0$ yield the same point X_0 of C, while every other point of C arises from a unique value of the ratio $\lambda : \mu$. If we now interpret (λ, μ) as a homogeneous projective parameter-pair on a projective line L_0, we have a correspondence τ between the points of C and the points of L_0 which is $(1, 1)$ except only that the single point X_0 of C has $n-1$ corresponding points (not necessarily distinct) on L_0. If the parameter-pair (λ, μ) is replaced by a single non-homogeneous parameter $\theta = \lambda/\mu$ (which must, of course, be allowed to take the improper value ∞ as well as all values in K) the parametric representation of C assumes the form

$$\frac{x_0}{-u_n(\theta,1)} = \frac{x_1}{\theta u_{n-1}(\theta,1)} = \frac{x_2}{u_{n-1}(\theta,1)}.$$

4.3. Polar curves

Returning yet again to equation (2), which we wrote on p. 8 in the form

$$J(\lambda,\mu) \equiv A_0\lambda^n + A_1\lambda^{n-1}\mu + \ldots + A_n\mu^n = 0,$$

we shall now use a non-homogeneous parameter $\theta = \lambda/\mu$ for the points of the line L determined by the fixed points $\mathbf{a}$ and $\mathbf{b}$. This line then meets C in the n points, distinct or otherwise, given by the values $\theta_1,\ldots,\theta_n$ of θ which satisfy the equation

$$J(\theta,1) \equiv A_0\theta^n + A_1\theta^{n-1} + \ldots + A_n = 0.$$

Now suppose that some one of the coefficients A_i in this equation is zero. If this is the case for one representation $\mathscr{R}$ it is also the case for every other allowable representation $\bar{\mathscr{R}}$. Change of the representation, in fact, being a homogeneous linear transformation of coordinates, leaves the values of $\theta_1,\ldots,\theta_n$ unaltered; and a change from the particular coordinate-triads (a_0,a_1,a_2) and (b_0,b_1,b_2) to other proportional triads which represent the same base points in $\mathscr{R}$ merely has the effect of multiplying $\theta_1,\ldots,\theta_n$ by a common factor. Since the equation $A_i = 0$ is equivalent to the equation $\sum \theta_1 \ldots \theta_i = 0$, its projective invariance follows at once; and we may now infer that this algebraic relation is the expression of a certain projective relation between the ordered pair of points $\mathbf{a}$, $\mathbf{b}$ and the curve C.

If $\mathbf{a}$ is kept fixed and $\mathbf{b}$ is such that $A_{n-r} = 0$, the locus of $\mathbf{b}$ is a curve, projectively determined by $\mathbf{a}$ and C, that is known as the rth polar of $\mathbf{a}$ with respect to C. We define it formally as follows.

DEFINITION. Let C be a curve of order n, given by an equation $f(x_0,x_1,x_2) = 0$, and let (a_0,a_1,a_2) be any point of the plane. Then the equation

$$\left(a_0\frac{\partial}{\partial x_0} + a_1\frac{\partial}{\partial x_1} + a_2\frac{\partial}{\partial x_2}\right)^r f(x_0,x_1,x_2) = 0,$$

provided that it is not identically satisfied, defines a curve $C^{(r)}(\mathbf{a})$ of order $n-r$, and this curve is called the *r-th polar of* $\mathbf{a}$ *with respect to* C, or the *polar* $(n-r)$-*ic of* $\mathbf{a}$ *with respect to* C.

The equation of $C^{(r)}(\mathbf{a})$ may also be written in the alternative form (cf. p. 11)

$$\left(x_0\frac{\partial}{\partial a_0}+x_1\frac{\partial}{\partial a_1}+x_2\frac{\partial}{\partial a_2}\right)^{n-r}f(a_0,a_1,a_2)=0. \qquad (6)$$

Every point $\mathbf{a}$ of S_2 now has a set of $n-1$ polar curves $C^{(1)}(\mathbf{a}),..., C^{(n-1)}(\mathbf{a})$, of orders $n-1,...,1$ respectively, with respect to C. Some of these may, however, be illusory for a particular choice of $\mathbf{a}$, their equations being satisfied identically. If $\mathbf{a}$ is a simple point of C, its polar line $C^{(n-1)}(\mathbf{a})$ necessarily exists and is the tangent to C at $\mathbf{a}$.

It will readily be seen that the polar curves just defined lead to a generalization, for arbitrary plane algebraic curves, of the polar theory of the conic. The basic equation $J(\lambda,\mu)=0$, from which the whole theory is deduced, is simply the general form of Joachimsthal's equation. In place of the harmonic property of pole and polar with respect to a conic we now have the following geometrical characterization of the set of polar curves of a point:

The fundamental property of $C^{(r)}(\mathbf{a})$, $r=1,...,n-1$, when this curve exists, is that any line which joins $\mathbf{a}$ to some point $\mathbf{b}$ of $C^{(r)}(\mathbf{a})$ meets C in n points such that the sum $\sum\theta_1...\theta_{n-r}$ of the products $n-r$ at a time of the parameters $\theta_i=\lambda_i/\mu_i$ of the points, relative to $\mathbf{a}$ and $\mathbf{b}$ in this order, is zero.

Two obvious properties of polar curves, of which the first is an interpretation of (5) and the second follows from (6), are the following.

THEOREM 8. *If $\mathbf{b}$ lies on $C^{(r)}(\mathbf{a})$, then $\mathbf{a}$ lies on $C^{(n-r)}(\mathbf{b})$.*

THEOREM 9. *The s-th polar of $\mathbf{a}$ with respect to $C^{(r)}(\mathbf{a})$ is the $(r+s)th$ polar of $\mathbf{a}$ with respect to C.*

Taking the equation of $C^{(r)}(\mathbf{a})$ in the form (6), and using Theorem 7, we obtain at once the following result.

THEOREM 10. *Any s-fold point of a curve C is at least an $(s-r)$-fold point of the r-th polar with respect to C of any point of the plane $(r<s)$.*

From Theorem 10 it follows that every first polar curve $C^{(1)}(\mathbf{a})$, when it exists at all, passes through all the multiple points of C, and in fact passes $(s-1)$-fold, at least, through every s-fold point of C. Suppose, now, that $\mathbf{b}$ is a simple point of C that lies on $C^{(1)}(\mathbf{a})$. Then, by Theorem 8, the polar line $C^{(n-1)}(\mathbf{b})$, i.e. the tangent to C at $\mathbf{b}$, passes through **a**. Conversely, every point of C that is a point of contact of a tangent which passes through **a** lies on $C^{(1)}(\mathbf{a})$; and we thus have the following theorem.

THEOREM 11. *The points of intersection of a curve C with the first polar $C^{(1)}(\mathbf{a})$ of any point $\mathbf{a}$ of the plane are* (i) *the multiple points of C and* (ii) *the points of contact of those tangents of C which pass through* **a**.

In order to examine in greater detail the connexion between the multiple points of C and the polar curves defined by C, we now take the equation of C in the special form referred to on p. 12, but with x_0, x_1, x_2 replaced by z, x, y respectively. Thus we suppose that C is given by an equation

$$z^{n-s}u_s + z^{n-s-1}u_{s+1} + \dots + u_n = 0 \quad (u_s \neq 0),$$

the reference point Z being an s-fold point of C. The reader may now verify the following statement.

If Z is an s-fold point of C, then Z is also s-fold for every one of its own existing polars $C^{(r)}(Z)$; and every such polar has the same tangent (if $s = 1$) or the same set of nodal tangents (if $s > 1$) as C at the point Z.

Now let us consider the polars, not of Z, but of a general point P of the plane. If P has coordinates (ζ, ξ, η), the equation of its first polar $C^{(1)}(P)$—the only one that we shall examine—may be written as

$$z^{n-s}v_{s-1} + z^{n-s-1}v_s + \dots + v_{n-1} = 0,$$

where v_i $(i = s-1, \dots, n-1)$ is a K-form in x and y of degree i, and, in particular,

$$v_{s-1} = \xi \frac{\partial u_s}{\partial x} + \eta \frac{\partial u_s}{\partial y}.$$

If $s > 1$, $C^{(1)}(P)$ has, in general, an $(s-1)$-fold point at Z, with nodal tangents given by the combined equation

$$\xi \frac{\partial u_s}{\partial x} + \eta \frac{\partial u_s}{\partial y} = 0.$$

If the s-fold point Z of C is ordinary, the s factors of u_s are distinct, and none of them can be a common factor of $\partial u_s / \partial x$ and $\partial u_s / \partial y$. In this case, therefore, no factor of u_s can be a factor of v_{s-1} for all values of the ratio $\xi : \eta$. We thus have the following result.

If $s \geqslant 2$ and C has an ordinary s-fold point at Z, then the first polar $C^{(1)}(P)$ with respect to C of any general point P of the plane has an $(s-1)$-fold point at Z; and the nodal tangents of $C^{(1)}(P)$ at Z are all distinct from the nodal tangents of C at Z.

The expression 'general point' in this statement means any point not lying on any of a certain finite number of lines through Z.

If $s = 1$, $C^{(1)}(P)$ does not in general pass through Z. For it to do so, we must have

$$v_0 \equiv \xi \frac{\partial u_1}{\partial x} + \eta \frac{\partial u_1}{\partial y} = 0,$$

i.e. by Euler's Theorem, $u_1(\xi, \eta) = 0$; and from this it follows that P must lie on the tangent to C at Z. Now suppose that the frame of reference is so chosen that the tangent to C at Z is the line $y = 0$. The equation of C may then be written in the form

$$z^{n-1}y + z^{n-2}(ax^2 + 2hxy + by^2) + \ldots + u_n = 0.$$

Let P be any point, other than Z, of the tangent at Z, i.e. any point $(\zeta, \xi, 0)$, with $\xi \neq 0$. The leading term in the equation of $C^{(1)}(P)$ is then $z^{n-2}v_1$, where

$$v_1 = 2\xi(ax + hy) + (n-1)\zeta y.$$

If $a \neq 0$, then $C^{(1)}(P)$ has a simple point at Z, and its tangent there is distinct from that of C at the same point. If $a = 0$, so that ZP has at least three coincident intersections with C at Z, then $C^{(1)}(P)$ either has a simple point at Z and touches C there, or (if $a = 0$ and $2h\xi + (n-1)\zeta = 0$) it has a double point at Z. We note only the following result.

*If T is the point of contact of a tangent from P to C, T and P being distinct, and if the tangent to C at T is ordinary (not inflexional)†
then $C^{(1)}(P)$ passes simply through T but does not touch C there.*

EXERCISES. (i) Write down the equations of the polar conic (first polar) and the polar line (second polar) of a point η with respect to the cubic curve C given by $x_0^3 + x_1^3 + x_2^3 = 0$. Deduce (1) that the polar conics of the points of any given line p form a pencil, and (2) that there exist at most four points which have p as polar line with respect to C.

(ii) Show that, in affine geometry, the mean centres of the sets of n points cut on a curve C by a system of parallel lines always lie on a line. [The line is the polar line, with respect to C, of the point at infinity common to the parallel lines.]

(iii) Show that the most general type of linear net of conics in the plane is the net of polar conics of all points of the plane with respect to a unique cubic curve.

4.4. Inflexions. The Hessian curve $H(C)$

If P is any simple point of a curve C, every line but one through P meets C once only there; but the exceptional line, the tangent

---

† A tangent is said to be inflexional (cf. § 4.4) if it meets the curve in more than two coincident points at its point of contact.

at P, meets C in at least two coincident points at P. Those points P of C which are such that the tangent at P meets C in more than two points there are referred to as inflexions of C. We say that such a point is an inflexion in the broad sense if the multiplicity of intersection is merely asserted to be greater than two, and an inflexion in the narrow sense if the multiplicity is specified as precisely three.

DEFINITION. An *inflexion* (in the broad sense) of a curve C is a simple point† of C which is such that the tangent at the point meets the curve in at least three coincident points there.

In order to discuss the properties of inflexions, we use the equation
$$J(\theta, 1) \equiv A_0 \theta^n + A_1 \theta^{n-1} + \dots + A_n = 0,$$
obtained on p. 13. The roots $\theta_1, \dots, \theta_n$ of this equation are the parameters of the points $\theta\mathbf{a} + \mathbf{b}$ in which the line joining two given points $\mathbf{a}$ and $\mathbf{b}$ is met by C. If $\mathbf{a}$ is a simple point of C and $\mathbf{b}$ is any point, other than $\mathbf{a}$, of the tangent at $\mathbf{a}$, then at least two of $\theta_1, \dots, \theta_n$ are infinite, and $A_0 = A_1 = 0$. The point $\mathbf{a}$ is an inflexion of C if and only if we also have $A_2 = 0$, i.e.
$$\left(b_0 \frac{\partial}{\partial a_0} + b_1 \frac{\partial}{\partial a_1} + b_2 \frac{\partial}{\partial a_2}\right)^2 f(a_0, a_1, a_2) = 0;$$
and this is the condition for $\mathbf{b}$ to lie on the polar conic $C^{(n-2)}(\mathbf{a})$ of $\mathbf{a}$. The condition is to hold for all points $\mathbf{b}$, except $\mathbf{a}$ itself, of the tangent to C at $\mathbf{a}$, and therefore, by Theorem 3, this tangent must be a component of $C^{(n-2)}(\mathbf{a})$. We thus have the following theorem, which gives a necessary and sufficient condition for a simple point of a curve to be an inflexion of the curve.

THEOREM 12. *A simple point P of a curve C is an inflexion if and only if its polar conic breaks up into the tangent at P and another line.*

The residual line may be called the *copolar line* of P, and it meets the inflexional tangent at a point which may be called the *conjoint* of P. The copolar of P (which is defined only when P is an inflexion) can never pass through P; for if P were a double point of its own polar conic it would have to be a double point of C.

The sufficient condition for P to be an inflexion of C which is given in Theorem 12 is unnecessarily strong, since, if the polar

† Inflexions at a multiple point of a curve can also be defined, but since these refer to branches at the multiple point we do not give the definition until later (cf. p. 76).

conic of a simple point P of C breaks up at all, one of its components has to be the tangent at P. For if P is simple for C it is also simple for its own polar conic $C^{(n-2)}(P)$, and the tangents at P to C and $C^{(n-2)}(P)$ are the same.

We see, then, that whether the polar conic of a *simple* point P of C is degenerate or proper gives us important information about P, telling us whether or not this point is an inflexion. If, on the other hand, the point P of C is not simple, its polar conic cannot be proper. If P is a double point of C, then $C^{(n-2)}(P)$ also has a double point at P, with the same nodal tangents, and it therefore breaks up into this pair of tangents. If, finally, P is a point of multiplicity greater than two on C, then its polar conic is illusory. These considerations suggest, as is in fact the case, that it would be worth while to consider C in relation to the locus of all points of S_2 which have a degenerate (or illusory) polar conic with respect to C. This important locus is known as the *Hessian curve* of C.

DEFINITION. If C is a curve of order n, with equation $f(x_0, x_1, x_2) = 0$, its *Hessian* $H(C)$ is the curve, of order $3(n-2)$, with equation

$$f_H(x_0, x_1, x_2) \equiv \frac{\partial(\partial f/\partial x_0, \partial f/\partial x_1, \partial f/\partial x_2)}{\partial(x_0, x_1, x_2)} = 0,$$

i.e. the curve given by the determinantal equation

$$\left| \frac{\partial^2 f}{\partial x_r \, \partial x_s} \right| = 0.$$

If $f_H(\mathbf{x})$ is identically zero or reduces to a constant, then C has no Hessian curve.

If $H(C)$ exists, then every point of it is such that its polar conic with respect to C is either degenerate or non-existent; and conversely, every point of S_2 with a degenerate or non-existent polar conic lies on $H(C)$. The Hessian curve of C, as we have now defined it, is therefore identical with the locus referred to immediately before the definition, and we may enunciate the following theorem.

THEOREM 13. *The points in which a curve C is met by its Hessian $H(C)$ are the inflexions and the multiple points of C.*

If, for example, C is a non-singular cubic curve, then $H(C)$ is likewise a cubic curve; and if the two curves C and $H(C)$ meet, as we should generally expect, in nine points, these nine points are the inflexions of C.

EXERCISES. (i) C is a cubic curve. Show that the Hessian $H(C)$ exists except when C is a triad of concurrent lines, and that $H(C)$ is also a cubic curve. Verify that, when C is a triad of non-concurrent lines (so that every point of it which is not an intersection of two of the lines can be regarded as an inflexion), $H(C)$ and C are the same curve.

(ii) Show that no irreducible cubic curve has more than nine inflexions; and show that the cubic curve with equation

$$x^3 + y^3 + z^3 = 3mxyz$$

has precisely nine inflexions for a general value of m, these inflexions being the intersections of the curve with the sides of the triangle of reference.

(iii) If I is an inflexion of an irreducible cubic curve C, the copolar line of I is called the *harmonic polar line* of I with respect to C. If a variable line through I meets this line in M and meets C in two further points P and Q, show that I and M separate P and Q harmonically.

(iv) Show that, if a cubic curve C has an inflexion I, then an allowable coordinate system can be chosen such that the equation of C takes the form

$$y^2z = m(x-az)(x-bz)(x-cz),$$

where m, a, b, c are constants. [The reference point Y is at I, YX is the inflexional tangent, and ZX is the harmonic polar of I.]

5. Linear systems of curves of order n

We have been dealing so far in this chapter with the methods by which the properties of any given plane algebraic curve C may be handled, but in the present section we shall be more concerned with aggregates of curves of some specified order than with individual curves.

Let C be a given curve of order n—or, as we shall now usually say, a given curve C^n. In any chosen representation $\mathscr{R}$ of S_2, C may be represented by an equation of the form

$$f(x_0, x_1, x_2) \equiv \sum c_{\alpha\beta\gamma} x_0^\alpha x_1^\beta x_2^\gamma = 0,$$

in which the summation extends over all ordered triads (α, β, γ) of non-negative integers such that $\alpha + \beta + \gamma = n$. We note at once that, since the number of terms in the equation is $\frac{1}{2}(n+1)(n+2)$ and only the ratios of the coefficients $c_{\alpha\beta\gamma}$ are significant, *the freedom of curves C^n in S_2 (i.e. the number of free parameters on which they depend) is $\frac{1}{2}n(n+3)$.*

We may take the coefficients $c_{\alpha\beta\gamma}$ in the equation $f(\mathbf{x}) = 0$ as *homogeneous coordinates of the curve C*, relative to the representation $\mathscr{R}$ of S_2, and we then obtain a one-one mapping of the curves C^n of S_2 on the points $(c_{\alpha\beta\gamma})$ of a projective space $\Sigma \equiv S_N(K)$ of dimensionality $N = \frac{1}{2}n(n+3)$. Any non-singular linear transformation

T of x_0, x_1, x_2 induces a linear transformation T' of the $c_{\alpha\beta\gamma}$; and since the transformation induced by T^{-1} is clearly inverse to T' it follows that T' is also non-singular. Thus any change of representation in S_2 induces an associated change of representation in Σ.

Any set of curves which is mapped on a linear subspace Σ'_r of Σ of dimensionality r is said to be a *linear system of curves C^n of freedom r*. In particular, the set of all curves C^n in S_2 is a linear system of freedom $\frac{1}{2}n(n+3)$, while any pencil of such curves is a linear system of freedom 1. More generally, the set of curves which is mapped on any algebraic manifold in Σ is said to be an *algebraic system of curves C^n in S_2*. Such a system consists of all the curves C^n whose co-ordinates $c_{\alpha\beta\gamma}$ satisfy a fixed set of homogeneous equations

$$F_i(c_{\alpha\beta\gamma}) = 0 \quad (i = 1,...,s),$$

with coefficients in K.

It follows from the algebraic theory of linear dependence that a linear system of curves C^n of freedom r can be obtained in two alternative ways:

(i) as the system of all curves C^n with equations of the form

$$f(\mathbf{x}; \boldsymbol{\lambda}) \equiv \sum_{i=0}^{r} \lambda_i f_i(\mathbf{x}) = 0, \tag{1}$$

where $f_0(\mathbf{x}),...,f_r(\mathbf{x})$ are $r+1$ fixed linearly independent K-forms in x_0, x_1, x_2 of degree n, and $\lambda_0,...,\lambda_r$ are any elements of K, not all zero;

(ii) as the system of all curves C^n whose coordinates satisfy a set of $\frac{1}{2}n(n+3)-r$ linearly independent linear equations

$$\sum A_{\alpha\beta\gamma} c_{\alpha\beta\gamma} = 0, \tag{2}$$

where the $A_{\alpha\beta\gamma}$ are elements of K, not all zero.

In (i) we construct an equation $f(\mathbf{x}; \boldsymbol{\lambda}) = 0$ with the requisite freedom by supplying parameters $\lambda_0,..,\lambda_r$, while in (ii) we reduce the freedom of an undetermined C^n from $\frac{1}{2}n(n+3)$ to r by imposing a set of linear conditions on its coordinates. The two procedures are equivalent to defining the image space Σ'_r of the system as the join of $r+1$ linearly independent points of Σ on the one hand, or as the intersection of $\frac{1}{2}n(n+3)-r$ linearly independent primes of Σ on the other.

In considering the definition of a linear system Λ of freedom r by linear conditions of the type (2), we note that there is only one general type of linear condition that admits by itself of immediate geometrical interpretation, namely the condition (2) which is such that $A_{\alpha\beta\gamma} = a_0^\alpha a_1^\beta a_2^\gamma$, where a_0, a_1, a_2 are the coordinates of a point

A of S_2. Such a condition means that C^n is required to contain the assigned point A; and we shall say that A is a *base point* of the set of curves C^n that satisfy the condition.

If a linear system Λ consists of all the C^n that contain s given base points $A_1,..., A_s$, the linear conditions imposed by these points are not necessarily linearly independent. Nevertheless, the set of s linear equations in the $c_{\alpha\beta\gamma}$ has a well-defined dimensionality d $(d \leqslant s)$; and if $A_{i_1},..., A_{i_d}$ are d of the assigned points which do impose linearly independent conditions, then all the C^n which pass through these d points necessarily pass also through the remaining $s-d$ points. A system Λ that is defined by base points in this way will sometimes be found to have additional (unassigned) base points, and it may even have base curves which are fixed components of all the curves of Λ.

EXAMPLES. (i) Let C_1^3, C_2^3 be two cubic curves which intersect (as is generally the case) in nine distinct points $A_1,..., A_9$. Then, since a C^3 has nine degrees of freedom, the conditions imposed by these nine points on cubic curves required to pass through them cannot be linearly independent. If the conditions imposed by $A_1,..., A_8$ are independent, then the system of cubic curves through these eight points is a pencil, and it therefore has A_9 as a ninth unassigned base point. (Cf. Exercise 19 at the end of the chapter.)

(ii) If A_1, A_2, A_3 are three collinear points, any conic through them all breaks up into the line of collinearity and a further line. Thus the system of all such conics has the line $A_1 A_2 A_3$ as a base curve.

As an immediate generalization of the single linear condition which imposes a point A as a base point on C^n we shall have a set of linear conditions which imposes A as a q-fold base point $(q \leqslant n)$ on C^n. If $f(x_0, x_1, x_2) = \sum c_{\alpha\beta\gamma} x_0^\alpha x_1^\beta x_2^\gamma$, the conditions in question are those which express the vanishing at A of all the derivatives of $f(x_0, x_1, x_2)$ of order $q-1$; their number is therefore $\frac{1}{2}q(q+1)$, and they are linearly independent, as may readily be verified by taking A to be the point $(1, 0, 0)$ in a suitable coordinate system. This brings us to the following definition of an important special type of linear system.

DEFINITION. A linear system Λ of C^n is said to be *complete with respect to the assigned base* $(A_1^{q_1}, A_2^{q_2},..., A_s^{q_s})$, or to be a system $C^n(A_1^{q_1}, A_2^{q_2},..., A_s^{q_s})$, if it consists of all C^n that have the assigned multiplicities q_i (at least) at the assigned points A_i $(i = 1,..., s)$.

The total condition on a C^n that it should belong to Λ is com-pounded evidently of s separate sets of linear conditions on the $c_{\alpha\beta\gamma}$, the set corresponding to any particular point A_i being composed of $\frac{1}{2}q_i(q_i+1)$ linearly independent conditions; but the aggregate of all the conditions in all the sets may well be redundant (i.e. not linearly independent). We define the *virtual freedom* $\bar{r}$ of Λ by the formula

$$\bar{r} = \tfrac{1}{2}n(n+3) - \tfrac{1}{2}\sum_{i=1}^{s} q_i(q_i+1),$$

observing that the actual or *effective freedom* r of Λ must satisfy the inequality $r \geqslant \bar{r}$. The difference $\epsilon = r - \bar{r}$, arising from the possible redundancy of the total set of $\frac{1}{2}\sum q_i(q_i+1)$ linear conditions involved, is called the *superabundance* of Λ with respect to its assigned base. Any system of superabundance zero is said to be *regular*.

We note finally that a system Λ, as above defined, may well be found to have additional unassigned base points, it may have base point multiplicities at some of the A_i that are greater than those assigned, and it may have base curves, that is to say fixed com-ponents of all the curves of the system.

In Chapter VI we shall have occasion to consider a further numerical characteristic of a linear system, namely its *grade* γ, defined as the maximum number of 'free' intersections (i.e. inter-sections not at base points) of any pair of curves of the system which do not have any common component that is not a base curve. We shall see in due course that multiplicities can be assigned to the intersections of two curves in such a way that (*a*) the total number of intersections of a C^m and a C^n with no common component is mn (p. 37) and (*b*) the multiplicity of intersection of two curves at a point which is p-fold for the one and q-fold for the other is at least equal to pq and may possibly be greater than pq (p. 94). It follows that the grade of the linear system $C^n(A_1^{q_1},..., A_s^{q_s})$ considered above has an upper bound

$$\bar{\gamma} = n^2 - \sum_{i=1}^{s} q_i^2,$$

i.e. that $\gamma \leqslant \bar{\gamma}$, provided only that the system has no base curve. We call the number $\bar{\gamma}$ just defined the *virtual grade* of the linear system (whether this has a base curve or not) and we call γ the *effective grade*.

EXAMPLES. (i) If A_1, A_2, A_3 are not collinear, the system $C^4(A_1^2, A_2^2, A_3^2)$ is such that $r = \bar{r} = 5$; $\gamma = \bar{\gamma} = 4$. If, however, A_1, A_2, A_3 are collinear, the system $C^4(A_1^2, A_2^2, A_3^2)$ has the line $A_1 A_2 A_3$ as a base curve, and in this case $r = 6, \bar{r} = 5; \gamma = 6, \bar{\gamma} = 4$.

(ii) If $A_1,..., A_9$ impose eight conditions on cubic curves required to pass through them, as in Example (i), p. 21, then the system $C^3(A_1,..., A_9)$ is such that $r = 1$, $\bar{r} = 0$; $\gamma = \bar{\gamma} = 0$.

6. Parametric curves

We now complete the present preliminary survey of algebraic curves in general by considering an important alternative way of defining some of these curves, namely by the use of parametric equations. We take first of all the simplest case of the rational parametric curve.

DEFINITION. A *rational parametric curve* is the aggregate of points obtained by substituting all values belonging to K, as well as the improper value ∞, for the indeterminate θ in a set of equations of the form

$$\frac{x_0}{\phi_0(\theta)} = \frac{x_1}{\phi_1(\theta)} = \frac{x_2}{\phi_2(\theta)}, \tag{1}$$

where ϕ_0, ϕ_1, ϕ_2 are K-polynomials in θ, not all of degree zero and not possessing a common factor which involves θ.

THEOREM 14. *Every rational parametric curve is an irreducible algebraic curve.*

Proof. Let C be a rational parametric curve, given by the parametric representation (1) above. We consider the set $\mathscr{F}$ of all K-forms $f(x_0, x_1, x_2)$ with the property that

$$f(\phi_0(\theta), \phi_1(\theta), \phi_2(\theta)) = 0$$

in the ring $K[\theta]$. This set $\mathscr{F}$ certainly contains at least one non-constant form, for among its elements is the θ-resultant $R(x_0, x_1, x_2)$ of the polynomials $x_0 \phi_1(\theta) - x_1 \phi_0(\theta)$ and $x_0 \phi_2(\theta) - x_2 \phi_0(\theta)$, which belong to $K[x_0, x_1, x_2][\theta]$. This resultant can be expressed as a linear combination of the two polynomials in question, and is accordingly zero when $\phi_i(\theta)$ is substituted for x_i ($i = 0, 1, 2$). Now, since there are non-constant forms in $\mathscr{F}$, we may suppose that some one of them, $\bar{f}(x_0, x_1, x_2)$ say, of minimum degree, has been selected. This form is necessarily irreducible; for if it could be expressed as a product of non-constant factors, these would all be forms (cf. p. 6) of lower degree than $\bar{f}(x_0, x_1, x_2)$, and, the ring $K[\theta]$ having no divisors of zero, at least one of them would belong to $\mathscr{F}$. Thus

$$\bar{f}(x_0, x_1, x_2) = 0$$

is the equation of an irreducible curve $\bar{C}$; and, since

$$\bar{f}(\phi_0(\theta_0), \phi_1(\theta_0), \phi_2(\theta_0)) = 0$$

for every element θ_0 of K, every point of C is a point of $\bar{C}$. But now, if $f(x_0, x_1, x_2)$ is any form in $\mathscr{F}$, the curve $f(x_0, x_1, x_2) = 0$ has infinitely many points, derived from the parametric equations (1), in common with the irreducible curve $\bar{C}$; and hence, by Theorem 2, $f(x_0, x_1, x_2)$ has $\bar{f}(x_0, x_1, x_2)$ as a factor. This is true, in particular, of $R(x_0, x_1, x_2)$; and therefore every point of $\bar{C}$ is a zero of the resultant $R(x_0, x_1, x_2)$, and consequently arises from the representation (1) for some value of θ, i.e. it is a point of C. This completes the identification of the parametric curve C with the irreducible algebraic curve $\bar{C}$, thus proving Theorem 14.

We shall see in due course that rational parametric curves form only a very special subclass of the class of all irreducible algebraic curves. In our next definition we seem, at first sight, to narrow this subclass still further, by imposing an additional restriction on the parametric curves; but it will appear in due course (see p. 171) that *all* rational parametric curves in fact satisfy the new condition, so that no limitation is actually involved.

DEFINITION. A rational parametric curve C is said to be a *rational curve* if it can be represented by equations of the form (1) in such a way that the resulting parametrization is *proper*, i.e. such that, with at most a finite number of exceptions, each point of C corresponds to only one value of the parameter θ.

In other words, a rational curve has a parametrization which puts its points into a general, though not necessarily un-exceptional, $(1, 1)$ correspondence with the points of a projective line. We showed, at the end of § 4.2, that any irreducible curve C^n with an $(n-1)$-fold point is rational, and we noted there that the multiple point might arise from as many as $n-1$ different values of the parameter. We shall see at a later stage that the number of values of θ that give rise to the same (exceptional) point P of a rational curve C is the number of 'places' on the curve at P.

For many purposes, and in order to avoid the use of the improper value ∞ of θ, it is convenient to replace θ by a homogeneous para-meter-pair (λ, μ) such that $\theta = \lambda/\mu$. Instead of (1) we then have equations

$$\frac{x_0}{\phi_0(\lambda, \mu)} = \frac{x_1}{\phi_1(\lambda, \mu)} = \frac{x_2}{\phi_2(\lambda, \mu)}, \tag{2}$$

where ϕ_0, ϕ_1, ϕ_2 are K-forms in λ and μ, of the same positive degree n, with no common factor. Also, supposing the parametrization to be proper, the points of the rational curve C defined by (2) are in general $(1, 1)$ correspondence with the points (λ, μ) of a projective line. We see at once that *if a rational curve C is given by a proper parametrization* (2), *then its order is equal to the common degree of the forms ϕ_0, ϕ_1, ϕ_2.* For a general line $u_0 x_0 + u_1 x_1 + u_2 x_2 = 0$ meets C in a number of distinct points equal to the order of C, each point being given by one value of the ratio $\lambda : \mu$; and hence the order of C is equal to the degree n of the form

$$U(\lambda, \mu) \equiv u_0 \phi_0(\lambda, \mu) + u_1 \phi_1(\lambda, \mu) + u_2 \phi_2(\lambda, \mu).$$

Furthermore, the conditions that (λ, μ) should be at least a double root of the equation $U(\lambda, \mu) = 0$ are $\partial U/\partial \lambda = \partial U/\partial \mu = 0$; and from this it follows that the equation of the tangent line to C at a simple point (λ, μ) is

$$\begin{vmatrix} x_0 & x_1 & x_2 \\ \dfrac{\partial \phi_0}{\partial \lambda} & \dfrac{\partial \phi_1}{\partial \lambda} & \dfrac{\partial \phi_2}{\partial \lambda} \\ \dfrac{\partial \phi_0}{\partial \mu} & \dfrac{\partial \phi_1}{\partial \mu} & \dfrac{\partial \phi_2}{\partial \mu} \end{vmatrix} = 0.$$

Hence *at most $2n - 2$ tangents to C pass through any general point of S_2.*

Finally, the conditions that (λ, μ) should be at least a triple root of the equation $U(\lambda, \mu) = 0$ are $\partial^2 U/\partial \lambda^2 = \partial^2 U/\partial \lambda \partial \mu = \partial^2 U/\partial \mu^2 = 0$; and from this it follows that the parameters of the inflexions of C are among the $3n - 6$ roots of the determinantal equation

$$\begin{vmatrix} \dfrac{\partial^2 \phi_0}{\partial \lambda^2} & \dfrac{\partial^2 \phi_1}{\partial \lambda^2} & \dfrac{\partial^2 \phi_2}{\partial \lambda^2} \\ \dfrac{\partial^2 \phi_0}{\partial \lambda \partial \mu} & \dfrac{\partial^2 \phi_1}{\partial \lambda \partial \mu} & \dfrac{\partial^2 \phi_2}{\partial \lambda \partial \mu} \\ \dfrac{\partial^2 \phi_0}{\partial \mu^2} & \dfrac{\partial^2 \phi_1}{\partial \mu^2} & \dfrac{\partial^2 \phi_2}{\partial \mu^2} \end{vmatrix} = 0.$$

Thus *the curve has at most $3n - 6$ inflexions.*

The reader may easily verify by examples that the numbers $2n-2$ and $3n-6$ mentioned above are upper bounds, attained in some cases but not in others, deficiencies occurring when C has cusps or other multiple points which are not ordinary.

NOTES AND EXERCISES ON CHAPTER I

1. Show that the only points of the plane that lie on any of their own polar curves with respect to a curve C are the points of C; also that the multiplicity of any such point on C is equal to the multiplicity of the point on each of its (existing) polar curves for C.

2. If C is any one of the curves (i) $Y^2 = X^3+1$, (ii) $Y = X^3-1$, (iii) $Y = X^2-Y^3$, (iv) $Y = X^3-Y^3$, (v) $X^3+Y^3 = 1$, find the polar conic of the origin O with respect to C and discuss in each case the intersections of this conic with C.

3. Give the appropriate definitions of the first, second,... polar sets of a given point of a line (or line of a pencil) with respect to a given set of n points of the line (or n lines of the pencil).

If A is an s-fold point of a curve C and P is any other point, show that the set of nodal tangents of $C^{(1)}(P)$ at A is the first polar set of AP with respect to the set of nodal tangents of C at A. (Cf. p. 15).

4. If C is a curve of order n, and two lines through a point A, not on C, meet C in sets of distinct points $(P_1,...,P_n)$ and $(Q_1,...,Q_n)$, show that A has the same polar line with respect to C and with respect to the curve composed of the n lines $P_i Q_i$.

5. Show that a line p is in general the polar line of each of four points—the poles of p—for a non-singular C^3, and that the corresponding numbers of poles of p for a nodal cubic and for a cuspidal cubic are 3 and 2.

Discuss the sets of poles of all lines p through an inflexion I of a non-singular C^3.

6. Show that the cubic with equation
$$12(x^3+y^3+z^3)-9xyz = (x+y+z)^3$$
has a node at $(1, 1, 1)$ and inflexions at the intersections of the line $x+y+z=0$ with the lines $x = 0$, $y = 0$, $z = 0$. Show also that these three lines have unique poles at $(-8, 1, 1)$, $(1, -8, 1)$, $(1, 1, -8)$ respectively.

7. If h is the harmonic polar line (cf. Exercise (iii), p. 19) of an inflexion I of an irreducible C^3, show that the curve is invariant under the harmonic plane homology with vertex I and axis h. Deduce the result:

Any two inflexions of an irreducible C^3 are collinear with a third.

8. If I is an inflexion of a curve C in the narrow sense, such that the inflexional tangent has precisely 3-point contact with C at I, show that I is a simple point of the Hessian $H(C)$, and that the tangents to C and $H(C)$ at I are distinct.

From this, in particular, as will follow from the results of Chapter II, we may deduce the result:

A non-singular C^3 has precisely nine inflexions.

9. If C is of order n, with equation $f(x, y, z) = 0$, show that

$$\frac{\partial(f_x, f_y, f_z)}{\partial(x, y, z)} = \frac{(n-1)^2}{z^2} \begin{vmatrix} f_{xx} & f_{xy} & f_x \\ f_{xy} & f_{yy} & f_y \\ f_x & f_y & \dfrac{n}{n-1}f \end{vmatrix},$$

and deduce that every intersection of C with the curve

$$f_x^2 f_{yy} + f_y^2 f_{xx} = 2f_x f_y f_{xy}$$

is either an inflexion or a multiple point of C, or an intersection of C with the line $z = 0$.

(From this last equation we may derive immediately, within the domain of the differential calculus, the usual characteristic property of inflexions of a curve $F(X, Y) = 0$, namely that they are points of the curve at which $d^2Y/dX^2 = 0$.)

10. *The two standard forms for a C^3*. By a suitable choice of the reference system (affine or projective) the equation of any non-singular C^3 may be reduced to either of the following standard forms:

    (I) $Y^2 = 4X^3 - g_2 X - g_3$ $(g_2, g_3 \in K)$,

    (II) $x^3 + y^3 + z^3 = 3mxyz$ $(m \in K)$.

The form (I), which also embraces nodal and cuspidal cubics, is the affine equivalent, with only trivial modifications, of that given in Exercise (iv) on p. 19. It is derived by taking any inflexion I of C as Y_∞, the tangent at I as the line at infinity, and the harmonic polar of I as the X-axis. The other eight inflexions then lie by pairs on four lines through I.

The form (II) is less easily established. By use of the basic property of the inflexions (Exercise 7 above), it may be shown (a) that there always exists a proper triangle XYZ (to be taken as triangle of reference) such that the nine inflexions of C lie by threes on YZ, ZX, and XY (not at X or Y or Z); (b) that the unit point may be so chosen that the nine inflexions are the intersections of YZ, ZX, XY with the sides $x+y+z = 0$, $x+\omega y+\omega^2 z = 0$, $x+\omega^2 y+\omega z = 0$ ($\omega^3 = 1$) of a second triangle; and (c) that C must then belong to the pencil of cubics $x^3+y^3+z^3 - 3xyz + \lambda xyz = 0$ defined by the two triangles (as triads of lines each meeting C in the same set of nine distinct points).

We may note, incidentally, that the pencil of cubics defined by (II) as m varies is such that all its members have the same set of inflexions (the base points of the pencil), and that the four curves of the pencil given by $m = \infty$, 1, ω, ω^2 are triangles.

11. *The nodal C^3*. Any irreducible C^3 with an ordinary node can have its equation reduced to the standard form $x^3+y^3 = xyz$, and then it admits the parametric representation $(t, t^2, 1+t^3)$. Show that the class of this curve (maximum number of tangents through any point) is 4, that the curve has three collinear inflexions, and that it is invariant for a group of six self-collineations of the plane.

12. *The cuspidal C^3*. A standard form for the equation of a cuspidal C^3 is $y^2z = x^3$. This curve is of class 3, has one inflexion, and is invariant for a 1-parameter group of self-collineations of the plane.

13. If k, a, b, c are non-zero constants such that $k \neq 1$ and a, b, c are all unequal, show that the parametric equations

$$x:y:z = (\theta-ka)(\theta-b)(\theta-c):(\theta-a)(\theta-kb)(\theta-c):(\theta-a)(\theta-b)(\theta-kc)$$

represent a C^3 which passes through X, Y, Z and has a node at $(1, 1, 1)$. Show that the condition for collinear points is $\theta_1\theta_2\theta_3 = kabc$, and that the line containing the three inflexions has equation

$$(b-c)(kbc-a^2)x+(c-a)(kca-b^2)y+(a-b)(kab-c^2)z = 0.$$

14. *Trinodal C^4*. Show that the equation of any C^4 with double points at X, Y, Z is of the form

$$(a,b,c,f,g,h\S yz, zx, xy)^2 = 0.$$

By use of the quadratic transformation $x' : y' : z' = yz : zx : xy$, or otherwise, show that any irreducible curve of the above type admits a proper parametric representation of the form

$$x : y : z = \Theta_2\Theta_3 : \Theta_3\Theta_1 : \Theta_1\Theta_2,$$

where Θ_1, Θ_2, Θ_3 are linearly independent quadratic polynomials in a parameter θ.

15. *Flecnode*. An ordinary node O of a curve C is termed a *flecnode* if each of the nodal tangents has four coincident intersections (at least) with C at O. If C has equation $0 = u_2(X,Y)+u_3(X,Y)+...+u_n(X,Y)$, show that the condition for O to be a flecnode is that u_2 should be a factor of u_3.

16. Show that the curve $(x^2+y^2)z^2 = x^2y^2$ has flecnodes at X, Y, Z, and obtain its parametric representation $(2\theta(1+\theta^2), 1-\theta^4, 2\theta(1-\theta^2))$.

Show that the points with parameters θ_1, θ_2, θ_3, θ_4 are collinear if

$$\theta_1\theta_2\theta_3\theta_4 = -1, \quad \sum_{i \neq j} \theta_i\theta_j = 0.$$

Deduce that the curve has no proper inflexions, but that it has four double tangents.

17. *The lemniscate.* Classify projectively the lemniscate with equation $(X^2+Y^2)^2 = a^2(X^2-Y^2)$, and show that it is a rational curve.

18. *Tricuspidal C^4*. Obtain the standard form

$$y^2z^2+z^2x^2+x^2y^2 = 2xyz(x+y+z)$$

for the equation of any (irreducible) tricuspidal C^4, and the parametric representation $(\theta^2(\theta-1)^2, (\theta-1)^2, \theta^2)$ of this curve. Show that its three cuspidal tangents are concurrent, that it is of class 3, that it has a unique double tangent $x+y+z = 0$, and that it has no inflexion.

19. *Nine associated points.* If it is assumed (in anticipation of results in Chapter II) that two cubic curves with no common component have at most nine common points, then it can be shown by elementary arguments that nine distinct points which form the complete intersection of two such curves C and C' have the property that any eight of them impose eight linearly independent conditions on cubics required to contain them. Thus the cubics through any eight of the points form a pencil, which must then be the pencil $C+\lambda C'$ defined by C and C'; and they pass, therefore, through the ninth point. Hence:

If two cubic curves with no common component intersect in nine points $A_1,..., A_9$, then every cubic through any eight of these points passes through the remaining one.

The points $A_1,..., A_9$ are then said to be *nine associated points* of S_2.

Thus, for example, if three lines meet a cubic C in point-triads (P_1, Q_1, R_1), (P_2, Q_2, R_2), (P_3, Q_3, R_3) such that P_1, P_2, P_3 are collinear and Q_1, Q_2, Q_3 are collinear, then R_1, R_2, R_3 are also collinear.

20. *Self-transformations of a non-singular C^3.* We single out two species of $(1, 1)$ correspondence between points P, P' of a non-singular cubic C:

   (i) a *τ-transformation* (involutory) which carries any point P of C into the third intersection P' of C with the line joining P to a fixed point A of C (the *vertex* of τ); and

   (ii) a *σ-transformation* (in general non-involutory) which is the product $\tau_2 \tau_1$ of any two τ-transformations τ_1 and τ_2.

Show that any product $\tau_3 \tau_2 \tau_1$ of three τ-transformations (and therefore also any product of any odd number of τ-transformations) is again a τ-transformation. [Let A_1, A_2, A_3 be the vertices of τ_1, τ_2, τ_3; let $A_1 A_3$ meet C again in B; and let $A_2 B$ meet C again in A_4. Then the nine points A_1, A_2, A_3, A_4, B, P, $\tau_1 P$, $\tau_2 \tau_1 P$, and $\tau_3 \tau_2 \tau_1 P$ are associated, and hence $\tau_3 \tau_2 \tau_1$ is the transformation τ_4 with vertex A_4.]

Show further that $\tau_4 \tau_3 = \tau_1 \tau_2$ if and only if $A_1 A_3$ and $A_2 A_4$ have the same residual intersection with C.

21. Show that the two sets of transformations τ and σ, as above defined, together constitute a group G of self-transformations of C, the σ-transformations alone constituting a subgroup G_1 of index 2 of G.

22. *Parametric representation of a non-singular C^3.* The standard form (I) (Exercise 10 above) for the equation of a non-singular cubic C leads directly to the transcendental parametric representation

$$X = \wp(u), \qquad Y = \wp'(u)$$

of C, where $\wp(u)$ is the Weierstrassian elliptic function of the parameter u, with periods ω_1, ω_2. Verify, then, that three points given by values u_1, u_2, u_3 of the parameter are collinear (i.e. they are the intersections of C with a line) if and only if $u_1 + u_2 + u_3 \equiv 0 \pmod{\omega_1, \omega_2}$.

Show also that τ-transformations and σ-transformations on C are represented in terms of the parametric representation by congruences of the form

$$u + u' \equiv a \quad \text{and} \quad u - u' \equiv b$$

respectively, where a and b are constants. Deduce the existence of three non-identical involutory σ-transformations.

23. *Further properties of a non-singular C^3.* If C is the cubic of the last example, show by use of the parametric representation that:

   (i) C has nine inflexions, lying by threes on twelve lines;

   (ii) four tangents can be drawn from any point of C (not an inflexion) to touch the curve elsewhere;

   (iii) the tangents to C at three collinear points meet C again in three collinear points;

(iv) if a C^n meets C in $3n$ points with parameters $u_1, ..., u_{3n}$, then $u_1 + u_2 + ... + u_{3n} \equiv 0 \pmod{\omega_1, \omega_2}$.

24. Show that there exist twenty-four solutions to the problem of inscribing a triangle XYZ in a given non-singular cubic curve C in such a way that the tangents to C at X, Y, Z meet C again at Y, Z, X respectively.

Derive a third standard form

$$yz^2 + zx^2 + xy^2 = mxyz$$

for the equation of a non-singular cubic.

25. *Modulus of a non-singular C^3.* If P is any point of a non-singular cubic C, then C meets the polar conic of P in six points, of which two coincide (in an obvious sense) at P while *the remaining four are always distinct among themselves*, even though one of them will coincide with P when P is an inflexion. [The reader should prove this for himself.] We may accordingly say that the four tangents t_1, t_2, t_3, t_4 of C that pass through P, excluding the tangent at P counted twice, are distinct among themselves for *every* position of P on C.

If C has equation $f(X, Y) = 0$, and if λ is any one of the cross-ratios of the pencil (t_1, t_2, t_3, t_4), then the symmetric function

$$\Lambda = \frac{4(1 - \lambda + \lambda^2)^3}{(\lambda + 1)^2 (\lambda - 2)^2 (2\lambda - 1)^2}$$

of the six cross-ratios of the above pencil is necessarily a rational function $\Lambda = \phi(X, Y)$ of the coordinates X, Y of P. Further, since no two of t_1, t_2, t_3, t_4 can ever coincide, so that λ never takes any of the values 0, ∞, or 1, it follows that $\phi(X, Y) \neq 1$ *for any position of P on C.*

From the equations $f(X, Y) = 0$ and $\Lambda = \phi(X, Y)$, it follows that Λ must either be a constant, or it must satisfy some irreducible K-equation $G(X, \Lambda) = 0$ of positive degrees in X and Λ. Since, however, there can be no finite or infinite value of X for which $G(X, 1) = 0$, the second alternative can hold only if every coefficient in $G(X, \Lambda)$, as a polynomial in X, has $\Lambda - 1$ as a factor, the irreducibility of $G(X, \Lambda)$ being thereby contradicted. It follows therefore that Λ is a constant. Hence *if P, Q are any two points of a non-singular cubic curve C, then, with a suitable pairing, the tetrads of tangents from P and Q to C (as above defined) are projectively equivalent.*

The constant Λ—a projective invariant—is called the *modulus* of C.

26. *Projective transforms of a non-singular C^3.* We refer the reader to Enriques-Chisini, *Lezioni sulla teoria geometrica delle equazioni e delle funzioni algebriche*, Vol. II, Chapter III, for detailed proofs and amplifications of the following results:

(i) Two (non-singular) cubics C, C' are projectively equivalent (i.e. each is the transform of the other by a plane collineation) if and only if they are *equimodular* ($\Lambda = \Lambda'$).

(ii) A non-singular cubic C admits always a *finite* group G of self-collineations of the plane. The order of G is in general 18; but for a *harmonic cubic* ($\Lambda = \infty$) it is 36, and for an *equianharmonic cubic* ($\Lambda = 0$) it is 54.

The group G_{18} in the general case contains (and is generated by) the nine harmonic homologies of the type referred to in Exercise 7.

27. *The rational normal curve $C^{(n)}$ of S_n.* Any rational n-ic curve of S_2, as we have defined it, has a proper parametric representation $(\Theta_0, \Theta_1, \Theta_2)$, where the Θ_i $(i = 0, 1, 2)$ are linearly independent n-ic polynomials in the parameter θ. It can therefore be regarded as the projection, from a space S_{n-3}, of a curve C of S_n with a parametric representation of the form

$$(\Theta_0, \Theta_1, ..., \Theta_n),$$

where $\Theta_0, ..., \Theta_n$ are $n+1$ linearly independent n-ic polynomials in θ. Every such curve C, however, is a projective transform of the *rational normal curve* $C^{(n)}$ of S_n with parametric representation $(\theta^n, \theta^{n-1}, ..., 1)$. Hence: *Every rational n-ic curve of S_2 can be obtained as a projection, from a suitable S_{n-3}, of the projectively unique rational normal curve $C^{(n)}$ of order n in S_n.*

Thus, in particular, any rational C^3 of S_2 is a projection of a twisted cubic $C^{(3)}$ from an external point A, the node or cusp of C^3 arising from the unique chord or tangent line of $C^{(3)}$ through A. Also, any rational C^4 of S_2 is a projection of a rational normal $C^{(4)}$ of S_4 from a line which does not meet this $C^{(4)}$; and the three chords of $C^{(4)}$ that (in general) meet the line project (in general) into three double points of C^4, though special cases arise from special positions of the line in relation to $C^{(4)}$.

28. *Image curve of an (m, n) correspondence.* If $F(X, Y)$ is any K-polynomial of effective degrees m and n in X and Y respectively, then the equation $F(X, Y) = 0$ defines an (m, n) correspondence τ between the complex variables X and Y. The same equation also defines a curve I of S_2—*the image curve of τ*—whose points represent all the pairs of corresponding values of X and Y. This curve I, augmented if need be by a multiple of the line at infinity, may always be supposed to be of order $m+n$ precisely; and it will then have an n-fold point at X_∞ and an m-fold point at Y_∞.

The *united points* of τ—values of X such that (X, X) is a corresponding pair—will be represented by the intersections of I with the line $X = Y$, their number, properly counted, being therefore $m+n$. The *critical values* of X— for which two at least of the corresponding values of Y are equal—correspond to ordinates that touch I (or pass through a multiple point of I other than X_∞ or Y_∞); their number is at most $2m(n-1)$. Similarly, the number of critical values of Y is at most $2n(m-1)$.

The correspondence is *irreducible* if I is irreducible (apart from any adjoined multiple of the line at infinity); and it is *symmetrical* if and only if I is symmetrical (in an obvious sense) about the line $Y = X$.

CHAPTER II

POINT-SETS IN S_2

1. Representation of point-sets by equations

WE have already seen in the previous chapter that every algebraic curve in S_2, being given by a single equation $f(x_0, x_1, x_2) = 0$, can be represented by a set of homogeneous coordinates; and we have also seen that the totality of curves of given order n can be mapped, without exception or ambiguity, on a projective space Σ of dimensionality $\frac{1}{2}n(n+3)$, each curve C^n of S_2 then having an image point in Σ. By such means we are able to give precision to the somewhat vague notion that algebraic curves can be treated as *geometric variables*, on which restrictions of various kinds can be imposed, such as, for instance, that of belonging to a specified pencil or other linear system of curves of order n. But the idea of a geometric variable is of much greater generality than this one example might suggest, and already in S_2 we have a second type of variable geometrical object that is of very great importance, namely the algebraic point-set.

DEFINITION. An *algebraic point-set* G of S_2 is a finite set of points $P_1, ..., P_s$, such that with each point P_i of the set is associated a positive† integer r_i, its *multiplicity* as a component of G. The *order* of the point-set is the sum $n = r_1 + ... + r_s$, i.e. the total number of points, each counted to its proper multiplicity.

For the purpose of treating point-sets as geometric variables, we need to find some way of endowing each set G with homogeneous coordinates that serve to identify it, so that any variation in G can then be interpreted as a corresponding variation of the image point of G in an appropriately chosen projective space Σ. The natural way in which we might hope to achieve this end is by finding a means of characterizing G completely by a single equation—as we were able to do for a curve in S_2—and then taking the coefficients in this equation as the required coordinates. It is not quite so obvious, however, how to do this for a point-set as it was for a

† For some purposes it is desirable to allow the r_i to be arbitrary rational integers. When this is done, a point-set for which all the r_i are positive is said to be an *effective* set.

plane curve; and a similar but much more acute difficulty will face us when we try to characterize by a single equation a space curve of order n, or indeed any (pure) manifold of dimensionality d in a projective space S_r. The solution of our present problem will, in fact, point the way to a general procedure which can be applied in all such cases (cf. Ch. IX).

1.1. Two-way forms

Let $\mathbf{a}$ and $\mathbf{b}$ be two points of a projective plane S_2, or of two projective planes S_2 and S_2'. The ordered pair of triads of numbers $\mathbf{a}$ and $\mathbf{b}$, which we shall denote by the symbol

$$(\mathbf{a}; \mathbf{b}) \equiv (a_0, a_1, a_2; b_0, b_1, b_2),$$

defines a new kind of object that we shall call a *two-way point* in a *two-way projective space* $S_{2,2}(K)$. It will be understood that, if λ and μ are any two non-zero elements of K, the symbol

$$(\lambda \mathbf{a}; \mu \mathbf{b}) \equiv (\lambda a_0, \lambda a_1, \lambda a_2; \mu b_0, \mu b_1, \mu b_2)$$

is another representation of the same (two-way) point as before. Plainly, then, $S_{2,2}$ has ∞^4 two-way points.

A *two-way K-form of degrees* (l, m) is a polynomial

$$f(\mathbf{x}, \mathbf{y}) \equiv f(x_0, x_1, x_2; y_0, y_1, y_2)$$

in the six indeterminates x_i, y_j which is homogeneous and of degree l in x_0, x_1, x_2 and homogeneous and of degree m in y_0, y_1, y_2, Every two-way form has well-defined degrees, with the single exception of the form which is identically zero. For this null two-way form the degrees are undefined. In the particular case in which one of the two degrees l and m of $f(\mathbf{x}; \mathbf{y})$ is zero, the two-way form is said to be *degenerate*, since when this is so the form reduces effectively to a one-way form.

A two-way point $(\mathbf{a}; \mathbf{b})$ of $S_{2,2}$ is said to be a *zero* of a two-way form $f(\mathbf{x}; \mathbf{y})$ if and only if $f(\mathbf{a}; \mathbf{b}) = 0$.

The above ideas obviously extend to two-way spaces $S_{p,q}$ in general, and also indeed to m-way spaces $S_{p_1, p_2, ..., p_m}$, the points of which are ordered m-ads of points taken respectively from m ordinary (one-way) projective spaces $S_{p_1}, S_{p_2}, ..., S_{p_m}$.

It may be shown, by an argument similar to that used on p. 6, that any factorization of a two-way form $f(\mathbf{x}; \mathbf{y})$, regarded as a polynomial in the six indeterminates x_i, y_j, is necessarily a resolution of it into two-way forms. The distinction between reducible and irreducible two-way forms is accordingly the same whether we regard these forms as two-way forms in two sets of three indeterminates or as polynomials in six indeterminates. For two-way forms, therefore, we have a resolution theorem that may be formulated in the following terms.

THEOREM 1. *For every two-way form $f(\mathbf{x}; \mathbf{y})$ there exists a decomposition $f = f_1^{\sigma_1} f_2^{\sigma_2} \ldots f_s^{\sigma_s}$ of the form into irreducible two-way factors, and this decomposition is essentially unique. If the degrees of f and f_i are (l, m) and (l_i, m_i) respectively, then $l = \sum \sigma_i l_i$ and $m = \sum \sigma_i m_i$.*

We conclude this section by recording a property of two-way equations that is analogous to the known property of plane algebraic curves (i.e. one-way equations) of being determined, apart from the multiplicities of their components, by the totalities of points which satisfy them (cf. Chapter I, § 3).

THEOREM 2. *If $f(\mathbf{x}; \mathbf{y})$ and $g(\mathbf{x}; \mathbf{y})$ are two-way forms, $f(\mathbf{x}; \mathbf{y})$ being irreducible, and if every zero of $f(\mathbf{x}; \mathbf{y})$ is a zero of $g(\mathbf{x}; \mathbf{y})$, then $f(\mathbf{x}; \mathbf{y})$ is a factor of $g(\mathbf{x}; \mathbf{y})$.*

Proof. The theorem is an immediate consequence of the last theorem in § 17 of Appendix A. From that theorem, indeed, we can deduce a stronger form of Theorem 2, in which the hypothesis 'every zero of $f(\mathbf{x}; \mathbf{y})$ is a zero of $g(\mathbf{x}; \mathbf{y})$' is replaced by 'every zero of $f(\mathbf{x}; \mathbf{y})$ which does not satisfy an arbitrary fixed two-way equation $h(\mathbf{x}; \mathbf{y}) = 0$ is a zero of $g(\mathbf{x}; \mathbf{y})$'.

COROLLARY. *If two two-way forms $f(\mathbf{x}; \mathbf{y})$ and $g(\mathbf{x}; \mathbf{y})$ have the same zeros, then they are composed of the same irreducible factors, though possibly with different exponents.*

1.2. Associated forms

We now return to the problem of representing an arbitrary point-set G by a single equation. Two different solutions are possible, since there are two ways in which we can represent a single point $\mathbf{a}$ by an equation:

(i) by means of the line-equation $a_0 u_0 + a_1 u_1 + a_2 u_2 = 0$;

(ii) by means of the two-way equation

$$|\mathbf{x}\ \mathbf{y}\ \mathbf{a}| \equiv \begin{vmatrix} x_0 & y_0 & a_0 \\ x_1 & y_1 & a_1 \\ x_2 & y_2 & a_2 \end{vmatrix} = 0.$$

The line-equation expresses algebraically the condition for a line **u** to pass through the point **a**, and the two-way equation expresses the condition for two points **x** and **y** to be collinear with this point.

If, now, a point-set G consists of points $\overset{i}{\mathbf{a}}$ with multiplicities r_i, it can be represented without ambiguity by either of the equations

$$G(\mathbf{u}) \equiv \prod_{i=1}^{s} (\overset{i}{a}_0 u_0 + \overset{i}{a}_1 u_1 + \overset{i}{a}_2 u_2)^{r_i} = 0$$

and

$$G(\mathbf{x}; \mathbf{y}) \equiv \prod_{i=1}^{s} |\mathbf{x} \ \ \mathbf{y} \ \ \overset{i}{\mathbf{a}}|^{r_i} = 0;$$

and the left-hand sides of these equations are called *associated forms* of the point-set G. Although the first of these forms—an ordinary form of degree n in the line-coordinates u_j—is at first sight the simpler of the two, we shall find that the second—a (highly special) two-way form of degrees (n, n) in the point-coordinates x_j and y_j— is equally fundamental, and in some ways more suggestive of possible generalization.

If we consider the totality of all sets G of given order n, the $\binom{n+2}{2}$ coefficients of any particular form $G(\mathbf{u})$ define an image point Γ of the corresponding set G in a projective space Σ of dimensionality $\binom{n+2}{2} - 1$, while the $\binom{n+2}{2}^2$ coefficients of $G(\mathbf{x}; \mathbf{y})$ define another image point Γ' of G in a projective space Σ' of dimensionality $\binom{n+2}{2}^2 - 1$. The new and unavoidable feature that is common to both these representations is that the totality of point-sets G of order n in S_2 is mapped, not on a full linear space, but on a manifold contained in a linear space Σ or Σ'. The mapping is in this respect more like the mapping of lines in S_3 on points of S_5 by means of their Grassmann coordinates p_{ik} than like the mapping of conics in S_2 on points of S_5 by means of their coefficients a_{ik}. The coefficients of a form of degree n in u_0, u_1, u_2 must, in fact, satisfy a fixed set of algebraic equations, not all linear, if the form is to be of the special type $G(\mathbf{u})$, i.e. a product of n homogeneous linear factors; and, similarly, the coefficients of a two-way form of degrees (n, n) must satisfy a set of algebraic equations if the form is to be resolvable completely into factors of the type $|\mathbf{x} \ \mathbf{y} \ \mathbf{a}|$. We obtain, therefore, by the procedures outlined, *two alternative mappings of the point-sets G of order n in S_2 on the points of certain image manifolds Ω and Ω' in* *higher spaces* Σ *and* Σ'; and these manifolds, as can be shown, are algebraic, i.e. definable by sets of algebraic equations.

The relation between the forms $G(\mathbf{u})$ and $G(\mathbf{x};\mathbf{y})$ is very close, the latter form being derivable from the former, as is evident, by replacing u_0, u_1, u_2 everywhere by $x_1 y_2 - x_2 y_1$, $x_2 y_0 - x_0 y_2$, $x_0 y_1 - x_1 y_0$ respectively. We may accordingly describe $G(\mathbf{x};\mathbf{y})$ as the *dispersed form* of $G(\mathbf{u})$.

EXAMPLES. (i) If $n = 1$, so that we are dealing with point-sets of order 1 (i.e. individual points), the model Ω, derived from $G(\mathbf{u})$, is the complete *projective plane* Σ_2. On the other hand, the general bilinear form $F(\mathbf{x};\mathbf{y}) \equiv \sum_{i=0}^{2} \sum_{k=0}^{2} a_{ik} x_i y_k$ has nine coefficients, which define a point (a_{ik}) of a projective space Σ'_8 of eight dimensions; and the condition that $F(\mathbf{x};\mathbf{y})$ should be of the form $G(\mathbf{x};\mathbf{y}) \equiv |\mathbf{x}\ \mathbf{y}\ \mathbf{a}|$ is that the matrix (a_{rs}) should be skew-symmetric. This gives six linearly independent homogeneous linear relations connecting the a_{ik}, so that Ω' is a plane in Σ'_8.

(ii) If $n = 2$, the condition that a general quadratic form $\sum_{i=0}^{2} \sum_{k=0}^{2} a_{ik} u_i u_k\ (a_{ik} = a_{ki})$ should be a form $G(\mathbf{u})$ is $|a_{rs}| = 0$, which is a single homogeneous cubic relation between the six coefficients a_{ik}, and the model Ω is therefore a *cubic primal* (fourfold) contained in Σ_5. On the other hand, a general two-way form

$$F(\mathbf{x};\mathbf{y}) \equiv \sum a_{i,k;i',k'}\, x_i x_k y_{i'} y_{k'}$$

of degrees $(2, 2)$ has thirty-six coefficients $a_{i,k;i',k'}$, and is represented by a point in Σ'_{35}. The conditions for such a form to reduce to the special type $G(\mathbf{x};\mathbf{y})$ are *first* that F should be a quadratic form $\sum_{p=0}^{2} \sum_{q=0}^{2} \alpha_{pq} U_p U_q$, where the U_j $(j = 0, 1, 2)$ are the three expressions of the form $x_i y_k - x_k y_i$, and *second* that the quadratic form should factorize. The first condition gives thirty linearly independent linear relations between the $a_{i,k;i',k'}$, and the second gives simply $|\alpha_{rs}| = 0$, which is a single cubic relation between the $a_{i,k;i',k'}$. Ω' is therefore a cubic fourfold in a space Σ'_5 subordinate to Σ'_{35}.

2. Multiplicities of intersection. Bézout's Theorem

We come now to an introductory treatment of one of the central theorems in the theory of plane algebraic curves. Although the theorem itself is neither abstruse nor difficult to prove, we shall find that it requires, for its full exploitation and development, the radically new methods and concepts that are to be discussed in the chapters which follow the present one.

THEOREM 3. (*Bézout's Theorem*). *Let C_1 and C_2 be algebraic curves in S_2, of orders n_1 and n_2, with no common component. Then C_1 and C_2 have only a finite number of common points $P_1,..., P_s$; and multiplicities $\sigma_1,..., \sigma_s$ can be assigned to these points, by a systematic procedure, in such a way that the sum $\sum_{i=1}^{s} \sigma_i$ is equal to $n_1 n_2$.*

The theorem asserts that a definition of the multiplicity of intersection σ of two curves at any common point P can be given, which is such that the set of common points of any two curves C_1 and C_2 is a point-set $C_1 . C_2$, the order of which is the product of the orders of the curves.

Proof. Let C_1 and C_2 be represented by equations $f_1(\mathbf{x}) = 0$ and $f_2(\mathbf{x}) = 0$, the forms $f_1(\mathbf{x})$ and $f_2(\mathbf{x})$ having no common factor. It follows then, by Theorem 3 of Chapter I, that C_1 and C_2 have only a finite number of common points $\overset{1}{\mathbf{a}},..., \overset{s}{\mathbf{a}}$.

Now let $\mathbf{y}$ and $\mathbf{z}$ be two undetermined points,† and let $\lambda \mathbf{y} + \mu \mathbf{z}$ be an undetermined point of the line joining them.

If
$$f_1(\lambda \mathbf{y} + \mu \mathbf{z}) \equiv A_0 \lambda^{n_1} + A_1 \lambda^{n_1-1} \mu + ... + A_{n_1} \mu^{n_1} \tag{1}$$
and
$$f_2(\lambda \mathbf{y} + \mu \mathbf{z}) \equiv B_0 \lambda^{n_2} + B_1 \lambda^{n_2-1} \mu + ... + B_{n_2} \mu^{n_2}, \tag{2}$$
then A_i $(i = 0,..., n_1)$ is a two-way form in $\mathbf{y}$ and $\mathbf{z}$ of degrees $(n_1 - i, i)$ and B_j is a two-way form of degrees $(n_2 - j, j)$. The resultant of the two forms (1) and (2) in λ, μ is then a polynomial $R(\mathbf{y}, \mathbf{z})$ in $y_0,..., z_2$. But, if A_i is reckoned as having weight i and B_j as having weight j, the resultant R consists of terms which are all of weight $n_1 n_2$ in the A_i and B_j together; and therefore $R(\mathbf{y}, \mathbf{z})$, when multiplied out, is a two-way form $R(\mathbf{y}; \mathbf{z})$ of degrees $(n_1 n_2, n_1 n_2)$. Now this resultant is zero if and only if the equations $f_1(\lambda \mathbf{y} + \mu \mathbf{z}) = 0$ and $f_2(\lambda \mathbf{y} + \mu \mathbf{z}) = 0$, regarded as equations for λ/μ, have a common root, i.e. if and only if some point of the line joining $\mathbf{y}$ and $\mathbf{z}$ is common to C_1 and C_2. It follows that the pairs of points $(\boldsymbol{\eta}, \boldsymbol{\zeta})$ which satisfy the equation $R(\mathbf{y}; \mathbf{z}) = 0$ are exactly the same as those which satisfy the equation $\prod_{i=1}^{s} |\mathbf{y} \ \mathbf{z} \ \overset{i}{\mathbf{a}}| = 0$. By

---

† We use this form of expression in order to bring out the simple idea behind the proof. If the reader so wishes, he will be able easily to reformulate the argument as a piece of pure algebra.

the Corollary to Theorem 2, therefore, $R(\mathbf{y}; \mathbf{z})$ may be expressed in the form

$$R(\mathbf{y}; \mathbf{z}) = k \prod_{i=1}^{s} |\mathbf{y} \ \mathbf{z} \ \overset{i}{\mathbf{a}}|^{\sigma_i},$$

where k is an element of K and $\sigma_1,...,\sigma_s$ are positive integers; and, because of the uniqueness of factorization of two-way forms, the expression is essentially unique. The exponents $\sigma_1,...,\sigma_s$ now give the required multiplicities of $\overset{1}{\mathbf{a}},...,\overset{s}{\mathbf{a}}$ as points of intersection of C_1 and C_2; and, since the two-way form $R(\mathbf{y}; \mathbf{z})$ has degrees $(n_1 n_2, n_1 n_2)$,

$$\sum_{i=1}^{s} \sigma_i = n_1 n_2.$$

That the definition that we have just given of the multiplicities σ_i is a satisfactory formalization of the intuitive notion of multiplicity of intersection (a notion which is only free from doubt and ambiguity in comparatively simple cases) cannot be guaranteed except by the proved efficacy of the definition in the further working out of our system—and the great value of the abstract concept of multiplicity of intersection, as we have now defined it, will in fact become fully apparent in the course of the development which is to follow. For the moment, we shall remark simply that our definition certainly satisfies the obvious requirement of being projectively invariant. For suppose the representation of S_2 is changed from $\mathscr{R}$ to $\bar{\mathscr{R}}$ by a transformation with matrix equation $\bar{\mathbf{x}} = \mathbf{A}\mathbf{x}$ ($|\mathbf{A}| \neq 0$). Then each bilinear form $|\mathbf{y} \ \mathbf{z} \ \mathbf{a}|$ is transformed according to the law

$$|\bar{\mathbf{y}} \ \bar{\mathbf{z}} \ \bar{\mathbf{a}}| = |\mathbf{A}| \, |\mathbf{y} \ \mathbf{z} \ \mathbf{a}|,$$

and $R(\mathbf{y}; \mathbf{z})$ is changed, by the linear transformation of the co-ordinates, into another two-way form $\bar{R}$ with the same degrees as R.

In conclusion, we observe that our definition of the multiplicities σ_i is well adapted only to theoretical use, since, even in the very simplest cases, the direct evaluation of the σ_i for a particular pair of curves would be so laborious as almost to preclude our attempting the undertaking. We can, however, reduce the task at least to more manageable proportions by a procedure of specialization, now to be explained.

2.1. Computation of the multiplicities σ_i

We start from the two-way equation

$$R(\mathbf{y}; \mathbf{z}) \equiv k \prod_{i=1}^{s} |\mathbf{y} \ \mathbf{z} \ \overset{i}{\mathbf{a}}|^{\sigma_i} = 0$$

of the intersection-set $G \equiv C_1 . C_2$; and we specialize this equation throughout by (i) replacing z_0, z_1, z_2 by x_0, x_1, x_2 (purely a change of notation), and (ii) replacing y_0, y_1, y_2 by 1, 0, 0. The change carries $R(\mathbf{y}; \mathbf{z})$ into a homogeneous polynomial $E(x_1, x_2)$ in x_1, x_2, namely

$$E(x_1, x_2) \equiv k \prod_{i=1}^{s} \begin{vmatrix} 1 & x_0 & \overset{i}{a_0} \\ 0 & x_1 & \overset{i}{a_1} \\ 0 & x_2 & \overset{i}{a_2} \end{vmatrix}^{\sigma_i}$$

$$\equiv k \prod_{i=1}^{s} (x_1 \overset{i}{a_2} - x_2 \overset{i}{a_1})^{\sigma_i}.$$

The form $E(x_1, x_2)$ is of degree $n_1 n_2$, and, *provided only that the reference point* $(1, 0, 0)$ *is not one of the common points of* C_1 *and* C_2, *it does not vanish identically.* Also $E(x_1, x_2)$ is the (λ, μ)-resultant of the forms

$$f_1(\lambda + \mu x_0, \mu x_1, \mu x_2) \quad \text{and} \quad f_2(\lambda + \mu x_0, \mu x_1, \mu x_2),$$

i.e. the λ-resultant of the polynomials $f_1(\lambda + x_0, x_1, x_2)$ and $f_2(\lambda + x_0, x_1, x_2)$, i.e. the x_0-resultant of $f_1(x_0, x_1, x_2)$ and $f_2(x_0, x_1, x_2)$. We now ask whether it is possible that two different irreducible factors of $R(\mathbf{y}; \mathbf{z})$ may be specialized to give identical factors of $E(x_1, x_2)$; and we see at once that this can occur only if two of the points $\overset{i}{\mathbf{a}}$ are collinear with X_0. We thus have the following theorem.

THEOREM 4. *Provided that the reference point* $X_0 \equiv (1, 0, 0)$ *is neither a common point of* C_1 *and* C_2, *nor a point collinear with two such common points, then the multiplicities of intersection* $\sigma_1, ..., \sigma_s$ *of* C_1 *and* C_2 *at their common points* $\overset{1}{\mathbf{a}}, ..., \overset{s}{\mathbf{a}}$ *are the exponents of the factors* $x_1 \overset{i}{a_2} - x_2 \overset{i}{a_1}$ $(i = 1, ..., s)$ *in the* x_0-*resultant* $E(x_1, x_2)$ *of* $f_1(x_0, x_1, x_2)$ *and* $f_2(x_0, x_1, x_2)$, *where* $f_1 = 0$ *and* $f_2 = 0$ *are the equations of* C_1 *and* C_2.

This is plainly an improvement, from a practical point of view, on our original definition of the σ_i. It is desirable, however, to modify the result still further, so that the multiplicities may be characterized directly in terms of the affine equations of the curves.

Let us suppose, then, that we go over to affine coordinates X, Y by writing $x_1/x_2 = X$, $x_0/x_2 = Y$.†

† A departure from the customary correspondence $x_1/x_0 = X$, $x_2/x_0 = Y$ is here necessary in order that the eventual result may be obtained in a convenient form.

The affine equations of C_1 and C_2 are

$$F_1(X, Y) \equiv f_1(Y, X, 1) = 0$$

and

$$F_2(X, Y) \equiv f_2(Y, X, 1) = 0.$$

The form $E(x_1, x_2)$ now gives the Y-resultant, $R(X)$ say, of $F_1(X, Y)$ and $F_2(X, Y)$; and all the factors of $E(x_1, x_2)$ are represented, and to the same powers, by corresponding factors of $R(X)$, with the exception only of any that may arise from points $\overset{i}{\mathbf{a}}$ for which $\overset{i}{a_2} = 0$. These latter would be common points of C_1 and C_2 on the line at infinity of the affine system. We thus have the following further theorem.

THEOREM 5. *Let C_1 and C_2 have equations $F_1(X, Y) = 0$ and $F_2(X, Y) = 0$ in an affine coordinate system, and let $R(X)$ be the Y-resultant of $F_1(X, Y)$ and $F_2(X, Y)$. Then, provided that* (i) Y_∞ *is not a common point of C_1 and C_2, and* (ii) *no two common points of the curves lie on the same ordinate, the multiplicities of intersection σ_i of C_1 and C_2 at all their finite common points (a_i, b_i) are the exponents of the corresponding factors $X - a_i$ of $R(X)$.*

If we have chosen the affine representation in such a way that none of the common points lies on the line at infinity, then $R(X)$ will be of degree $n_1 n_2$, and *all* the multiplicities of intersection will be given by $R(X)$. Also, we shall have in that case explicitly

$$R(X) = k \prod_{i=1}^{s} (X - a_i)^{\sigma_i}.$$

Neither Theorem 4 nor Theorem 5 is of much value for the practical computation of multiplicities of intersection; but the theorems do bring us much nearer to our objective of being able to evaluate these numbers, since they characterize them in ways which are within the range of the new methods which we shall develop in the succeeding chapters.

NOTES AND EXERCISES ON CHAPTER II

1. *Coordinates of an unordered point-pair of S_1.* An unordered point-pair of S_1 is defined by an affine equation $a_0 - 2a_1 X + a_2 X^2 = 0$ or by a homogeneous equation $a_0 x_0^2 - 2a_1 x_0 x_1 + a_2 x_1^2 = 0$, and all such point-pairs can accordingly be mapped on the points (a_0, a_1, a_2) of a projective-plane S_2. Verify that the map, in this representation, of the repeated points of S_1 is the conic $C^{(2)}$ with parametric equations $x_0 : x_1 : x_2 = \theta^2 : \theta : 1$, and discuss the other properties of the representation.

2. *The rational normal curve* $C^{(n)}$ *of* S_n. If $(a_0, ..., a_n)$ is a homogeneous coordinate vector of a point of S_n, the curve $C^{(n)}$ with parametric equations

$$a_0 : a_1 : ... : a_n = \lambda^n : \lambda^{n-1} : ... : 1$$

is called a *rational normal curve of order* n in S_n. If the general point $(a_0, ..., a_n)$ of S_n is taken to be the image of the unordered set of points of S_1 defined by the equation

$$a_0 x_0^n - \binom{n}{1} a_1 x_0^{n-1} x_1 + ... + (-1)^n a_n x_1^n = 0,$$

show that $C^{(n)}$ is the map, in this representation, of all the n-fold points of S_1.

Discuss this representation in the cases $n = 3, 4$, and 5. Show in particular, with a proper interpretation of the term 'general' in each case, that (i) the general binary cubic form $F_3(x_0, x_1)$ over K can be expressed as a sum of two cubes of linear forms, and (ii) the general binary quintic form $F_5(x_0, x_1)$ can be expressed as a sum of fifth powers of three linear forms.

3. *The two-way space* $S_{1,1}$; *the ordered pairs of* S_1. The two-way space $S_{1,1}$ of points $(x_0, x_1; y_0, y_1)$ can be envisaged as the space of ordered pairs of points $\mathbf{x} = (x_0, x_1)$ and $\mathbf{y} = (y_0, y_1)$ of a line S_1. The *Segre model* of $S_{1,1}$, or of the ordered pairs $(\mathbf{x}, \mathbf{y})$ of S_1, is defined by the equations

$$X_0 : X_1 : X_2 : X_3 = x_0 y_0 : x_0 y_1 : x_1 y_0 : x_1 y_1,$$

which map each point of $S_{1,1}$ on a point of the quadric surface $W_{1,1}$ with equation $X_0 X_3 = X_1 X_2$ in projective space S_3.

Discuss this representation, and examine in particular the systems of point-pairs $(\mathbf{x}, \mathbf{y})$ that correspond to generators of each system on $W_{1,1}$ and to plane sections of $W_{1,1}$.

4. *The two-way space* $S_{2,2}$; *the ordered point-pairs of* S_2. Proceeding as in Exercise 3, we define the Segre model of $S_{2,2}$ as the four-fold (4-parameter) locus $W_{2,2}$ in S_8 with parametric equations

$$X_{ij} = x_i y_j \quad (i, j = 0, 1, 2),$$

the effective parameters being the ratios x_1/x_0, x_2/x_0, y_1/y_0, y_2/y_0; and $W_{2,2}$ is therefore the model of the ordered point-pairs $(\mathbf{x}, \mathbf{y})$ of S_2.

Show that $W_{2,2}$ has two doubly infinite systems of planes ξ and η, such that any plane ξ represents all pairs $(\mathbf{x}, \mathbf{y})$ for which $\mathbf{x}$ is a fixed point, with a similar interpretation of planes η. Show further that $W_{2,2}$ contains a quadruply infinite family of quadric surfaces ω, each of which represents pairs $(\mathbf{x}, \mathbf{y})$ such that $\mathbf{x}$ lies on a given line p and $\mathbf{y}$ on a given line q. Discuss the incidence relations of members of the systems (ξ), (η), and (ω); and discuss also the representation on $W_{2,2}$ of coincident point-pairs $(\mathbf{x}, \mathbf{x})$.

Show further that every section of $W_{2,2}$ by a prime S_7 of S_8 maps the point-pairs $(\mathbf{x}, \mathbf{y})$ of a correlation $\sum a_{rs} x_r y_s = 0$ (possibly singular) of S_2; and discuss, more generally, the model on $W_{2,2}$ of the aggregate of point-pairs $(\mathbf{x}, \mathbf{y})$ that satisfy any two-way K-equation $F(\mathbf{x}; \mathbf{y})$ of degrees m and n in the x_i and y_j.

5. *The model* $\Omega^{(2)}$ *of the unordered point-pairs of* S_2. The coordinates of any unordered point-pair (P, Q) of S_2 being taken (as on p. 35) to be the six coefficients a_{ij} in the associated quadratic form $\sum a_{ij} u_i u_j$ of the pair, we thereby obtain a representation of all the pairs (P, Q) on all the points of a cubic primal $\Omega^{(2)}$ with equation $|a_{ij}| = 0$ in S_5. Establish the following properties of $\Omega^{(2)}$:

(i) Every line of S_5, if it does not lie on $\Omega^{(2)}$, meets it in at most three points.

(ii) $\Omega^{(2)}$ has two doubly-infinite systems (π) and (λ) of generating planes, of which any π maps pairs (P, Q) of which one point is fixed, while any λ maps pairs (P, Q) such that each of P and Q lies on one and the same fixed line of S_2.

(iii) The repeated points (P, P) of S_2 are mapped on the points of a certain surface F—called a *Veronese surface*—on $\Omega^{(2)}$, and F meets every plane λ in a conic and every plane π in only a single point.

Show further that F is a *double surface* on $\Omega^{(2)}$, in the sense that any line of S_5 drawn through a point of F, and not lying entirely on $\Omega^{(2)}$, meets $\Omega^{(2)}$ in at most one further point.

Note. The above mapping of unordered point-pairs (P, Q) of S_2 on points of $\Omega^{(2)}$ is subordinate to the mapping of all conic envelopes of S_2 on points of S_5; and its properties may be conveniently investigated against this background.

6. *The model $\Omega^{(3)}$ of unordered point-triads of S_2.* The model $\Omega^{(3)}$, analogous to $\Omega^{(2)}$, of the unordered triads (P, Q, R) of S_2 is a six-fold locus in S_9, the equations defining this locus representing the conditions on the coefficients in a ternary cubic form $F_3(u_0, u_1, u_2)$ for the form to decompose into linear factors. Discuss the representation on $\Omega^{(3)}$ of (i) the totality of coincidence triads (P, P, P), and (ii) an aggregate of triads of the form (P, P, Q), where P is fixed and Q is variable.

7. *Intersections of a curve with a line.* To verify directly that the multiplicities of the intersections of a curve C with a line L, as defined in Chapter I, § 4.1, are the same as those resulting from the general definition given in § 2 of the present chapter, we may proceed as follows.

We take the line, as we may, to have equation $x_0 = 0$, and we suppose that C has equation $f(x_0, x_1, x_2) = 0$, where f is of degree n and does not have x_0 as a factor. Further, let the distinct intersections of C and L be

$$\mathbf{a}^{(i)} \equiv (0, a_1^{(i)}, a_2^{(i)}) \quad (i = 1, ..., s).$$

We verify at once then that the multiplicities of these intersections, according to the first definition, are the numbers σ_i occurring in the factorization

$$f(0, x_1, x_2) = k \prod_1^s (a_2^{(i)} x_1 - a_1^{(i)} x_2)^{\sigma_i} \quad (k \in K).$$

The two-way form $R(\mathbf{y}, \mathbf{z})$ relevant to the second definition is the resultant of the equations $f(\lambda \mathbf{y} + \mu \mathbf{z}) = 0$ and $\lambda y_0 + \mu z_0 = 0$, this being the same as the resultant of the equations

$$f(0, \lambda y_1 + \mu z_1, \lambda y_2 + \mu z_2) = 0 \quad \text{and} \quad \lambda y_0 + \mu z_0 = 0.$$

Since

$$f(0, \lambda y_1 + \mu z_1, \lambda y_2 + \mu z_2) = k \prod_1^s (\lambda(a_2^{(i)} y_1 - a_1^{(i)} y_2) + \mu(a_2^{(i)} z_1 - a_1^{(i)} z_2))^{\sigma_i}$$

we have

$$R(\mathbf{y}, \mathbf{z}) = k \prod_1^s (z_0(a_2^{(i)} y_1 - a_1^{(i)} y_2) - y_0(a_2^{(i)} z_1 - a_1^{(i)} z_2))^{\sigma_i},$$

so that
$$R(\mathbf{y}, \mathbf{z}) = \pm k \prod_1^s |\mathbf{y} \ \mathbf{z} \ \mathbf{a}^{(i)}|^{\sigma_i}$$

as required.

8. Show that Theorem 5 is applicable in the case when C_1 and C_2 are the conics $Y = X^2$ and $Y = (X-Y)^2$, and that in this case $R(X) = X^3(X-2)$. Verify by elementary methods, and with the aid of a figure, that the conics have 3-point contact at $(0, 0)$ and a simple intersection at $(2, 4)$.

Obtain the same results by use of the X-resultant $R(Y)$.

9. Verify that, if C_1 and C_2 are the conics with equations

$$X^2(1-a) + aY^2 - Y = 0, \qquad X^2(1-a) + aY^2 - Y + (\lambda X + \mu Y)^2 = 0,$$

where a, λ, μ are constants, then

$$R(X) = X^2\{(a\lambda^2 + \mu^2(1-a))X + \lambda\mu\}^2,$$
$$R(Y) = Y^2\{(a\lambda^2 + \mu^2(1-a))Y - \lambda^2\}^2.$$

Discuss, with rough sketches, the application of Theorem 5 to C_1 and C_2 (when this is appropriate) for all sets of values of a, λ, μ.

10. If C_1 and C_2 are respectively the cuspidal cubic $Y^2 = X^3$ and the conic $Y^2 + 2Y - 3X^2 = 0$, verify that

$$R(X) = X^3(X-1)^2(X-4),$$

and hence discuss the multiplicities of intersection of the curves at their common points. Illustrate your results by a rough sketch.

11. *Simple intersections.* Prove directly, by use of Theorem 5, that if C_1 and C_2 (having no common component) have each a simple point at P, then their multiplicity of intersection at P is 1 if their tangents at P are distinct, and is not less than 2 if their tangents are coincident.

[*Hint.* Take P as origin $(0, 0)$, remove the obvious factor X from the determinant $R(X)$, and evaluate the determinant $[X^{-1}R(X)]_{X=0}$ by Laplace's method as the product of a 2×2 determinant by another determinant.]

12. Verify by use of Theorem 5 that, if C_1 and C_2 each have a double point at P, then their multiplicity of intersection at P is not less than 4.

[*Hint.* Take P as origin and derive the factor X^4 of $R(X)$ by considering the last three columns of $R(X)$.]

13. The two cubic curves with equations

$$Y = aX^2 + 2hXY + bY^2 + U_3(X, Y),$$
$$Y = a'X^2 + 2h'XY + b'Y^2 + U_3'(X, Y)$$

are such that they have no common component and no intersection other than the origin on the axis OY. Prove that $a = a'$ is a necessary and sufficient condition for their multiplicity of intersection at O to be at least 3.

14. If P is any common point of C_1 and C_2, show that the multiplicity of P as an intersection of C_1 with the s-fold curve C_2 is s times the multiplicity of intersection of C_1 and C_2 at P.

CHAPTER III

TRANSCENDENTAL POINTS OF S_2

1. Transcendental points

A POINT of $S_2(K)$ is defined by means of a triad of coordinates (a_0, a_1, a_2) in some allowable representation $\mathscr{R}$ of S_2; and these coordinates have hitherto been restricted, by definition, to the elements of K. To make possible the developments which we have in mind, however, we now need to relax this restriction, generalizing the concept of point by allowing the coordinates to be taken from an extension field K' of K, instead of confining them to K itself. From now on, therefore, we shall be dealing both with points in the strict sense, which we distinguish as the *ground points* of $S_2(K)$, and also with certain ideal points, which we refer to as *transcendental points* of $S_2(K)$.

The distinction between actual and ideal points of a space, to which we shall now give a precise meaning, is by no means unfamiliar, even in more elementary geometry. We make use of it, for instance, when we adjoin imaginary points and points at infinity (real as well as imaginary) to the real euclidean plane. Again, the same notion comes into play, if only implicitly, when we refer to a 'general' or 'variable' point of the plane or of a locus in the plane; for neither the point (X, Y) with current coordinates X, Y, nor the point $(\theta^2, \theta, 1)$ of the conic $x_1^2 = x_2 x_0$, where θ is a parameter, is a point in the strict sense. The extension of the idea of point that is involved in such examples is, however, slight; for both (X, Y) and $(\theta^2, \theta, 1)$ can be regarded as point-schemata, which give rise to well-defined points whenever definite numbers are substituted for the variables X and Y, or θ. Conceptual extension can accordingly be avoided by use of an appropriate circumlocution. But the situations which we now envisage demand, on the contrary, a real extension of ideas, for we certainly do not wish to interpret as schemata the new generalized points which we are about to introduce. These points are to be conceived as objects in their own right, being elements of the geometrical system no less than the ground points. In order to illustrate the change of outlook involved, we shall first of all take the 'general point' $(\theta^2, \theta, 1)$ of the conic s with equation

$x_1^2 = x_2 x_0$, and show how it may be regarded as an actual geometric entity.

Let θ be an *indeterminate*, in the sense current in algebra—i.e. a formal constituent of the symbolism, concerning which nothing is postulated beyond the fact that it can be manipulated in accordance with specific rules (the same as the rules which govern calculation with elements of K). Thus θ is not to be understood as a variable with a range of values; it is a new entity which is to be handled formally in the same way as the elements of the ground field. We now possess extended possibilities of calculation; and we are able, in particular, to look upon $(\theta^2, \theta, 1)$ as a triad of coordinates of a point, since the same kind of algebraic operations can be carried out on $(\theta^2, \theta, 1)$ as on (a_0, a_1, a_2), where a_0, a_1, a_2 are all in K. The 'point' $(\theta^2, \theta, 1)$, moreover, may reasonably be said to lie on the conic s, since its coordinates formally satisfy the equation of s.

Having once adjoined to the ground field K the new symbol θ, and laid down the rules of calculation which govern its use, we are able to construct a whole family of new symbolic objects, which we call *rational functions* of θ. These are expressions of the form

$$\frac{a_m \theta^m + a_{m-1} \theta^{m-1} + \ldots + a_0}{b_n \theta^n + b_{n-1} \theta^{n-1} + \ldots + b_0},$$

the a_i and b_j being elements of K. When equality, addition, subtraction, multiplication, and division of such expressions are defined formally in conformity with the familiar rules of elementary algebra, the set of all rational functions of θ becomes a field, and we call it the field $K(\theta)$ of (formal) rational functions in the indeterminate θ over the field K. $K(\theta)$ has a subfield, consisting of all the constant rational functions a_0/b_0, which is isomorphic with K and which, by a widely used procedure of identification, may be identified with K itself. Thus $K(\theta)$ is an *extension field* of K; and it is just because formal calculations involving the 'point' $(\theta^2, \theta, 1)$ can be regarded as calculations within the extended field $K(\theta)$ that we are able to work with this 'point' as if it were an actual point of $S_2(K)$. We shall henceforth be more explicit in this respect, and we shall refer to $(\theta^2, \theta, 1)$ as a triad of coordinates of a *transcendental point* of $S_2(K)$, meaning thereby a point, in a generalized sense, with coordinates in a field which is an extension of the ground field. The precise definition of transcendental point runs as follows.

DEFINITION. If $\mathscr{R}$ is any allowable representation of $S_2(K)$, and if α_0, α_1, α_2 are any three elements, not all zero, of some extension field K' of K (i.e. some field K' which has K as a subfield) then we say that α_0, α_1, α_2 are homogeneous coordinates, relative to $\mathscr{R}$, of a point P. If there exists a non-zero element λ of K' such that $\lambda\alpha_0$, $\lambda\alpha_1$, $\lambda\alpha_2$ are all in K, P is a *ground point* of $S_2(K)$; otherwise it is a *transcendental point* of $S_2(K)$. The equations of transformation (with coefficients in K) from $\mathscr{R}$ to any other allowable representation $\overline{\mathscr{R}}$ of $S_2(K)$ apply equally to ground points and transcendental points.

Note. To be a transcendental point of $S_2(K)$ with coordinates in K' is not the same thing as to be a ground point of $S_2(K')$; and it is the last sentence of the above definition that makes this distinction clear. The allowable changes of coordinate representation for points of $S_2(K)$, whether these are ground points or transcendental points, have coefficients in K, while the allowable changes for points of $S_2(K')$ have coefficients in K'. It follows, therefore, that the distinction between ground points and transcendental points is projective, being unaffected by any allowable change of the representation $\mathscr{R}$. An analogous situation arises, of course, when imaginary points are adjoined, as ideal points, to the real euclidean or projective plane.

Suppose now that a particular choice has been made of the extension field K' of K. Then there are infinitely many transcendental points of $S_2(K)$ which have coordinates in K'. If we are only interested in some particular one of these points, $\boldsymbol{\alpha}$ say, it may happen that the extension of K to K' is unnecessarily wide, since there is a proper subfield K'' of K' in which the ratios between α_0, α_1, and α_2 are all contained. For every transcendental point $\boldsymbol{\alpha}$, in fact, there is a minimal choice of extension field of K which contains the ratios of α_0, α_1, and α_2, and we shall denote by K_α the smallest extension field with this property.

Suppose, for definiteness, that $\alpha_0 \neq 0$. Then K_α must contain the ratios α_1/α_0 and α_2/α_0; and it is easily seen that in this case K_α is generated over K by these two ratios, i.e. it consists of all those elements of K' that can be expressed rationally in terms of α_1/α_0 and α_2/α_0, with coefficients in K. It should be noted, however, that not every rational function over K of two indeterminates yields an element of K_α when α_1/α_0 and α_2/α_0 are substituted for the indeterminates; for an element of K_α will only be obtained if the denominator, after substitution, is different from zero. It is also to be noted that two different rational functions may yield the same element of K_α. (Cf. the detailed discussions of extension fields later in this chapter and in Chapter VII.)

We now give a formal definition of K_α.

DEFINITION. The *minimum field of definition K_α* of a point α of $S_2(K)$ is the extension field of K that is generated by those of the six ratios α_i/α_j for which the denominator is different from zero, i.e. the smallest field which contains all the elements of K and also these ratios.

Remarks. (i) Plainly $K_\alpha = K$ if α is a ground point, and K_α is a proper extension of K if α is transcendental. (ii) Since K is algebraically closed, it has no proper *algebraic* extensions (cf. Chapter VII, § 2, and Appendix A, §§ 11, 13). Thus α is a transcendental point if and only if K_α is transcendental over K.

We now observe that two different transcendental points may be only formally distinct, having all their most important properties in common although their sets of coordinate ratios are distinct from each other. Trivial examples of points which are only formally distinct from $(\theta^2, \theta, 1)$ are $(\phi^2, \phi, 1)$ and $(1, \theta, \theta^2)$; and a slightly less trivial example of a point only formally distinct from the same point $(\theta^2, \theta, 1)$ is $((1+\theta)^2, 1+\theta, 1)$. We shall see at a later stage that the properties which a transcendental point has in common with all those points that are only formally distinct from it, relative to the ground field K, are of great importance; and for this reason we adopt the following definition.

DEFINITION. Two extension fields K' and K'' of K are said to be *equivalent extensions* of K if there exists an isomorphism $K' \cong K''$ between them which leaves every element of K invariant (briefly, an *isomorphism over K*). Two transcendental points α and β of $S_2(K)$ are said to be *isomorphically equivalent* if they correspond in an isomorphism over K between K_α and K_β.

THEOREM 1. *If α and β are isomorphically equivalent transcendental points, then any K-equation which is satisfied by either of them is also satisfied by the other.*

Proof. If $f(\alpha_0, \alpha_1, \alpha_2) = 0$, where $f(x_0, x_1, x_2)$ is a K-form, then any isomorphism over K between K_α and K_β in which α corresponds to β carries the relation $f(\alpha_0, \alpha_1, \alpha_2) = 0$ into $f(\beta_0, \beta_1, \beta_2) = 0$.

Transcendental points, as we have defined them, are simply

points with coordinates in an extension field of K but not in K itself, and the concept of transcendental point is thus a very general one. We shall find it convenient to lay down a further definition, making a distinction between two different kinds of transcendental point which has the effect of separating off those transcendental points which interest us most at the moment from those which do not so immediately concern us.

DEFINITION. A transcendental point is *of the first kind* if it satisfies at least one K-equation $f(x_0, x_1, x_2) = 0$, and *of the second kind* if it does not satisfy any such equation.

2. Basic types of extension field

The concept of transcendental point has been defined in terms of an extension field K' of K which may be of any kind whatever; but the types of extension that actually arise when we use this concept in algebraic geometry are comparatively few. One of the main purposes for which we introduce transcendental points into our geometrical system is to secure the existence of suitable parametric representations of all the curves that we wish to consider. Given any algebraic equation $F(X, Y) = 0$, we want to be able to express the pairs of values of X and Y which satisfy the equation in terms of a parameter, u say, In a few favourable cases such expression is possible by means of rational functions—e.g. $X = cu$, $Y = c/u$ for the hyperbola $XY - c^2 = 0$ —but such cases are exceptional. For most algebraic curves we have to use infinite power series $\sum_{k=N}^{\infty} a_k u^k$ instead of rational functions, and for certain purposes it is even desirable to work with series of fractional powers of u. We are led in this way to consider various types of expression involving the parameter u, such as rational functions and formal series of integral or fractional powers; and each such type of expression yields a corresponding type of extension field of K. The fields thus obtained all have one feature in common, namely that they can be derived from K by some kind of constructive extension, using an indeterminate u; and the systematic development of those parts of our system of algebraic geometry which depend on the parametrization of curves will be based upon the construction of appropriate extension fields of K by so-called symbolic adjunction. Since, however, this algebraic process is wholly abstract, whereas the classical algebraic geometry from which our system is ultimately derived is presented in the literature in a very different way, we shall prefix to our more formal development a short account of the historical origins of the methods which we now prefer to use.

The method of symbolic adjunction was introduced into mathematics for the purpose of making possible a purely algebraic treatment of the roots of algebraic equations. The older way of developing a theory of the roots of equations with real coefficients was first of all to extend the system of real numbers to the more comprehensive system of complex numbers, and then to base the subsequent discussion on the Fundamental Theorem of Algebra, by virtue of which every equation with real coefficients has a root in the complex domain. This theorem, however, is not purely algebraic, and can only be proved by methods which belong properly to analysis; and to bring in analytical ideas unnecessarily is felt by algebraists to be unsatisfactory. Not only are there aesthetic objections to such a course, but there are also logical grounds on which a purely algebraic treatment is to be preferred. Algebra, which is based on finite operations, is logically simpler than analysis, with its limiting processes and its topological foundation; and looked at from the point of view of metamathematics, where logical niceties are of the first importance, algebra does not involve as much by way of logical presuppositions as analysis does. There is thus good reason for insisting that theories which are essentially algebraic shall be treated purely algebraically. A clear account of how this end is achieved in the case of algebraic equations is to be found in Chapter V of van der Waerden's *Modern Algebra*, where it is shown how, when an equation with coefficients in a particular field $\mathscr{K}$ is given, an extension of $\mathscr{K}$ can always be constructed, by use of symbolic adjunction, which is such that the given equation has a root in the extended field.

Now there is a close analogy between an *algebraic number*, which is a root of an algebraic equation $f(x) = 0$ over a given field $\mathscr{K}$, and an *algebraic function*, which is a root of an algebraic equation $f(x, y) = 0$ that serves to determine a dependent variable y implicitly as a function of an independent variable x. And in much the same way as one kind of symbolic adjunction enables us to construct an extension field $\mathscr{K}'$ of $\mathscr{K}$ in which a given $\mathscr{K}$-equation $f(x) = 0$ has a root, so another kind of symbolic adjunction enables us to construct certain extension fields $K|x|$ and $K^*|x|$ of the ground field K in which any K-equation $f(x, y) = 0$ can be solved explicitly for y as a 'function' of x.

In order to trace this idea to its origin, we must go back for a moment to the theory underlying the classical mode of treatment of algebraic functions. The ground field K is here understood, of course, to be the field of all complex numbers. Let us consider an irreducible polynomial $f(x, y)$ in two indeterminates x, y, with coefficients in K. It is shown in the theory of functions of a complex variable that the equation $f(x, y) = 0$ determines y as a many-valued function of x. More precisely, if the degree in y of $f(x, y)$ is n, there are n function elements $y_1, ..., y_n$, and these behave in the following manner in the neighbourhood of any particular value a of x. If a is not one of a certain finite set of *critical values* of x, then the values of $y_1, ..., y_n$ at a are all distinct, and each of the function elements $y_1, ..., y_n$ behaves as a one-valued function of the complex variable x in the neighbourhood of $x = a$, being expressible as a convergent power series in $x - a$ provided that $|x-a|$ does not exceed a suitably chosen positive quantity δ. But if a is a critical value of x, some of the y_i are associated in *cycles*, the k elements $y_1, ..., y_k$ of a cycle then being expressible as fractional power series in $x - a$ (namely, ordinary power series in $(x-a)^{1/k}$) in such a way that $y_1, ..., y_k$ are permuted cyclically if $e^{2\pi i/k}(x-a)^{1/k}$ is substituted for $(x-a)^{1/k}$ in the series representing them. The fractional power series, once again, converge to $y_1, ..., y_k$ whenever $|x-a|$ is less than a certain positive quantity. Such expansions in series of the function elements $y_1, ..., y_n$, defined by an equation $f(x, y) = 0$ of degree n in y, are known as *Puiseux series*; and the classical theory of algebraic functions is based on their Puiseux expansions, considered in relation to the Riemann surface for y as a many-valued function of x.†

It is part of our purpose in this book to show how such recourse to the theory of functions can be made unnecessary by constructing, by symbolic adjunction, fields of *formal* power series, integral and fractional, in which every algebraic equation $f(x, y) = 0$ may be solved directly for y in terms of x. In this way we arrive at series

---

† Puiseux's original memoir 'Recherches sur les fonctions algébriques' appeared in the *Journal de Mathématiques pures et appliquées*, **15** (1850). A simple modern account of the behaviour of the set of function elements $y_1, ..., y_n$ is to be found in Chapter II of van der Waerden's *Einführung in die algebraische Geometrie*. A standard work on the theory of algebraic functions is K. Hensel and G. Landsberg, *Theorie der algebraischen Funktionen einer Variabeln* (Leipzig, 1902).

formally the same as those obtained in the classical theory; but
since the formal series are now themselves the immediate objects of
interest, being elements of the extension field in which we are
operating, we do not have to ask whether there are 'values' to which
they converge. This is our most immediate gain when we introduce
the notion of transcendental point. Instead of being obliged to
investigate the properties of any given curve $F(X, Y) = 0$ by
examining the behaviour of Y, treated as an n-valued function of
the complex variable X, in the neighbourhood of any value $X = a$,
we now have only to solve the equation $F(X, Y) = 0$ *algebraically*
for Y in the field $K^*|X-a|$ of fractional power series in $X-a$,
obtaining as its roots $Y_1,..., Y_n$ a set of formal series which we can in
principle actually construct. All that then remains to be done is to
study the properties of the n transcendental points (X, Y_i); and this
again is a matter of algebra only, not of analysis.

We now turn to detailed consideration of the types of extension
of the ground field K with which we shall be concerned in the
subsequent chapters of this book. These are four in number, and
are as follows:

(i) the field $K(u)$ of *rational functions over K in an indeterminate
    u*;

(ii) the field $K|u|$ of *extended (formal) power series over K in u*;

(iii) the field $K^*|u|$ of *extended fractional power series over K in u*;

(iv) the field K_C of *rational functions on an irreducible curve C*
    of $S_2(K)$.

The extensions $K(u)$, $K|u|$, and $K^*|u|$ of K can all be obtained
from K, as we shall see, by the method of symbolic adjunction.
The fourth type of extension K_C, on the contrary, will be formed
in a different way, as a class of objects dependent on a given irredu-
cible curve C. Whereas the fields $K(u)$, $K|u|$, and $K^*|u|$ provide
our basic equipment for the parametrization of all algebraic curves,
K_C is itself obtained from a particular curve C. This field K_C is, as
we shall find, the basis of what we call the *invariantive geometry of
the curve C*, that is to say the totality of properties of C which are
left invariant by every 'birational' transformation of C into
another irreducible curve C'.

2.1. The integral domain $K[u]$ and the field $K(u)$

Although the formal treatment of polynomials and rational
functions is well known, we shall summarize the details here, both

for the sake of completeness of the systematic development and also to facilitate comparison with the treatments of power series which follow.

We begin by considering K-polynomials in an indeterminate u, each of these being simply a formal expression of the type

$$k_0 + k_1 u + \ldots + k_n u^n,$$

n being any non-negative integer, the k_i all being elements of K, and u being the letter whose sole function is to be a constituent in formal expressions. If operations of addition and multiplication of such formal polynomials are now defined by taking over, as definitions in the new abstract system, the rules already familiar from elementary algebra (or, as we shall say, if we adopt the 'natural' definitions of addition and multiplication) the set of all K-polynomials in u becomes a ring $K[u]$. The ring is actually an integral domain, and we may therefore embed it in a field of quotients by taking the set of all ordered pairs (f, g) of polynomials for which $g \neq 0$, separating this set into its equivalence classes with respect to the equivalence relation $(f_1, g_1) \sim (f_2, g_2)$ which holds if and only if $f_1 g_2 - f_2 g_1 = 0$ in $K[u]$, and then regarding these equivalence classes as elements in a new system. In this way we arrive at the field $K(u)$ of (formal) rational functions of u over K, and, if each element k of K is now identified with the equivalence class which contains the particular ordered pair $(k, 1)$, K itself is contained in $K(u)$. Each element of $K(u)$ has infinitely many representations by an ordered pair (f, g) of polynomials in $K[u]$, all pairs of the appropriate equivalence class being equally admissible. Using the customary notation for rational functions, we may then write the element, in infinitely many ways, as a quotient f/g.†

Suppose, now, that α is a transcendental point of $S_2(K)$ which is defined in $K(u)$. Then α_0, α_1, α_2 are rational functions of u, and since the coordinates are homogeneous we may reduce these functions to polynomials by multiplying through by a suitable polynomial factor. The point accordingly possesses a representation

$$\alpha_i = f_i(u) \quad (f_i(u) \in K[u], \quad i = 0, 1, 2).$$

† Any reader who is more interested in the development of the system of algebraic geometry than in logical clarification of its algebraic foundation may, without risk, think of f/g as a quotient in the ordinary naïve sense; and any reader who wants full details of the construction of fields of quotients will find them in van der Waerden's *Modern Algebra*, Chap. III.

In an affine coordinate system, any two elements a_1, a_2 of $K(u)$ which are not both in K define a transcendental point (a_1, a_2).

It is readily seen that any transcendental point of $S_2(K)$ that is defined in $K(u)$ must be of the first kind. For elimination of u between a pair of equations

$$X = a_1(u), \quad Y = a_2(u) \qquad (a_i(u) \in K(u), \quad i = 1, 2),$$

is always possible, and it yields a non-zero polynomial $F(X, Y)$ which is such that $F(a_1(u), a_2(u)) = 0$ in $K(u)$. A transcendental point that is defined in $K(u)$ may be called, for brevity, a *rational transcendental point*.

EXERCISE. Find rational transcendental points on each of the curves (a) $x_0^2 + x_1^2 + x_2^2 = 0$; (b) $x_1^3 + x_2^3 = x_0 x_1 x_2$; (c) $x_0 x_2^2 = x_1(x_0 + x_1)^2$.

2.2. The integral domain $K\{u\}$ and the field $K|u|$

Instead of extending K to an integral domain by forming *finite* formal sums

$$k_0 + k_1 u + \dots + k_n u^n,$$

we may take instead the *infinite* formal sums

$$p(u) \equiv k_0 + k_1 u + k_2 u^2 + \dots \quad (k_i \in K),$$

or *formal power series* in u; and once again, when addition and multiplication have their natural definitions, the extended system is an integral domain. We denote the domain of all formal power series in u, with coefficients belonging to K, by $K\{u\}$. If we identify any power series $p(u)$ for which $k_i = 0$ for $i = n+1, n+2, \dots$ with the corresponding polynomial $k_0 + k_1 u + \dots + k_n u^n$, we can regard $K\{u\}$ as containing $K[u]$ as a subdomain; and thus $K \subset K[u] \subset K\{u\}$.

$K\{u\}$ has a *multiplicative identity element* $1 = 1 + 0 . u + 0 . u^2 + \dots$; and every $p(u)$ such that $k_0 \neq 0$ is a *unit* of $K\{u\}$, that is to say there is an element $p'(u)$ in $K\{u\}$ such that $p'(u)p(u) = 1$. We can in fact determine the coefficients k_i' of $p'(u)$ in succession from the equation

$$(k_0' + k_1' u + k_2' u^2 + \dots)(k_0 + k_1 u + k_2 u^2 + \dots) = 1 + 0 . u + 0 . u^2 + \dots$$

by equating coefficients of ascending powers of u. This procedure, in other words, yields a recursive definition of the k_i'.

Any non-zero element $p(u)$ of $K\{u\}$, i.e. any formal power series in which the coefficients are not all zero, can be written in the form

$$p(u) \equiv u^n U,$$

where n is a non-negative integer and U is a unit of $K\{u\}$. The formal quotient of two series

$$p_1(u) \equiv u^{n_1} U_1 \quad \text{and} \quad p_2(u) \equiv u^{n_2} U_2$$

can then be written in the form

$$p_1(u)/p_2(u) \equiv u^{n_1-n_2} V,$$

where n_1-n_2 can be positive, negative, or zero, and

$$V = U_1/U_2 = U_2' U_1$$

is again a unit of $K\{u\}$. We see in this way that *the field of quotients $K|u|$ of $K\{u\}$ can be taken to be the system of all extended formal power series*

$$P(u) \equiv k_0 u^N + k_1 u^{N+1} + \dots \quad (k_i \in K), \tag{1}$$

with at most a finite number of terms with negative exponent. Since every rational function of u is formally expressible in the form (1) (by use of the binomial theorem, for example), $K|u|$ is an extension of $K(u)$.

If $P(u)$ does not have every coefficient zero, its leading exponent N is called its *order*, and we denote this number by $O(P(u))$. The null series—the zero element of $K|u|$—is taken conventionally to be of order ∞.

A transcendental point which is defined in $K|u|$ will often be referred to, for brevity, as a *formal transcendental point*. Such a point may be of the first or of the second kind. If, for example, we take an equation $f(u, v) = 0$, for which 0 is not a critical value of u (see p. 50) then this equation, as will appear, can be solved for v as a power series $p(u)$ in u; and then the formal transcendental point with affine representation $(u, p(u))$ is certainly of the first kind, since $f(u, p(u)) = 0$. The formal transcendental point $(u, s(u))$, on the other hand, where $s(u) = u - u^3/3! + \dots$ is the familiar power series for $\sin u$, is of the second kind, since u and $\sin u$ are not connected by any algebraic equation.

If a point $\boldsymbol{\alpha}$ is defined in $K|u|$, we can always arrange, by multiplying through if necessary by a power of u, that its homogeneous coordinates satisfy the following conditions:

    (i) $\alpha_0, \alpha_1, \alpha_2$ all belong to $K\{u\}$, i.e. they are elements of $K|u|$ of non-negative order;

    (ii) one, at least, of $\alpha_0, \alpha_1, \alpha_2$ is a unit of $K\{u\}$, i.e. an element of $K|u|$ of order 0.

When this has been done, we shall say that the representation is *in standard form*. We can, of course, go still further and ensure, by dividing throughout by a unit of $K\{u\}$, that one, at least, of the coordinates is unity. When this also has been done (and, as a rule, when the first of the three coordinates has the value unity) we shall say that the representation has been *normalized*. Putting the same thing in a different way, we may say that a homogeneous representation of a formal transcendental point is *in normal form* if it can be written as $(1, \xi_1, \xi_2)$, where $O(\xi_1) \geqslant 0$ and $O(\xi_2) \geqslant 0$. The point is thus a 'finite' point, and its affine coordinates ξ_1 and ξ_2 are both in $K\{u\}$.

If the element 0 of K is substituted for the indeterminate u in the standardized coordinates α_0, α_1, α_2 of a formal transcendental point $\boldsymbol{\alpha}$, a ground point $(\bar{\alpha}_0, \bar{\alpha}_1, \bar{\alpha}_2)$ is obtained, and we call this point $\bar{\boldsymbol{\alpha}}$ the *centre* of α. We can also define, in a similar way, the centre of a rational transcendental point, but in this case the notion is of little interest. The relation between formal transcendental points and their centres, on the contrary, will prove to be of great importance in the development of our system.

EXERCISES. (i) Verify that the point $(1, u, u^2+u^4+u^6+...)$ is a transcendental point, with centre $(1, 0, 0)$, of the curve $x_0 x_1^2 = x_2(x_0^2-x_1^2)$.

(ii) Find a formal power series $p(u)$ such that $(1, u, p(u))$ is a (normalized) transcendental point of the curve $x_1^3+x_2^3 = x_0 x_1 x_2$.

2.3. The integral domain $K^*\{u\}$ and the field $K^*|u|$

The entire intersection theory of algebraic curves is essentially simplified and facilitated, as we shall see below, if we proceed one stage further with the sequence of extensions $K \to K(u) \to K|u|$ of the ground field. We need, in fact, to consider formal series of a more general type than power series in u, namely power series in an arbitrary fractional power $u^{1/n}$ of u. The precise definition of the type of series that we introduce runs as follows.

DEFINITION. A formal series
$$k_0 u^{\nu_0}+k_1 u^{\nu_1}+... \quad (k_i \in K, \quad i = 0, 1,...),$$
in which $\nu_0, \nu_1,...$ is a strictly increasing sequence of rational numbers, will be called an (*extended*) *fractional power series* if and only if there exists a positive integer n such that $\nu_0, \nu_1,...$ are all integral multiples of the unit fraction $1/n$.

This definition implies that the number of negative exponents in the sequence $\nu_0, \nu_1,...$ is finite. If there are no negative exponents at all, the series is said to be *ordinary*, and it is then an element of the ring $K\{u^{1/n}\}$ for the appropriate value of n. If the series is *extended*, i.e. not necessarily ordinary, we can only assert that it belongs to the field $K|u^{1/n}|$.

The least positive integer n such that a given fractional series belongs to $K|u^{1/n}|$ is called the *index* of the series. If the index is 1 the series may be identified with a formal power series in u, possibly extended, as defined in § 2.2; and this shows that $K|u|$ is a subset of the set of all extended fractional power series in u. We shall now show that the latter set can readily be made into a field $K^*|u|$ which is an extension of the field $K|u|$.

Let $Q_1(u)$ and $Q_2(u)$ be fractional power series, of indices n_1 and n_2 respectively. Since both series may be written as formal power series in $u^{1/n_1 n_2}$, natural definitions of addition and multiplication are available. With these definitions, the set of all ordinary fractional series in u is an integral domain $K^*\{u\}$, and the set of all extended fractional series is a field $K^*|u|$, which is the field of quotients of this integral domain.

The units of $K^*\{u\}$ are those ordinary fractional series

$$k_0 + k_1 u^{\nu_1} + k_2 u^{\nu_2} + \dots$$

which begin with a non-zero term k_0, independent of u; and every unit of $K^*\{u\}$, being a unit of some ring $K\{u^{1/n}\}$, has a reciprocal in $K^*\{u\}$. Every non-zero element of $K^*|u|$ may be written in the form

$$Q(u) \equiv u^N U(u),$$

where $U(u)$ is a unit of $K^*\{u\}$ and N is a rational number. The number N, which is uniquely determined by $Q(u)$, is a very important character of the series, and we accordingly give it a special name (cf. p. 54).

DEFINITION. The *order* $O(Q(u))$ of any (non-zero) fractional power series $Q(u)$ is the rational number N which occurs as the exponent of u when $Q(u)$ is written in the form $u^N U(u)$, where $U(u)$ is a unit of the ring $K^*\{u\}$.

The transcendental points of $S_2(K)$, defined in $K^*|u|$, that we shall have occasion to use will nearly all be of the form $(1, a+u, Q(u))$, with $a \in K$ and $Q(u) \in K^*|u|$; and in fact they will usually arise as points with affine coordinates $(a+u, Q(u))$. When we need a name for such points we shall call then *fractional transcendental points*.

If $Q(u)$ is of index n, so that it may be written as a formal power series $P(u^{1/n})$ in $u^{1/n}$, and if ζ is a primitive nth root of unity, we shall call the $n-1$ series

$$Q_i(u) \equiv P(\zeta^i u^{1/n}) \quad (i = 1,...,n-1),$$

the *conjugates* of $Q(u)$ in $K*|u|$; and the points $(1, a+u, Q_i(u))$ will be called the *conjugate points* of the point $(1, a+u, Q(u))$. Thus, for example, $(1, u, u^{\frac{1}{2}})$ is a fractional transcendental point of the conic $x_2^2 - x_0 x_1 = 0$, and $(1, u, -u^{\frac{1}{2}})$ is its unique conjugate.

It follows from the theorem which we discuss in Appendix B (Theorem 1, p. 83) that, if any K-polynomial $F(X, Y)$ in X and Y is arranged as a polynomial in Y with coefficients in $K[X]$,

$$\Phi(Y) \equiv a_0(X)Y^n + a_1(X)Y^{n-1} + ... + a_n(X),$$

then $\Phi(Y)$ decomposes completely over $K*|X|$ into linear factors, so that

$$\Phi(Y) \equiv a_0(X) \prod_{i=1}^{n} (Y - Q_i(X)) \quad (Q_i(X) \in K*|X|).$$

Each of the points $(X, Q_i(X))$ is then (in general) a fractional transcendental point of the curve $F(X, Y) = 0$.

We note finally, that *if $Q(u) \equiv P(u^{1/n})$ is a fractional power series of index n, then the fractional transcendental point $(1, a+u, Q(u))$, as well as each of its conjugates, is isomorphically equivalent to the formal transcendental point $(1, a+v^n, P(v))$.* For the correspondence $u^{1/n} \leftrightarrow v$ (or $\zeta^i u^{1/n} \leftrightarrow v$, as the case may be) defines an isomorphism over K between the fields $K|u^{1/n}|$ and $K|v|$, and thus induces the necessary isomorphism over K between the minimum fields of definition of the points in question.

2.4. The field K_C of rational functions on an irreducible curve C

The extension of K to K_C, as we have already indicated, is different from the extensions of K to $K(u)$, $K|u|$, and $K*|u|$ in that K_C is constructed as an adjunct to a particular irreducible curve C, and not as a totality of formal expressions built up by use of an indeterminate u. In order to obtain this field K_C, we begin by introducing, in as natural a manner as possible, the concept of a *rational function on an irreducible curve C*; and for this purpose it is convenient to use an affine coordinate system, in which C has an equation $f(X, Y) = 0$, where $f(X, Y) \in K[X, Y]$.

Adopting, for the moment, the point of view of the theory of functions, let us consider an arbitrarily chosen rational function $\phi(X, Y)$ of two variables X and Y. Thus $\phi(X, Y)$ is a quotient $F(X, Y)/G(X, Y)$ of two polynomials, which may be supposed to have no non-constant common factor, and the denominator $G(X, Y)$ is not the zero polynomial. The function $\phi(X, Y)$ associates with every ground point of the plane, except only those points which lie on the curve $G(X, Y) = 0$, a definite value; and we may say further, if we choose, that the function takes the improper value ∞ at every point of $G(X, Y) = 0$ which is not also a point of $F(X, Y) = 0$. If, now, (X', Y') denotes a variable point P of the irreducible curve C then, provided that $G(X, Y)$ is not divisible by $f(X, Y)$, the expression

$$\phi(P) \equiv F(X', Y')/G(X', Y')$$

defines a function on the curve, since it takes a definite value at every point of the curve, with at most a finite number of exceptions. Such a function of $\phi(P)$ is called a *rational function on C*, and we obtain it from a rational function $\phi(X, Y)$ in the ordinary sense simply by restricting the domain of the pair of variables (X, Y) to the set of pairs of values which satisfy the equation $f(X, Y) = 0$ of C.

Now the polynomials $F(X, Y)$ and $G(X, Y)$ which occur in the expression for $\phi(X, Y)$ are not uniquely determined by the rational function, since every pair $\lambda F(X, Y)$ and $\lambda G(X, Y)$ will do as well, where λ is any non-zero element of K. When we turn from $\phi(X, Y)$ to the restricted function $\phi(P) \equiv \phi(X', Y')$, the arbitrariness of $F(X, Y)$ and $G(X, Y)$ is increased still further; for the condition for $F_1(X, Y)/G_1(X, Y)$ and $F_2(X, Y)/G_2(X, Y)$ to take the same values at all points of C where both values are defined is clearly

$$F_1(X, Y)G_2(X, Y) - F_2(X, Y)G_1(X, Y) \equiv 0 \quad (\bmod f(X, Y)).$$

We shall find it convenient to write this congruence relation in the form

$$F_1(X, Y)/G_1(X, Y) \sim F_2(X, Y)/G_2(X, Y) \quad (\bmod f(X, Y)). \quad (2)$$

It is, of course, an equivalence relation; and it accordingly separates the class of all formal expressions $F(X, Y)/G(X, Y)$, such that F and G are coprime and $G \not\equiv 0 \pmod{f}$, into disjoint congruence classes. Each such congruence class is the complete set of expressions $F(X, Y)/G(X, Y)$ which correspond to some rational function $\phi(P)$ on C. The congruence class defined by a particular expression

F/G will be denoted by $\{F/G\}$; and any member of the class may be taken as the representative which serves to define it.

The above analysis of the intuitive notion of a rational function on a curve shows how a formal theory of such functions may be constructed. We begin with the field $K(X, Y)$ of formal rational functions over K in two indeterminates X and Y, and we select from this field the set of all those of its elements which can be written in the form F/G, where $G \not\equiv 0 \pmod{f}$ in $K[X, Y]$. Adopting (2) as a formal definition, we now introduce a relation of congruence for the elements F/G of this set; and we take the congruence classes $\{F/G\}$ yielded by this relation as the *rational functions on C*. We shall assume, from now on, that rational functions on an irreducible curve have been defined in this way; and we shall consistently use the symbol $\{F/G\}$ to denote the rational function on C that is determined by the formal rational function $F(X, Y)/G(X, Y)$.

EXAMPLE. Whatever irreducible curve is taken as C, every element k of K, and more generally every K-polynomial $F(X, Y)$, defines a rational function $\{k\}$ or $\{F\}$ on C. Provided that C is not the line $X = 0$, the expressions $1/X$ and $(X^2+Y^2)/X$ define rational functions $\{1/X\}$ and $\{(X^2+Y^2)/X\}$ on C. If C is the proper conic $Y^2-X = 0$, then $\{X/Y\}$ and $\{Y\}$ both denote the same rational function on C, which may be identified with the parameter θ in the canonical representation $X:Y:1 = \theta^2:\theta:1$.

EXERCISES. (i) Show that, if homogeneous coordinates (x_0, x_1, x_2) are used instead of affine coordinates (X, Y), every rational function on a curve C can be defined by a formula $f(x_0, x_1, x_2)/g(x_0, x_1, x_2)$, in which f and g are K-forms of the same degree; and adapt the foregoing theory of rational functions on C to the case of a homogeneous coordinate representation.

(ii) Prove that the concept of rational function on C is projective (i.e. invariant with respect to change of allowable representation $\mathscr{R}$ of S_2).

Let us now consider the totality of all rational functions $\phi(P) \equiv \{F/G\}$ on C. It is easily verified that the operations of addition, subtraction, multiplication, and division by a non-zero element, as ordinarily defined for rational functions, are compatible with the congruence relation $F_1/G_1 \sim F_2/G_2 \pmod{f}$, so that if, for instance, $F_1/G_1 \sim F_2/G_2$ and $F_1'/G_1' \sim F_2'/G_2'$, then

$$(F_1 G_1' + F_1' G_1)/G_1 G_1' \sim (F_2 G_2' + F_2' G_2)/G_2 G_2'$$

and
$$F_1 F_1'/G_1 G_1' \sim F_2 F_2'/G_2 G_2';$$

and we are therefore at liberty to define addition of congruence classes by putting $\{F/G\}+\{F'/G'\} = \{F/G+F'/G'\}$, and to define the other rational operations similarly. When this is done, the totality of congruence classes becomes an extension field K_C of K. Verification of the field axioms for the system presents no difficulty, and the new field can be treated as an extension of K since the elements $\{k\}$, with $k \in K$, form a subfield isomorphic with K. The zero element of K_C is, of course, the congruence class $\{0\}$, i.e. the rational function on C (in the original sense) which takes the value zero at every point of the curve.

It follows from the definition of the four rational operations in K_C that, if $\phi(X, Y)$ is any rational function over K of X and Y, then $\phi(\{X\}, \{Y\}) = \{\phi(X, Y)\}$ in K_C. We may therefore say that the two elements $\{X\}$ and $\{Y\}$ of K_C *generate* this field as an extension of K.

3. Generic points of irreducible curves

In this concluding section of the present chapter we shall establish the fundamental connexion that exists between transcendental points of the first kind in $S_2(K)$ and irreducible curves of $S_2(K)$. We shall also obtain a result which shows how intimate is the relation between any irreducible curve C of $S_2(K)$ and the function field K_C to which it gives rise.

THEOREM 2. *Every transcendental point of the first kind in S_2 belongs to one and only one irreducible curve C of S_2. Conversely, every irreducible algebraic curve possesses a transcendental point.*

Proof. Let $\boldsymbol{\alpha}$ be any transcendental point of S_2 of the first kind, its coordinates $\alpha_0, \alpha_1, \alpha_2$ belonging to some extension field K' of K. Then the set $\mathscr{F}$ of all non-zero K-forms $f(x_0, x_1, x_2)$ with the property that $f(\alpha_0, \alpha_1, \alpha_2) = 0$ is not empty, and we may suppose that a form $h(x_0, x_1, x_2)$, of lowest possible degree, is selected from $\mathscr{F}$. Such a form is necessarily irreducible; for, if it had non-trivial factors, at least one of these would be a form in $\mathscr{F}$ of lower degree than $h(\mathbf{x})$. In order to prove the first part of the theorem we have only to show that $h(\mathbf{x})$ is, to within a factor in K, the only irreducible form in $\mathscr{F}$. This follows from the fact that the point $\boldsymbol{\alpha}$ is transcendental, which means that at least one of the ratios of $\alpha_0, \alpha_1, \alpha_2$, say α_0/α_1, exists but is not an element of K. For suppose that $g(x_0, x_1, x_2) = 0$ is any K-equation that is satisfied by $(\alpha_0, \alpha_1, \alpha_2)$; and let $R(x_0, x_1)$ be the x_2-resultant of the polynomials $g(x_0, x_1, x_2)$ and $h(x_0, x_1, x_2)$. Since the equations $g(\alpha_0, \alpha_1, x_2) = 0$ and $h(\alpha_0, \alpha_1, x_2) = 0$ for x_2 have the common root α_2, it follows that $R(\alpha_0, \alpha_1) = 0$. But K is algebraically closed, and α_0/α_1 does not belong to it, from which it follows that α_0/α_1 is not a root of any K-equation. Therefore $R(x_0, x_1) = 0$ in $K[x_0, x_1]$; and this means that $g(x_0, x_1, x_2)$ and $h(x_0, x_1, x_2)$ have a common factor belonging to $K[x_0, x_1][x_2]$. Since $h(x_0, x_1, x_2)$ is irreducible in $K[x_0, x_1, x_2]$, it now follows that $h(x_0, x_1, x_2)$ is a factor of $g(x_0, x_1, x_2)$. The set $\mathscr{F}$ of all non-zero K-forms $g(\mathbf{x})$ for which $\boldsymbol{\alpha}$ is a zero therefore consists of all the multiples of the irreducible K-form $h(\mathbf{x})$ by other K-forms $q(\mathbf{x})$. There is thus a unique irreducible curve which contains the transcendental point $\boldsymbol{\alpha}$, namely the curve $h(\mathbf{x}) = 0$.

The first part of the theorem is now proved. To prove the second part we consider any irreducible curve C in relation to its function field K_C, using the notation of § 2.4. The field K_C may be generated over K by the two particular rational functions $\{X\}$ and $\{Y\}$ on C; and, since $f(\{X\}, \{Y\}) = \{f(X, Y)\} = 0$ in K_C, the point of S_2 with affine coordinates $(\{X\}, \{Y\})$ is a transcendental point of C.

COROLLARY 1. *If an algebraic curve D contains a transcendental point of an irreducible algebraic curve C, then D has C as a component.*

COROLLARY 2. *Any irreducible algebraic curve C has a transcendental point $\boldsymbol{\xi}$ with the field K_C as its minimum field of definition $K_{\boldsymbol{\xi}}$.*

EXERCISE. Show that, if C^* is a reducible curve, there is no point of C^* with the property that any curve D which contains it necessarily contains the whole of C^*.

We have now reached a stage in the development of our system of geometry where we are able to make precise the notion of a generic point of a curve, and thereby to give fully satisfactory answers to such questions as 'What is meant by the assertion that $(\theta^2, \theta, 1)$ is a "general" point of the conic $x_1^2 - x_2 x_0 = 0$?' (cf. p. 44).

DEFINITION. A *generic point* of an irreducible algebraic curve C is a point of C which is such that any K-equation which is satisfied by it is satisfied by every point of C.

THEOREM 3. *A point of an irreducible algebraic curve C in $S_2(K)$ is a generic point of C if and only if it is a transcendental point of $S_2(K)$.*

Proof. Suppose, first, that P is a transcendental point of C. It then follows from Theorem 2 that P is a generic point of C.

Now suppose it is given that P is a generic point of C, and suppose, if possible, that P is not transcendental. Then P is a ground point of S_2, i.e. a point (a, b) such that a and b are in K. Thus P satisfies the K-equations $X = a$ and $Y = b$; and, since P is generic for C, every point of C satisfies these same equations. This is clearly impossible, and therefore P cannot be a ground point.

If we take an arbitrary transcendental point $\boldsymbol{\alpha}$, then (provided that it is of the first kind, i.e. capable of being a point of an algebraic curve) it is a generic point of one and only one irreducible curve. If, on the other hand, we start with an irreducible curve, it certainly has one generic point, namely the point with affine coordinates $(\{X\}, \{Y\})$; and it may have more than one. The conic $x_1^2 - x_2 x_0 = 0$, for example, has not only the point $(\theta^2, \theta, 1)$ as a generic point, but also every point derived from this by a homographic substitution $\theta = (a\phi + b)/(c\phi + d)$, $ad - bc \neq 0$. It is now natural to ask how any two transcendental points which are generic points of the same irreducible curve must be related to each other; and this question finds an answer in the next theorem.

THEOREM 4. *Two transcendental points $\boldsymbol{\alpha}$ and $\boldsymbol{\beta}$ of the first kind are generic points of the same irreducible curve C if and only if they are isomorphically equivalent.*

Proof. First let $\boldsymbol{\alpha}$ and $\boldsymbol{\beta}$ be generic points of the same irreducible curve C. We may suppose that, after a change of coordinate system if necessary, neither α_0 nor β_0 is zero. Then, if $X = x_1/x_0$ and $Y = x_2/x_0$ are taken as affine coordinates, the representations (a_1, a_2) and (b_1, b_2) of the points $\boldsymbol{\alpha}$ and $\boldsymbol{\beta}$ are given by $a_i = \alpha_i/\alpha_0$, $b_i = \beta_i/\beta_0$. The fields $K_{\boldsymbol{\alpha}}$ and $K_{\boldsymbol{\beta}}$ are then $K(a_1, a_2)$ and $K(b_1, b_2)$. In order to show that they are isomorphic over K by an isomorphism which makes $\boldsymbol{\alpha}$ correspond to $\boldsymbol{\beta}$, we map $K(a_1, a_2)$ on $K(b_1, b_2)$ in the following manner. Any element ξ of $K(a_1, a_2)$ may be expressed as a rational function $F(a_1, a_2)$ over K; and we map it on the corresponding rational function $F(b_1, b_2)$ of b_1 and b_2, which we call ξ'. This prescription, however, is only significant if we can be certain that we shall arrive at the same element ξ' whichever of the possible expressions for ξ we take as our $F(a_1, a_2)$. Suppose a second of these expressions is $G(a_1, a_2)$. Then if $F(X, Y) \equiv F_1(X, Y)/F_2(X, Y)$ and $G(X, Y) \equiv G_1(X, Y)/G_2(X, Y)$, where F_1, F_2, G_1, $G_2 \in K[X, Y]$, the point (a_1, a_2) lies on the curve D with equation $F_1 G_2 - F_2 G_1 = 0$. D thus contains a generic point of C, from which it follows that it has C as a component (Theorem 2, Corollary 1), and hence that it contains every point, generic or otherwise, of C. So the equation

$F_1 G_2 - F_2 G_1 = 0$ is satisfied, in particular, by (b_1, b_2); and therefore $F(b_1, b_2) = G(b_1, b_2)$. We have thus defined a $(1, 1)$ correspondence $\xi \leftrightarrow \xi'$ between $K(a_1, a_2)$ and $K(b_1, b_2)$, and this correspondence is plainly an isomorphism over K which is such that $a_1 \leftrightarrow b_1$ and $a_2 \leftrightarrow b_2$. This proves that $\boldsymbol{\alpha}$ and $\boldsymbol{\beta}$ are isomorphically equivalent transcendental points.

If, conversely, two transcendental points $\boldsymbol{\alpha}$ and $\boldsymbol{\beta}$ are isomorphically equivalent, by an isomorphism $K_{\boldsymbol{\alpha}} \cong K_{\boldsymbol{\beta}}$, and $\boldsymbol{\alpha}$ is a generic point of an irreducible curve C with equation $f(x_0, x_1, x_2) = 0$, the isomorphism carries the relation $f(\alpha_0, \alpha_1, \alpha_2) = 0$ into $f(\beta_0, \beta_1, \beta_2) = 0$, thus showing that $\boldsymbol{\beta}$ is also a point of C; and since $\boldsymbol{\beta}$ is transcendental, it is generic for C.

We conclude this chapter with a theorem which makes explicit the fundamental connexion between the concepts of the minimum field of definition of a transcendental point and the field of rational functions on an irreducible curve.

THEOREM 5. *The minimum field of definition of any generic point of an irreducible algebraic curve C is isomorphic over K with the field K_C of rational functions on C.*

Proof. The assertion follows at once from Theorem 4, since C has a generic point $(\{X\}, \{Y\})$ with K_C as its minimum field of definition.

NOTES AND EXERCISES ON CHAPTER III

In the exercises which follow, the symbols u, v will always represent indeterminates.

1. The point $(1, u^2 + u^3, u^4)$ is transcendental of the first kind over K. Show that its minimum field of definition is $K(u)$ and find the unique irreducible algebraic curve which contains it.

[*Hint.* If we write $X = u^2 + u^3$, $Y = u^4$, then

$$u = \frac{X^3 - 3XY - 3Y^2 + 2X^2 - 2Y}{Y(Y+4)}$$

and

$$X^4 - 2YX^2 - 4XY^2 + Y^2 - Y^3 = 0.]$$

2. Show that the minimum field of definition of the point $(u^3, u^6 + 1, u^5 + u)$ is $K(\alpha)$, where $\alpha = u + 1/u$; and verify that the point in question is a generic point of the curve

$$x_0 x_1^2 = (x_2 - x_0)^2 (x_2 + 2x_0).$$

3. If ξ and η, being each transcendental over K, satisfy the relation $\xi^2 + \eta^2 = 1$, define an isomorphism over K between the field $K(\xi, \eta)$ and the field $K(u)$.

[*Answer.* The substitutions

$$\xi \to \frac{1-u^2}{1+u^2}, \quad \eta \to \frac{2u}{1+u^2}, \quad \text{and} \quad u \to \frac{\eta}{1+\xi}$$

define such an isomorphism.]

4. Write down the coordinates of a formal transcendental point of the curve $X^2+Y^2 = 1$ with centre at the point $(\cos\alpha, \sin\alpha)$, where $\alpha \in K$. Write down also the coordinates of a fractional transcendental point of the same curve, of the form $(1, 1+u, P(u))$, where $P(u) \in K^*|u|$.

5. By use of the parametric representation $(\theta/(1+\theta^3), \theta^2/(1+\theta^3))$ of the curve $X^3+Y^3 = XY$, determine two essentially distinct formal transcendental points of the curve with centres at the origin; and show also how to obtain a formal transcendental point of the curve with centre at the real point at infinity on the curve.

[*Solution.* For the first two points, replace θ by u and by $1/u$ respectively, and expand the rational functions of u as power series; for the last point replace θ by $u-1$ and proceed similarly.]

6. Investigate, for all values of the constant a, the transcendental points of the form $(X, P(X-a))$ that belong to the curve $Y^3 = \dfrac{X(X-1)}{(X+1)^2}$, the symbol $P(X-a)$ denoting any formal or fractional power series in $X-a$.

7. If $\{X\} = \xi$, $\{Y\} = \eta$ are the equivalence classes of rational functions, on the curve $Y^2 = X$, defined by X and Y, prove that (i) $\eta^2 = \xi$, (ii) there exists a K-isomorphism between $K(\xi, \eta)$ and $K(u)$, and (iii) every element of $K(\xi, \eta)$ can be expressed in the form $\Xi + \eta\Xi'$, where $\Xi, \Xi' \in K(\xi)$.

[*Solution.* For (ii), the required isomorphism is defined by the substitutions $\xi, \eta \to u^2, u$, and $u \to \eta$. For (iii), we use the relation $\eta^2 = \xi$ to reduce any element $\zeta = P(\xi,\eta)/Q(\xi,\eta)$ of $K(\xi,\eta)$ $(P(X,Y), Q(X,Y) \in K[X,Y]$, $Q(\xi,\eta) \neq 0)$ to the form $(A+B\eta)/(C+D\eta)$, where $A, B, C, D \in K[\xi]$; and then, having multiplied numerator and denominator by $C-D\eta$, we use the same relation to reduce the resulting fraction to the form $\Xi + \eta\Xi'$.]

8. *Rational curves.* An irreducible curve C is *rational* if its function field K_C is isomorphic over K to the field of rational functions $K(u)$ of an indeterminate u. Verify that this new definition agrees with that given (provisionally) in § 6 of Chapter I.

Deduce that C is rational if and only if there exists a rational function ϕ on C such that $K_C = K(\phi)$.

9. Find, on each of the curves C with equations (i) $X^2+Y^2 = 1$, (ii) $Y^2 = X(X-1)^2$, (iii) $x_1^2 x_2^2 + x_2^2 x_0^2 = x_0^2 x_1^2$, a rational function ϕ such that $K_C = K(\phi)$.

10. *Cremona transformations.* Two equations

$$X' = \phi_1(X,Y), \qquad Y' = \phi_2(X,Y),$$

where $\phi_1, \phi_2 \in K(X,Y)$, are said to define a *Cremona transformation* of the plane if they can be solved rationally in the form

$$X = \psi_1(X',Y'), \qquad Y = \psi_2(X',Y'),$$

where $\psi_1, \psi_2 \in K(X',Y')$. If such a transformation carries an irreducible curve C into another irreducible curve C', show that the fields K_C and $K_{C'}$ are isomorphic over K.

Apply the special quadratic transformation $X' = X$, $Y' = Y/X$ in this way to show that (i) the quartic curve with equation $(Y-X^2)^2 = XY^2$ is rational, and (ii) the function field of the sextic curve $Y^3 = X^3 - X^6$ is isomorphic over K to that of the cubic curve $X^3 + Y^3 = 1$.

11. If (a, b, c) and (a', b', c') are two sets of three unequal constants, prove that the function fields of the two cubic curves with equations

$$Y^2 = (X-a)(X-b)(X-c),$$
$$Y^2 = (X-a')(X-b')(X-c')$$

are isomorphic over K if $(a-b)/(a-c) = (a'-b')/(a'-c')$.

12. *Transcendental lines of S_2.* The equation of a transcendental line of S_2—dual of a transcendental point—is not a K-equation; and hence such a line, regarded as an aggregate of points, is not a K-curve of the class exclusively considered so far, but falls within the general class of 'transcendental curves' defined by equations with coefficient ratios in some proper extension of K (cf. Chapter 6, § 2). This explains, for example, why the transcendental line with equation $X = uY$ can intersect the K-curve $Y^2 = X$ in a generic point (u^2, u) of the latter, as well as in the ground point $(0, 0)$.

CHAPTER IV

CURVILINEAR BRANCHES

1. Points and branches

In the preceding chapter we introduced the concept of a *formal transcendental point* of $S_2(K)$, this being a point that can be represented, in standard form, by a sector $\mathbf{a}(u)$ with elements in $K\{u\}$, and which has associated with it a ground point $\mathbf{a}(0)$ called its *centre*. The points so defined were regarded essentially as additional geometric entities adjoined to the plane $S_2(K)$, but in fact they can be given a more suggestive interpretation as parametric representations—in a certain abstract sense—of *curvilinear branches* of S_2. This is indeed the sense in which points whose coordinates are formal power series in a parameter first came to be introduced into algebraic geometry (cf. our remarks on the classical analytic theory on p. 50), and it is the researches on that basis, going back to Puiseux, that provide the essential motivation for the formal theory of branches that we now propose to develop. The reader may find it useful, in this connexion, to compare van der Waerden's use of a *local uniformizing parameter (Ortsuniform-isierende)* in §§ 14, 20 of his *Einführung*.

For the better orientation of our ideas, we may begin by considering an example of an ordinary parametric representation taken from coordinate geometry. In homogeneous rectangular Cartesian coordinates, the parametric equations

$$x : y : z = 1-u^2 : 2u : 1+u^2$$

represent a circle, and the centre of this parametrization, obtained by putting $u = 0$, is the point $(1, 0, 1)$. There are, however, infinitely many similar parametrizations of the same circle, also centred at the point $(1, 0, 1)$, as for example

$$x : y : z = 2v+1 : 2v^2+2v : 2v^2+2v+1.$$

In this situation, the geometric object in view is the circle, which may be regarded as originating in the point $(1, 0, 1)$, and we have a class of rational parametrizations of the circle, centred at $(1, 0, 1)$. In the more general situation now to be envisaged, a formal transcendental point is the analogue of the parametrization, and a curvilinear branch is the analogue of the circle.

Our intention is, then, to define a branch by means of a class of *associated* formal transcendental points, all having the same centre and all related to each other by operations of parametric substitution. For the purpose of defining the precise character of the association that will bind together those transcendental points which correspond to the same branch, we must first set out the basic facts that we shall need in connexion with the fundamental operation of substituting one formal power series in another.

2. Properties of substitution in a power series

In this section we shall be concerned with substitutions $u \to s(v)$, in which $s(v)$ is any non-unit of $K\{v\}$:

$$s(v) \equiv k_m v^m + k_{m+1} v^{m+1} + \dots \quad (k_i \in K, \, m \geqslant 1, \, k_m \neq 0). \quad (1)$$

Such substitutions have certain simple properties, now to be established, which the reader will at once recognize as being analogous to formal properties of power series that are commonplace in analysis. These properties, however, belong strictly to the algebraic part of the theory of such series, and there is no implied reference in the notion of *formal* substitution to convergence or to any other analytical concept, any more than there is in the assertion of the existence of a formal power series.

(i) The substitution $u \to s(v)$, i.e. the substitution for u of the power series (1) in v, carries every element $P(u)$ of $K|u|$ into a well-defined element $Q(v)$ of $K|v|$; and the mapping of $P(u)$ on to $Q(v)$ is readily seen to be a homomorphism of $K|u|$ into $K|v|$. If the order of $P(u)$ is n, then that of $Q(v)$ is mn. The order m of the substituted series $s(v)$ is called the *index* of the substitution.

(ii) If $u \to s(v)$ and $v \to t(w)$ are two substitutions, then $u \to r(w) \equiv s(t(w))$ is also a substitution, and the successive substitutions $u \to s(v)$, $v \to t(w)$ carry any element $P(u)$ of $K|u|$ into the same element $R(w)$ of $K|w|$ as the single substitution $u \to r(w)$.

(iii) The substitution $u \to s(v)$ is said to be *regular* if and only if it is of index 1; and, when this is the case, it has a unique inverse $v \to s^{-1}(u)$ such that $s(s^{-1}(u)) = u$ and $s^{-1}(s(v)) = v$. For, if we substitute the power series

$$t(u) \equiv b_1 u + b_2 u^2 + \dots$$

for v in $s(v)$, the equation

$$s(t(u)) = u$$

determines the coefficients $b_1, b_2, \ldots$ successively (i.e. recursively), and the series thus obtained has the required properties. When the substitution $u \to s(v)$ is regular, the correspondence $P(u) \leftrightarrow P(s(v))$ is an isomorphism between $K|u|$ and $K|v|$, and the correspondence $P(u) \leftrightarrow P(s(u))$ is an automorphism of $K|u|$. The set of all *regular* substitutions $u \to s(u)$ is plainly a group with respect to the composition defined in (ii).

(iv) If $P(u) \equiv c_m u^m + c_{m+1} u^{m+1} + \ldots$ ($c_i \in K$, $m \neq 0$, $c_m \neq 0$) is an element of $K|u|$ of positive or negative (integral) order m, then there exists an element $p(u)$ of $K\{u\}$, of order 1, such that $P(u) = (p(u))^m$. In other words, $P(u)$ can be derived from the simple power v^m of v by a regular substitution $v \to p(u)$. For, if we put

$$p(u) = b_1 u + b_2 u^2 + \ldots,$$

where b_1 is any mth root of c_m, then the equation

$$c_m u^m + c_{m+1} u^{m+1} + \ldots = (b_1 u + b_2 u^2 + \ldots)^m,$$

that is

$$c_m + c_{m+1} u + \ldots = (b_1 + b_2 u + \ldots)^m,$$

yields a recursive determination of $b_2, b_3, \ldots$.

3. Quasi-branches

We shall now use the transformation of substitution in a power series to group together all the formal transcendental points which are to be taken as defining any particular branch. We shall, for logical reasons, actually identify the branch with the class of equivalent transcendental points, although it would perhaps be intuitively more natural to think of the branch as a new entity, derived from the class of equivalent points by abstraction. When we come to the details of the identification, two somewhat different courses are open to us. We can define equivalence of formal transcendental points either by reference to the full set of substitutions $u \to s(v)$ or by reference to the subset of regular substitutions. The first way of proceeding brings us more directly to the concept of branch that we require; but the second way is algebraically preferable in that the set of regular substitutions is a group. We shall accordingly prefer to develop the theory in two stages, first introducing an intermediate type of entity, which we call a quasi-branch, by use of regular substitutions only, and then combining sets of related quasi-branches into single branches.

DEFINITION. Two formal transcendental points $\mathbf{a}(u)$ and $\mathbf{b}(u)$ are said to be *substitutionally equivalent* if and only if there exists a regular substitution $u \to s(u)$† which carries one into the other, i.e. which is such that

$$a_i(s(u)) = \rho b_i(u) \quad (i = 0, 1, 2),$$

where $\rho \in K|u|$ is a factor of proportionality.

Since the set of all regular substitutions is a group, the relation of substitutional equivalence introduced here is an equivalence relation in the usual sense, and it accordingly determines a separation of the class of all formal transcendental points of $S_2(K)$ into disjoint equivalence classes.

DEFINITION. A *quasi-branch* $\tilde{\alpha}$ in S_2 is a complete class of substitutionally equivalent formal transcendental points of S_2.

This last definition states, effectively, that a quasi-branch is a formal transcendental point, defined only to within arbitrary regular substitution for the parameter. If $\mathbf{a}(u)$ represents any formal transcendental point of the class defining $\tilde{\alpha}$, we shall say that the coordinate-triad $\mathbf{a}(u)$ is a *representation* of the quasi-branch. Often indeed, we shall refer to 'the quasi-branch $\mathbf{a}(u)$'; and on occasion we shall refer to the equations

$$x_i = a_i(u) \quad (i = 0, 1, 2)$$

as a *set of equations of* $\tilde{\alpha}$. All the representations of a given quasi-branch correspond to transcendental points with the same centre, and we call this ground point the *centre of the quasi-branch*.

DEFINITION. A quasi-branch $\tilde{\beta}$, represented by $\mathbf{b}(v)$, is *minimal* if there exists no quasi-branch $\mathbf{a}(u)$ such that $\mathbf{b}(v)$ is the transform of $\mathbf{a}(u)$ by a substitution $u \to s(v)$ of index $m > 1$. A quasi-branch that is not minimal is *redundant*.

The reader will be able to verify that the property of $\tilde{\beta}$ specified in this definition is in fact independent of the particular choice of a representation $\mathbf{b}(v)$ for $\tilde{\beta}$, so that the definition is legitimate. A simple example of a redundant quasi-branch is $(1, u^2, u^4)$, which is derived from the minimal quasi-branch $(1, u, u^2)$ by applying the substitution $u \to u^2$ of index 2.

† It is sometimes more convenient to take a substitution as $u \to s(v)$ and sometimes more convenient to take it as $u \to s(u)$, and we adopt no rigid convention in this matter.

Consider, now, any pair of quasi-branches $\tilde{\alpha}$ and $\tilde{\beta}$, given by $\mathbf{a}(u)$ and $\mathbf{b}(v)$ respectively, such that $\mathbf{b}(v)$ is the transform of $\mathbf{a}(u)$ by a substitution $u \to s(v)$ of index $m > 1$. We assert that $\tilde{\beta}$ is uniquely determined by $\tilde{\alpha}$ and the integer m, so that we may legitimately refer to $\tilde{\beta}$ as *the redundant transform* $\tilde{\alpha}^{(m)}$ of $\tilde{\alpha}$ *of index m*. To prove this we note first of all that, by property (iv) of § 2, we can write $s(v) = (p(v))^m$, where $p(v)$ is of order 1. The transformation of $\tilde{\alpha}$ into $\tilde{\beta}$ can therefore be effected by the successive substitutions $u \to w^m$ and $w \to p(v)$, of which the first is dependent only on the integer m and the second is regular. It follows that all representations which are obtainable from the particular representation $\mathbf{a}(u)$ of $\tilde{\alpha}$ by a substitution of order m are substitutionally equivalent to the representation $\mathbf{a}(u^m)$, and they accordingly all belong to the same quasi-branch. All that we now have to prove is that this quasi-branch is independent of the original choice of a representation $\mathbf{a}(u)$ for $\tilde{\alpha}$; and in order to do this we shall suppose that $\mathbf{a}'(u)$ is any other representation of $\tilde{\alpha}$. Then $\mathbf{a}'(u) = \rho\mathbf{a}(t(u))$, where $t(u)$ is regular, and $\mathbf{a}'(u^m) = \sigma\mathbf{a}(t(u^m))$. Since $t(u^m)$ is of order m, we can write $t(u^m) = (t'(u))^m$, where $t'(u)$ is regular; and therefore $\mathbf{a}'(u^m)$ is obtainable from $\mathbf{a}(u^m)$ by the regular substitution $u \to t'(u)$, i.e. $\mathbf{a}(u^m)$ and $\mathbf{a}'(u^m)$ are substitutionally equivalent, as required.

If, now, we take any minimal quasi-branch $\tilde{\alpha}$, this has a redundant transform $\tilde{\alpha}^{(m)}$ for each positive integer m. A question that we must obviously ask is whether, when we begin by taking a redundant quasi-branch $\tilde{\beta}$, there necessarily exists some minimal quasi-branch $\tilde{\alpha}$ such that $\tilde{\beta}$ occurs among the redundant transforms of $\tilde{\alpha}$; and we shall now give an affirmative answer to this question by showing that every quasi-branch $\tilde{\beta}$ is either itself minimal or else is a redundant transform of a unique minimal quasi-branch $\tilde{\alpha}$. In order to do this, we shall begin by introducing the very important idea of *canonical representation of a quasi-branch*.

Let $\tilde{\beta}$ be any given quasi-branch. Then, by suitable choice of the coordinate representation of S_2 and of the factor of proportionality, we can arrange for $\tilde{\beta}$ to have a normalized representation $(1, b_1(v), b_2(v))$ $(b_1(v), b_2(v) \in K\{v\})$. The centre of $\tilde{\beta}$ is the point $(1, a, b) \equiv (1, b_1(0), b_2(0))$; and we may write $b_1(v) = a+h(v)$, $b_2(v) = b+k(v)$, where $h(v)$ and $k(v)$ are of positive orders μ and ν. The case in which $h(v)$ or $k(v)$ is zero (of order ∞) is trivial, and we suppose it excluded. If, now, we go over to affine coordinates $X = x_1/x_0$ and $Y = x_2/x_0$, the quasi-branch $\tilde{\beta}$ has the finite centre

(a, b), and its equations are

$$X - a = h(v), \quad Y - b = k(v).$$

Since $O(h(v)) = \mu$, we may put $h(v) = (p(v))^{\mu}$, where $O(p(v)) = 1$; and if we now make the substitution $v \to p^{-1}(u)$ we obtain a new representation of $\tilde{\beta}$ in the form

$$\left. \begin{aligned} X - a &= u^{\mu} \\ Y - b &= c u^{\nu} + c' u^{\nu'} + \dots \end{aligned} \right\}, \tag{1}$$

where $c, c', \dots \in K$, $c, c', \dots \neq 0$, $0 < \mu$, and $0 < \nu < \nu' < \dots$. Any representation of a quasi-branch in this form will be said to be *canonical*.

We now return to our problem of determining those minimal quasi-branches $\tilde{\alpha}$ which are such that $\tilde{\alpha}^{(m)} = \tilde{\beta}$ for some m. Any such quasi-branch $\tilde{\alpha}$ must have the same centre (a, b) as $\tilde{\beta}$, and we may suppose it to have a canonical representation (in the same coordinate system as has been used for $\tilde{\beta}$)

$$\left. \begin{aligned} X - a &= t^{\mu_1} \\ Y - b &= d t^{\nu_1} + d' t^{\nu_1'} + \dots \end{aligned} \right\}. \tag{2}$$

The quasi-branch $\tilde{\alpha}^{(m)}$ is then given by

$$\left. \begin{aligned} X - a &= t^{m \mu_1} \\ Y - b &= d t^{m \nu_1} + d' t^{m \nu_1'} + \dots \end{aligned} \right\}; \tag{3}$$

and for $\tilde{\alpha}^{(m)}$ and $\tilde{\beta}$ to be the same quasi-branch the representations (1) and (3) must be substitutionally equivalent. Thus there must exist a regular substitution $t \to s(u)$ such that

$$\left. \begin{aligned} (s(u))^{m \mu_1} &= u^{\mu} \\ \text{and} \qquad d(s(u))^{m \nu_1} + d'(s(u))^{m \nu_1'} + \dots &= c u^{\nu} + c' u^{\nu'} + \dots \end{aligned} \right\}. \tag{4}$$

Hence $m \mu_1 = \mu,$

and $s(u) = \zeta u,$

where ζ is a μth root of unity.

The second of equations (4) then gives

$$c u^{\nu} + c' u^{\nu'} + \dots = d(\zeta u)^{m \nu_1} + d'(\zeta u)^{m \nu_1'} + \dots$$
$$= \zeta^{m \nu_1} d u^{m \nu_1} + \zeta^{m \nu_1'} d' u^{m \nu_1'} + \dots.$$

Hence we have $m \nu_1 = \nu, \quad m \nu_1' = \nu', \quad \dots,$

and also $\zeta^{\nu} d = c, \quad \zeta^{\nu'} d' = c', \quad \dots.$

Thus $\tilde{\alpha}$ is given by

$$\left.\begin{aligned}X-a &= t^{\mu/m} \\ Y-b &= \zeta^{-\nu}ct^{\nu/m}+\zeta^{-\nu'}c't^{\nu'/m}+\ldots \\ &= c(\zeta^{-m}t)^{\nu/m}+c'(\zeta^{-m}t)^{\nu'/m}+\ldots\end{aligned}\right\}. \tag{5}$$

We thus obtain μ possible representations for $\tilde{\alpha}$, corresponding to the μ values for ζ; but since the regular substitution $t \to \zeta^m v$ carries (5) into the representation

$$\left.\begin{aligned}X-a &= v^{\mu/m} \\ Y-b &= cv^{\nu/m}+c'v^{\nu'/m}+\ldots\end{aligned}\right\}, \tag{6}$$

the μ representations all yield the same quasi-branch $\tilde{\alpha}$.

The results established by the above argument may now be summed up in the following theorem.

THEOREM 1. *If* $X-a = u^\mu$, $Y-b = cu^\nu+c'u^{\nu'}+\ldots$ *is any canonical representation of a quasi-branch* $\tilde{\beta}$, *then* $\tilde{\beta}$ *is minimal if and only if the highest common factor of the (possibly infinite) set of integers* $\mu, \nu, \nu',\ldots$ *is unity. If* $\tilde{\beta}$ *is redundant, the highest common factor of* $\mu, \nu, \nu',\ldots$ *being* m, *then* $\tilde{\beta}$ *is the redundant transform, of index* m, *of a unique minimal quasi-branch* $\tilde{\alpha}$. *In the latter case,* $\tilde{\alpha}$ *is given by the representation* (6) *above.*

4. The geometry of branches

As we explained on p. 68, quasi-branches are not themselves the geometric objects that we ultimately wish to study, and we have only introduced them in order to simplify the initial stages of the theory of branches. We shall now group together any minimal quasi-branch $\tilde{\alpha}$ and its redundant transforms $\tilde{\alpha}^{(2)}$, $\tilde{\alpha}^{(3)},\ldots$, which differ from it in little more than the manner in which they are represented, and we shall regard all these quasi-branches as corresponding to one and the same *branch* α. More precisely, *a formal transcendental point* $\mathbf{a}(u)$ *will be said to be a representation of the branch* α *if and only if it is a representation of some one of the quasi-branches* $\tilde{\alpha}$, $\tilde{\alpha}^{(2)}$, $\tilde{\alpha}^{(3)},\ldots$. Any formal transcendental point which represents $\tilde{\alpha}$ will be said to be a *minimal representation* of α, and any such point which belongs to $\tilde{\alpha}^{(m)}$ $(m > 1)$ will be said to be a *redundant representation* of α of *redundancy* m. We shall normally think of branches as specified by suitable minimal representations.

The study of branches is in itself a large and interesting subject, but at this stage it would be inappropriate to attempt even a superficial survey of all its ramifications. All that we propose to do here is to give as much of the theory as is necessary for the purposes of the next chapter, on multiplicities of intersection, and to suggest as briefly as possible the lines along which the theory can be developed.

We first remark that the branches of S_2 may be sorted into two categories, comprising respectively those which are *algebraic* and those which are *non-algebraic*, the distinction between the two types of branch corresponding to that already made between the two kinds of transcendental point. A formal transcendental point $\mathbf{a}(u)$ is of the first kind if and only if its coordinates $a_i(u)$ are connected by a K-equation; and since any such algebraic relation is plainly invariant with respect to substitution for the parameter, we may say that *a branch α with representation $\mathbf{a}(u)$ is algebraic if and only if the transcendental point $\mathbf{a}(u)$ is of the first kind.* If the transcendental point is of the first kind, then it belongs to a unique irreducible algebraic curve C (Theorem 2, p. 60), and in this case we say that α is a *branch of C.* If, on the other hand, the point is of the second kind, the branch is not a branch of any algebraic curve at all. Although it is evident from this that only algebraic branches are directly relevant to the study of algebraic curves, most of the rest of this chapter in fact applies, with at most minor variations, to both types of branch equally.

The geometry of any branch α is concerned primarily with the relations between α and the totality of all algebraic curves in S_2; and the first characteristic of the relationship of any such curve C to α is a certain non-negative integer (possibly ∞) which we call the *order of C on α.*

DEFINITION. Let C be an algebraic curve of S_2, not necessarily irreducible, with equation $f(x_0, x_1, x_2) = 0$, and let $\mathbf{a}(u)$ be a minimal representation *in standard form*† of a branch α. Then, if the power series $f(\mathbf{a}(u))$ is not the zero element of $K\{u\}$ its order is called the *order $O_\alpha(C)$ of C on α*, and if $f(\mathbf{a}(u)) = 0$ the order $O_\alpha(C)$ is taken conventionally to be ∞. The number $O_\alpha(C)$ is also referred to as the *order $O_\alpha(f)$ of the K-form $f(\mathbf{x})$ on α.*

The uniqueness of the integer $O_\alpha(C)$, as we have defined it, is assured by the requirement that the minimal representation $\mathbf{a}(u)$

---

† For the definition of standard form, see p. 55.

of α shall be in standard form. For any other minimal representation $\mathbf{b}(u)$ of α, also in standard form, is given by

$$b_i(u) = p(u)a_i(s(u)) \quad (i = 0, 1, 2),$$

where the substitution $u \to s(u)$ is regular and where $p(u)$ is a unit of $K\{u\}$. If the degree of the homogeneous polynomial $f(\mathbf{x})$ is n, we then have

$$f(\mathbf{b}(u)) = (p(u))^n f(\mathbf{a}(s(u))),$$

and therefore

$$O(f(\mathbf{b}(u))) = O(f(\mathbf{a}(s(u)))) \geqslant O(f(\mathbf{a}(u))).$$

Since the substitution $u \to s(u)$, being regular, possesses an inverse, we can show in the same way that $O(f(\mathbf{a}(u))) \geqslant O(f(\mathbf{b}(u)))$, and therefore $O(f(\mathbf{b}(u))) = O(f(\mathbf{a}(u)))$, as required.

The property of α of associating, in the way described, with every K-form $f(\mathbf{x})$ a definite non-negative integer (or else ∞) is often expressed by saying that α determines a *valuation* $v(f) \equiv O_\alpha(f)$ of the whole aggregate of such forms into the set $E\ \{0, 1, 2,...\}$ or the set $E \cup \{\infty\}$.

The set of all possible orders $O_\alpha(C)$, obtained by taking for C the different algebraic curves of S_2, i.e. the set of all possible values $v(f)$ for varying f, is an additive semigroup G, called the *characteristic semigroup of the branch* α. In saying that G is a semigroup, we mean simply that if $g_{(1)}$ and $g_{(2)}$ are any two members of G, distinct or coincident, then $g_{(1)}+g_{(2)}$ is also a member of G; and this follows at once from the relation $O_\alpha(f_1 f_2) = O_\alpha(f_1)+O_\alpha(f_2)$. In writing down the characteristic semigroup of any given branch (or at least a few of the smaller elements of the semigroup) we usually arrange the elements in an increasing sequence

$$G \equiv \{g_0, g_1, g_2,...\} \quad (g_0 = 0),$$

which is or is not closed by the element ∞ according as α is algebraic or non-algebraic. Structural features of the characteristic semigroup G will obviously furnish a preliminary classification of branches. For a deeper study of a branch α we also need to consider, in addition to the numbers g_i, the actual aggregates† H_i of forms $f(\mathbf{x})$ such that $O_\alpha(f) \geqslant g_i$. The properties of the resulting sequence $\{H_0, H_1, H_2,...\}$ of aggregates of forms with successively higher order on α constitute the geometry of α.

† These aggregates of forms are of the special type known as *homogeneous ideals*. See Appendix A, § 15.

From this brief indication of how the geometry of branches would be developed in general, we now turn to the elementary details that we shall need very soon.

4.1. The order of a branch

Consider a branch α, with centre A, and let C be any curve of the plane. Then it is evident that $O_\alpha(C) = 0$ if and only if C does not pass through A. The least value that $O_\alpha(C)$ can take for a curve C which passes through A is g_1. We call g_1 the *order of the branch* α, and we usually denote it by m.

Suppose now that α has a *normal* minimal representation

$$\mathbf{a}(u) \equiv (1, a_1(u), a_2(u)).$$

Then clearly $$m = \min_{i=1,2} O(a_i(u) - a_i(0)),$$

and the equations of α take the form

$$x_0 = 1, \quad x_1 = a_1 + b_1 u^m + ..., \quad x_2 = a_2 + b_2 u^m + ...,$$

where b_1 and b_2 are not both zero.

If L is any line, with equation $l_0 x_0 + l_1 x_1 + l_2 x_2 = 0$, L passes through the point A if and only if

$$l_0 + l_1 a_1 + l_2 a_2 = 0; \tag{1}$$

and, when this condition is satisfied, the order of L on α is

$$O_\alpha(L) = O(l_0 + l_1(a_1 + b_1 u^m + ...) + l_2(a_2 + b_2 u^m + ...))$$
$$= O((l_1 b_1 + l_2 b_2) u^m + ...).$$

Hence $O_\alpha(L) = m$, except only when l_0, l_1, l_2 satisfy the condition

$$l_1 b_1 + l_2 b_2 = 0. \tag{2}$$

It follows that every line through A has order m on α, with the single exception of the unique line whose coordinates l_0, l_1, l_2 satisfy both (1) and (2). This line, which has order $m' > m$, is called the *tangent to the branch* α. We have thus proved that *if a branch α with centre A is of order m, then the order on α of every line through A, except only the tangent to the branch, is equal to m.*

A branch is said to be *linear* if its order is equal to 1 and *non-linear* if its order is greater than 1.

In addition to the order m, we now define, for any branch α, a second important number n. This is to be the excess $m' - m$ of the order of the tangent to the branch over the order of any other line through A. The two numbers m and n are sometimes called the

characteristic numbers of α, and they alone are sufficient to characterize a few of the simplest types of branch.† Thus, for example, we
have a finer classification of linear branches ($m = 1$) into those of
general type ($n = 1$), those which are *inflexional* in the strict sense
($n = 2$), those which are *undulatory* ($n = 3$), and so on. A branch
with characteristic numbers $m = 2$, $n = 1$ is of the type known as
the *simple cuspidal branch*, while a $(2, 2)$ branch is said to be a
ramphoid cusp (*Schnabelspitze*).

It should be noted that any curve C which passes simply through
A and does not touch the branch tangent has order m on α, while a
curve through A which touches the branch tangent has order
$m'' > m$ on α. It may be seen that the least value of m'' for any of
the curves which touch the branch tangent is either $m+n$ or $2m$
according as $n \leqslant m$ or $n \geqslant m$; and this least value is the member
g_2 of the sequence $\{g_i\}$. Thus, for example, if α is a branch with
$m = 2$ and $n = 3$, then $g_2 = 4$ (the order on α of a repeated line
that is distinct from the tangent to the branch) while

$$g_3 = 5 = m+n.$$

4.2. The reduced equations of a branch. Some simple types of branch

With due precautions, the order $O_\alpha(C)$ of the curve C on the
branch α and the order m of the branch itself, which we have
defined with reference to a system of homogeneous coordinates,
can be handled also by means of affine coordinates. Thus if C has an
affine equation $F(X, Y) = 0$ and α has a *minimal* affine representation $(X(u), Y(u))$ then, *subject only to the restriction that the centre of
α must be a finite point*, the order $O_\alpha(C)$ is equal to $O(F(X(u), Y(u)))$.
We shall refer to this number also as the order $O_\alpha(F)$ of the polynomial $F(X, Y)$ on α. If $(X(u), Y(u))$ has its centre at infinity it is
necessary, of course, to revert to homogeneous coordinates and
the original definition. The order of the branch α—again subject
to the same restriction as above—is the lesser of the two orders
$O(X(u)-X(0))$ and $O(Y(u)-Y(0))$, the series $X(u)$ and $Y(u)$ being
necessarily elements of $K\{u\}$ in this case.

For the detailed study of a given branch α, the use of affine
coordinates has obvious advantages; and still more convenient is
the use of a canonical representation of α relative to axes AX and

† Cf. van der Waerden's remarks on this classification, illustrated by diagrams,
on p. 76 of his *Einführung*.

AY that intersect in the centre A of α and are such that one of them, AX, lies along the tangent to the branch. With this choice of the coordinate system, we obtain the *reduced equations* of α, which take the form

$$X = u^m, \quad Y = c_1 u^{m_1} + c_2 u^{m_2} + \cdots,$$

where $c_i \neq 0$, $i = 1, 2, \ldots$; $0 < m < m_1 < m_2 \ldots$; and the highest common factor of $m, m_1, m_2, \ldots$ is unity. Clearly, $m_1 = m + n$.

The very special case $X = u, Y = 0$ (in which there are no non-zero coefficients c_i) arises when α is a branch of a line, namely the line AX.

We conclude this section with a brief list of reduced equations of branches of some of the simplest types.

(i) *The linear branch* $(m = 1, n \geqslant 1)$
$$X = u, \quad Y = a_2 u^2 + a_3 u^3 + \cdots.$$
Any or all of the coefficients a_i may be zero.
$$G = \{0, 1, 2, \ldots\}, \text{ as already stated.}$$

(ii) *The simple cusp* $(m = 2, n = 1)$
$$X = u^2, \quad Y = a_3 u^3 + a_4 u^4 + \cdots \quad (a_3 \neq 0).$$
$$G = \{0, 2, 3, \ldots\}.$$

(iii) *The double cusp*† $(m = 2, n \geqslant 2)$
$$X = u^2, \quad Y = a_4 u^4 + a_5 u^5 + \cdots \quad (a_5 \neq 0).$$
$$G = \{0, 2, 4, 5, \ldots\}.$$

(iv) *The cubical cusp* $(m = 3, n = 1)$
$$X = u^3, \quad Y = a_4 u^4 + a_5 u^5 + \cdots \quad (a_4 \neq 0).$$
$$G = \{0, 3, 4, 6, 7, 8, \ldots\}.$$

(v) *The cubo-quadratic cusp* $(m = 3, n = 2)$
$$X = u^3, \quad Y = a_5 u^5 + a_6 u^6 + \cdots \quad (a_5 \neq 0).$$
$$G = \{0, 3, 5, 6, 8, 9, 10, \ldots\}.$$

(vi) *The general monomial branch* $(n = m_1 - m)$
$$X = u^m, \quad Y = u^{m_1}, \quad (m, m_1) = 1.$$
$G = \{rm + sm_1\}$, where r and s denote arbitrary non-negative integers.

---

† The *double cusp* is here defined as a branch with reduced equations of the form stated. Except when $a_4 = 0$ it is the simplest type of ramphoid cusp. A ramphoid cusp $(m = n = 2)$ of the sth type can be defined as a branch with reduced equations of the form
$$X = u^2, \quad Y = a_4 u^4 + a_6 u^6 + \cdots + a_{2s+2} u^{2s+2} + a_{2s+3} u^{2s+3} + \cdots,$$
where $a_4 \neq 0$ and $a_{2s+3} \neq 0$.

Only in the last case is α necessarily algebraic (being contained in the algebraic curve $X^{m_1} - Y^m = 0$).

In each of the cases given, the reader should construct examples of polynomials whose orders on the branch in question are the stated elements of G.

5. Analytic equivalence of branches

We now mention briefly one further development of the theory of branches. The ring of formal power series in a single indeterminate u may be extended to the ring $K\{u, v\}$ of formal power series in two indeterminates u and v, any element $P(u, v)$ of this wider ring being of the form

$$P(u, v) \equiv P_0 + P_1(u, v) + P_2(u, v) + \ldots,$$

where $P_i(u, v)$ is a K-form of degree i in u and v together. By use of the properties of this ring we may then define *local analytic transformations* of the type

$$\left. \begin{array}{l} X' = (aX + bY) + Q_2(X, Y) + Q_3(X, Y) + \ldots \\ Y' = (cX + dY) + R_2(X, Y) + R_3(X, Y) + \ldots \end{array} \right\},$$

where $ad - bc \neq 0$; and these transformations possess inverses of the same type. Any such transformation carries a branch α, with centre at the origin $(0, 0)$ of (X, Y), into a branch α' with centre at the origin $(0, 0)$ of (X', Y'); and any two branches α and α' which can be related in this way are said to be *analytically equivalent*. The properties of branches which are invariant with respect to local analytic transformations will obviously be of especial importance and generality. Investigation of such properties constitutes what is called the *analytic theory of branches* (cf. p. 101).

The difference between this very general theory and the projective theory of branches is illustrated, for example, by the fact that in the analytic theory all linear branches are equivalent. This means, in other words, that the linear branch, from the point of view of the analytic theory, is a unique geometric object; and the same is also true, for example, of the simple cuspidal branch (cf. p. 77). For branches in general, in S_r as in S_2, the investigation of analytic invariants is a development of considerable interest and importance (cf. Chapter XI, § 12).

NOTES AND EXERCISES ON CHAPTER IV

1. Show that the branch α, defined by the equations

$$x_0 : x_1 : x_2 = 1+2u+u^2 : -1-2u : 1+2u+u^2+u^4+u^5,$$

admits of the canonical representation

$$X+1 = v^2, \qquad Y-1 = v^4+3v^5+6v^6+\dots,$$

where $X = x_1/x_0$ and $Y = x_2/x_0$. Deduce that both representations are minimal, the order of α being 2, its centre being $(1, -1, 1)$, and its branch tangent having equation $x_0 = x_2$.

Show also that the semigroup of orders of all forms $f(x_0, x_1, x_2)$ (or polynomials $F(X, Y)$) on α is $\{0, 2, 4, 5+k\}$ $(k = 0, 1, 2,\dots,\infty)$, the branch being contained in the curve with equation

$$X^3Y^2+2(2, 10, 11, 4\!\!\!)\!(X, 1)^3Y-(1, 9, 26, 26, 9\!\!\!)\!(X, 1)^4 = 0.$$

2. A representation of a branch α is given in the form

$$x_0 : x_1 : x_2 = 1-u : 1-u+u^2 : 2-2u-u^2+\sum_0^\infty u^{4+i}.$$

Show that the normal representation, obtained by dividing throughout by $1-u$, is redundant, being derivable by the substitution $v \to \sum_0^\infty u^{2+i}$ from the minimal affine representation

$$X-1 = v, \quad Y-2 = -v+v^2;$$

and hence deduce that α is a linear branch, with centre $(1, 1, 2)$ and with branch tangent $3x_0-x_1-x_2 = 0$.

3. Show that the branch with canonical representation $X = u^4$, $Y = u^6+u^7$ admits of the alternative canonical representation

$$Y = v^6, \quad X = v^4-\tfrac{2}{3}v^5+\tfrac{2}{3}v^6+\dots.$$

Compute the semigroup of the branch.

4. If $c_{00} \neq 0$ and $P_j(u) = c_{0j}+c_{1j}u+c_{2j}u^2+\dots$ $(j = 0, 1, 2)$, show that a necessary condition for a branch with equations of the form

$$x_0 : x_1 : x_2 = P_0(u) : P_1(u) : P_2(u)$$

to be of order not less than n is that the rank of the $3 \times n$ matrix (c_{ij}) $(i = 0,\dots, n-1; j = 0, 1, 2)$ should be 1. Explain the insufficiency of the condition.

[*Hint.* Replace x_1 and x_2 by the new coordinates $\bar{x}_1 = x_1-c_{01}c_{00}^{-1}x_0$, $\bar{x}_2 = x_2-c_{02}c_{00}^{-1}x_0$.]

5. If $a_2 \neq 0$, show that there exists a conic with order at least 6 on the linear branch $X = u$, $Y = a_2u^2+a_3u^3+\dots$ if and only if

$$a_2^2a_5-3a_2a_3a_4+2a_3^3 = 0.$$

6. Show that the aggregate of all branches representable in the form

$$X = a+bu^m, \quad Y = P(u),$$

where m is any positive integer, a and b are arbitrary constants, and $P(u)$ is any element of $K\lfloor u\rfloor$, is composed of the two classes:

    (i) all branches with finite centres,

    (ii) all branches with Y_∞ as centre and with branch tangent not along the line at infinity.

[*Note.* Except for the trivial class of branches each of which is actually contained in a line $X = a$ (the case when $b = 0$), we may suppose that $b = 1$, and when, in addition, $P(u)$ is of non-negative order, we obtain all other branches with finite centres. Suppose, then, that $b = 1$ and that $P(u) = u^{-n}S(u)$, where n is a positive integer and $S(u)$ is a unit of $K\{u\}$. If we write $T(u) = (S(u))^{-1}$, the equations of the branch take the normal form

$$x_0 = u^n T(u), \quad x_1 = u^n(a + u^m)T(u), \quad x_2 = 1;$$

and the branch therefore has centre at Y_∞ and tangent not along the line at infinity (since $O\{u^n(a + u^m)T(u)\} \geqslant n$). The converse follows readily.]

    7. Classify, in the manner of the preceding example, the branches that admit of representation in the form

$$X = u^{-m}, \quad Y = P(u),$$

where m is any positive integer and $P(u)$ is any element of $K\lfloor u\rfloor$.

    8. Write down, for each of the six branch types listed on p. 77, the simplest equation of an algebraic curve with a branch of that type at the origin.

[Thus, for example, the curve $(Y - X^2)^2 = X^5$ has a (ramphoid) double cusp at O.]

    9. By solving the equation for X (in terms of Y), or by any other method, show that the curve with equation

$$X^2 + XY^2(1 + Y) - Y^5 = 0$$

has two linear branches at the origin O, each of which has OY as branch tangent.

Hence show, by applying the quadratic transformation $X = X'$, $Y = X'Y'$ to the curve with equation

$$(Y^2 - X^3)(Y^3 - X^4) = 2X^7,$$

that this curve also has two branches at O, and describe the character of these branches.

    10. *Semigroup of a branch.* The semigroup G of a branch α is the aggregate of numbers g each of which is the order on α of at least one curve C. In other words, if $X = P(u)$, $Y = Q(u)$ is a *minimal* representation of α, with the centre of α at the finite point $(P(0), Q(0))$, then G is the aggregate of orders $O\{F(P(u), Q(u))\}$ for all non-zero $F(X, Y) \in K[X, Y]$. The semigroup $G^{(s)}$ of a quasi-branch $\tilde{\alpha}^{(s)}$, redundant transform of index s of the minimal quasi-branch $\tilde{\alpha}$, is sometimes defined for obvious reasons to be the aggregate of numbers sg such that $g \in G$.

The characteristic structure of G was first investigated by R. Apéry (*Comptes Rendus*, **222** (1946), 1189–1200; see also the references quoted in § 11 of Chapter XI). In particular, Apéry proved (i) that G is *unitary*, which means that there exists an N_0 such that G contains all integers $N \geqslant N_0$, and in addition (ii) that G is *symmetric*, which means that there exists an integer A such that if two integers a, b satisfy the relation $a+b = A$ then one of them belongs to G and the other does not. These properties, however, are not sufficient to ensure that a semigroup G of non-negative integers is the semigroup of some branch α.

11. *Monomial branch*. If G is the semigroup of the monomial branch $X = u^m$, $Y = u^n$ $(m, n > 0, (m, n) = 1)$, then G (excluding ∞) consists of all integers of the form $pm+qn$ with $p, q \geqslant 0$, and is said to be generated by m, n. We then have the simple result:

If G is the semigroup of integers generated by the two mutually prime positive integers m, n, then G contains every integer $N \geqslant N_0$, where $N_0 = mn - m - n + 1$; and N_0 is the least integer with this property.

The following simple proof of this result was furnished by J. E. Reeve.

Proof. The result follows at once from the two statements:

  (i) $mn - m - n$ does not belong to G,

  (ii) if $N > mn - m - n + 1$, and if $N \in G$, then $N - 1 \in G$.

To prove (i), we suppose, if possible, that $mn - m - n = pm + qn$ with $p, q \geqslant 0$ (p, q being integers). Then $m(p+1) = n(m - q - 1)$; whence, since $(m, n) = 1$, it follows that $n \mid (p+1)$ and $m \mid (q+1)$. Writing $p+1 = nn_1$, $q+1 = mm_1$, where $m_1, n_1 > 0$, we have

$$m . nn_1 = n(m - mm_1);$$

whence, since $m, n > 0$, it follows that $m_1 + n_1 = 1$, in contradiction to $m_1, n_1 > 0$.

To prove (ii), since $N \in G$ we may write $N = pm + qn$ with $p, q \geqslant 0$; and hence, since $N \geqslant mn - m - n + 2$, we have

$$pm + qn - 1 \geqslant mn - m - n + 1.$$

Let x, y be integers such that $mx + ny = 1$. Then

$$pm + qn - mx - ny \geqslant mn - m - n + 1;$$

whence $$\frac{p - x + 1}{n} + \frac{q - y + 1}{m} \geqslant 1 + \frac{1}{mn} > 1.$$

From this it follows that an integer λ exists such that

$$\frac{-q + y - 1}{m} < \lambda < \frac{p - x + 1}{n};$$

so that $$p - x - \lambda n \geqslant 0 \quad \text{and} \quad q - y + \lambda m \geqslant 0,$$

and hence $$N - 1 = (p - x - \lambda n)m + (q - y + \lambda m)n \in G.$$

12. *Analytic transformations*. Show that any linear branch is analytically equivalent to the linear line-branch $X = u, Y = 0$; that any simple cuspidal branch is analytically equivalent to the branch $X = u^2, Y = u^3$; and that any double cuspidal branch is analytically equivalent to the branch $X = u^2$, $Y = u^5$. Discuss the corresponding problem for cubical cuspidal branches.

13. Prove that the semigroup G of a branch is an analytic invariant of the branch.

14. Show that the branches $X = u^3$, $Y = u^7$ and $X = u^3$, $Y = u^7 + u^8$ are not analytically equivalent (cf. Chapter XI, Exercise 13).

15. By using Theorem 9 of Chapter V, show that any local analytic transformation can be written, except possibly for a necessary interchange of X' and Y', in the form

$$X' = (X - a_1 Y - a_2 Y^2 - ...)U,$$
$$Y' = (Y - b_1 X - b_2 X^2 - ...)V,$$

where a_i, $b_j \in K$ $(i, j = 1, 2, ...)$, $a_1 b_1 \neq 1$, and U, V are units of the ring $K\{X, Y\}$ (cf. Chapter V, § 7.1).

MULTIPLICITIES OF INTERSECTION

1. Puiseux's Theorem

IN Chapter I we defined an irreducible algebraic curve C of $S_2(K)$ as the aggregate of points (i.e. ground points) which satisfy an irreducible K-equation; but since then we have been working our way towards a new and much deeper conception of C as an aggregate of algebraic branches, each branch having for its centre a ground point of C, and each branch being sufficient by itself to determine C completely. Such a reorientation of ideas would not be acceptable unless the new conception took all the ground points of C into account; and one of our first tasks in the present chapter will be to show that every ground point of C is the centre of at least one, but never of an infinite number, of the branches of C. Furthermore, our motive in introducing the new conception was the hope that it would illuminate the mysteries of multiplicity of intersection which we encountered in Chapter II, and we now wish to show that it makes possible a complete solution of that particular problem.

The theory of branches, and indeed our entire undertaking, is founded upon a certain algebraic theorem, of great power, which isolates an essential algebraic constituent of the classical analytical theory of algebraic functions. The theorem can be stated very simply, but the proof of it is long and not particularly easy, and it is most appropriately given separately (see Appendix B).

THEOREM 1 (*Puiseux's Theorem*). *The field $K^*|u|$ of fractional power series in a single indeterminate u, with coefficients in the complex field K, is algebraically closed.*

2. Fractional representation of branches

Since we shall be largely concerned throughout this chapter with affine branch-representations of the form

$$X = a + w^\nu, \quad Y = P(u), \tag{1}$$

where ν is a positive integer and $P(u)$ belongs to $K|u|$, it is convenient to note once for all the following precise characterization of the branches that can be represented in this way. *A branch, not actually contained in a line parallel to OY, admits of representation in the form* (1) *if and only if either* (i) *it has a finite centre, or* (ii) *it has centre at* Y_∞ *and branch tangent distinct from the line at infinity* (cf. Chapter IV, Exercise 6).

If the representation (1) is minimal, we refer to the fractional transcendental point

$$(X, P((X-a)^{1/\nu})) \tag{2}$$

as a *fractional representation, of index* ν, *of the branch* α in question. In this representation the expression $X-a$, or X' say, is to be looked on as the parameter. Since X' is transcendental over K, it behaves as an indeterminate; and we have, moreover, $X = X'+a$.

We also frequently say, more conveniently still, that the branch α is represented by the *fractional equation*

$$Y = P((X-a)^{1/\nu}). \tag{3}$$

If we do this, however, we have to bear in mind the fact that the same branch α is represented equally by ν different equations

$$Y = P(\zeta^i(X-a)^{1/\nu}) \quad (i = 0,...,\nu-1), \tag{4}$$

where ζ is a primitive νth root of unity; for all of these equations lead back to the same representation (1). Thus *a branch* α, *with a minimal representation of the form* (1), *has a cycle of* ν *distinct representations by fractional equations* (4). *Further, provided that* $O(P(u)) \geqslant 0$, *the branch is of order* ν *if the branch tangent is not parallel to* OY, *and of order* $\nu_1 < \nu$ *otherwise.*

Thus, for example, the linear branch $X = u^2$, $Y = u$, with OY as tangent, has the cycle of two fractional equations $Y = X^{\frac{1}{2}}$ and $Y = -X^{\frac{1}{2}}$.

3. Places on a curve

If a branch belongs to a curve C, then its centre is a point of C. The terms 'point of C' and 'centre of a branch of C' are not, however, synonymous, since the second is more specific than the first. We shall often find it convenient and expressive to use a language of *places* in preference to that of branches, since the new usage reflects faithfully the significant relation between the branches of C and the ground points on which they are centred.

DEFINITION. If P is the centre of a branch of a curve C, then the branch will be called a *place on* C *at* P, and it will usually be denoted by a script capital, such as $\mathscr{P}$, corresponding to the italic letter used for the point.

Our first object in this section will now be to investigate those places on a given irreducible curve C which have their centres on a given line L.

We take L as the axis OY of an affine coordinate system, and we suppose for simplicity that the line at infinity in this system is so chosen that Y_∞ is not on C. Then the equation of C may be written as

$$f(X, Y) \equiv Y^n + a_1(X)Y^{n-1} + \ldots + a_n(X) = 0, \qquad (1)$$

where n is the order of C, and $a_i(X) \in K[X]$ $(i = 1, \ldots, n)$. The ordinates of the n ground points $P_1, \ldots, P_n$ of C (not necessarily all distinct) that lie on OY are then the roots $b_1, \ldots, b_n$ of the equation

$$f(0, Y) \equiv Y^n + a_1(0)Y^{n-1} + \ldots + a_n(0) = 0.$$

In virtue of Puiseux's Theorem (p. 83) we know that equation (1) for Y can be solved completely in the fractional field $K^*|X|$; and we may therefore write

$$f(X, Y) = \prod_{i=1}^{n} (Y - P_i(X)), \qquad (2)$$

where the $P_i(X)$ are elements of $K^*|X|$. It follows that the n fractional transcendental points

$$(X, P_i(X)) \quad (i = 1, \ldots, n)$$

all belong to C and all have their centres on OY. Since none of these centres is Y_∞, the $P_i(X)$ are all of non-negative order,† i.e. they are in $K^*\{X\}$.

Now let $\mathscr{P}$ be any place on C with its centre at a point P of OY. By § 2, the place (i.e. branch) has a canonical representation of the form

$$X = u^\nu, \quad Y = b + b'u^{\nu'} + b''u^{\nu''} + \ldots, \qquad (3)$$

where $0 < \nu, 0 < \nu' < \nu'' < \ldots$, and the highest common factor of $\nu, \nu', \nu'', \ldots$ is 1; and this representation yields in turn a cycle of ν fractional representations

$$(X, P^{(\alpha)}(X)) \quad (\alpha = 0, \ldots, \nu - 1), \qquad (4)$$

where $\qquad P^{(\alpha)}(X) = b + b'\zeta^{\alpha\nu'}X^{\nu'/\nu} + b''\zeta^{\alpha\nu''}X^{\nu''/\nu} + \ldots,$

ζ being a primitive νth root of unity. Since the branch (3) belongs to C, the ν fractional points (4) must also be points of C, and the ν series $P^{(\alpha)}(X)$ must therefore be roots of equation (1). Thus each place on C at a point of OY gives rise to a cycle of distinct roots of

† This can also be seen directly; for if $O(P(X)) = -\mu$ $(\mu > 0)$, then
$$O(f(X, P(X))) = -n\mu,$$
so that $P(X)$ cannot be a root of (1).

(1); and conversely, as is obvious, each root of (1) belongs to precisely one such cycle, associated with a place on C at a point of OY.

We observe finally that, since $f(X, Y)$ is irreducible over K, all the roots $P_i(X)$ of (1) are distinct. For any multiple root would be a common root of $f(X, Y) = 0$ and $(\partial/\partial Y)f(X, Y) = 0$, and then $f(X, Y)$ and $(\partial/\partial Y)f(X, Y)$ would have a common factor, involving Y, in $K[X, Y]$. We can therefore assert the following theorem.

THEOREM 2. *With the above hypotheses and notation, the n roots $P_i(X)$ of equation* (1), *which are necessarily distinct, form a number $s \leqslant n$ of non-overlapping cycles*

$$\Pi_j = \{P_1^j, ..., P_{\nu_j}^j\} \quad (j = 1, ..., s).$$

Each of the cycles Π_j corresponds to a place $\mathscr{P}_j$ on C with centre on OY, and each place of C with centre on OY arises from one of the cycles.

In equation (2) we can equate the terms on each side which are independent of X, and we then have

$$f(0, Y) = \prod_{i=1}^{n} (Y - P_i(0)).$$

But the roots of the equation $f(0, Y) = 0$ are $b_1, ..., b_n$, and so we may put
$$b_i = P_i(0) \quad (i = 1, ..., n).$$

The centre of the place $\mathscr{P}_j$ corresponding to the cycle Π_j is the point $(0, P_i(0))$, i.e. the point $(0, b_i)$, where $P_i(X)$ is any one of the roots belonging to the cycle Π_j. Thus to every cycle of ν_j fractional series there correspond ν_j equal numbers among the b_i; and so we obtain the following further result.

THEOREM 3. *Once again with the hypotheses and notation of Theorem 2, if B is any intersection of C with OY, then B is the centre of one or more places on C; and the multiplicity of B as an intersection of C with OY is equal to the sum of the lengths of the cycles Π_j corresponding to all the places on C with centre at B.*

From the foregoing discussion of the places on a given curve C which have their centres on an arbitrary line, we can now infer the following general theorem concerning places on a curve.

THEOREM 4. *Every point of an irreducible curve C is the centre of at least one place on C, and it may be the centre of several places, though only of a finite number.*

COROLLARY 1. *If C has p distinct places $\mathscr{P}_1, ..., \mathscr{P}_p$ at an s-fold point P, then the sum of the orders† of $\mathscr{P}_1, ..., \mathscr{P}_p$ is s. And if σ is the sum of the orders of those of the places $\mathscr{P}_i$ which have a given nodal tangent T at P as branch tangent, then σ is equal to the multiplicity of T in the set of s nodal tangents at P.*

Proof. If we take affine coordinates with P as origin, and make use of the discussion leading up to Theorem 4, the proof is quite straightforward, and it may be left as an exercise for the reader (cf. Exercise 11, p. 106).

COROLLARY 2. *A curve C has a single linear branch at each of its simple points, and the tangent to C at the point coincides with the tangent to the branch.*

The proof is immediate.

The broad result of Theorem 4 and its corollaries is that we are now in a position to regard an irreducible curve C as an aggregate of places (i.e. algebraic branches) rather than an aggregate of ground points. The correspondence between places and points is one-one *in general*, but certain multiple points of C may be the centres of more than one place. The notion of the places on a curve may now be extended to reducible as well as irreducible curves by the following simple definition.

DEFINITION. If C is a reducible curve, consisting of components C_i with multiplicities m_i, the *places on C* are all the places on the components of C, each counted to the multiplicity of that component to which it belongs.

All the results that have been obtained for places on irreducible curves can now be extended, with appropriate adjustments, to places on reducible curves.

Our way of defining the concept of place on a curve, which will be found to play a fundamental role in the theory of algebraic curves that we are about to develop, may perhaps seem too abstract to have much connexion with geometrical intuition. It may help the reader to see the connexion if he thinks of the intuitively evident fact that when a curve has a node there are two points of the curve which fall at a particular point of the plane, the two points being

---

† It may perhaps be helpful to remind the reader that the order of a place $\mathscr{P}$ on C (i.e. a branch of C) is not necessarily the same as the length of the cycle of roots of equation (1) that corresponds to $\mathscr{P}$. Thus, if $\mathscr{P}$ has the representation (3), the cycle in question has length ν, while the order of $\mathscr{P}$ is the smaller of ν and ν'.

approached quite differently along the curve, while when a curve has a cusp there is only one point of the curve at that point of the plane. We shall be able to infer from our abstract theory that a curve has two places at a node but only one at a cusp. The representations of these places as branches, by formal power series, can be looked upon as parametric representations of the neighbourhoods on the curve of the places in question, and in the older Puiseux theory they were arrived at more or less in this way.

3.1. Curves which contain the point Y_∞

In the analysis of the preceding section we chose our affine coordinate system, for the sake of simplicity, in such a way that Y_∞ did not lie on the curve C that was under consideration. If we now remove this restriction, supposing only that C is irreducible and is not a line parallel to OY, then the equation of C takes, as compared with (1), the more general form

$$F(X, Y) \equiv a_0(X)Y^m + a_1(X)Y^{m-1} + \ldots + a_m(X) = 0, \qquad (5)$$

where m may be any positive integer that does not exceed the order n of C, and $a_0(X)$ is a non-zero polynomial in X of degree not exceeding $n-m$. As before, we have a factorization

$$F(X, Y) \equiv a_0(X) \prod_{i=1}^{m} (Y - P_i(X)), \qquad (6)$$

where the $P_i(X)$ are elements of $K^*|X|$; but some of the series $P_i(X)$ may now be of negative order if $a_0(X)$ has some positive power of X as a factor, that is to say if the line $X = 0$ is a branch tangent to C at its $(n-m)$-fold point Y_∞.

We shall leave the reader to verify that the roots of equation (5) once again distribute themselves into cycles corresponding to places on C with centres on OY, except that *a place at Y_∞ is represented in this way by a cycle of roots of* (5) *if and only if its branch tangent is OY.* Any place on C at Y_∞ which has a finite line $X = a$ as branch tangent will correspond to a cycle of roots of the equation $F(X, Y) = 0$ when this is solved for Y in the appropriate field $K^*|X-a|$; but no place on C at Y_∞ with the line at infinity as branch tangent is associated in this way with any cycle of roots of

$$F(X, Y) = 0.$$

4. Multiplicity of intersection in terms of order

In the previous chapter we defined the order on a branch α of S_2 of a curve D (or of a K-form $f(x_0, x_1, x_2)$ or a K-polynomial $F(X, Y)$).

When α is a place $\mathscr{P}$ on an irreducible curve C, this order will be called the *order of D* (or of $f(x_0, x_1, x_2)$ or $F(X, Y)$) *at the place $\mathscr{P}$ on C*. If C is reducible, and $\mathscr{P}$ is a place on a component C_i of multiplicity m_i in C, then the order of D at the place $\mathscr{P}$ on C will be taken to be m_i times its order at $\mathscr{P}$ on C_i.

The concept that we now possess of the order of one curve at a definite place on another curve has an immediate and fruitful application to the problem of characterizing adequately the multiplicity of intersection of two curves at a point which is common to them both; and our next task will be to re-examine, in the light of the innovations we have made, the definition which we gave in Chapter II of the multiplicity of a point P as an intersection of two curves C and D. We shall find that we are able in this way to give more point to Bézout's Theorem (p. 37). The basic connexion between the order of one curve at a place on another and the multiplicity of intersection of two curves at a particular point is established by the theorem which follows. We shall state this theorem, for simplicity, only for the case in which neither of the two curves concerned has any multiple component, although such an assumption is not really necessary and can easily be dispensed with afterwards.

THEOREM 5. *If P is any intersection of two curves C and D which have no common component, and neither of which has any multiple component, then the multiplicity of intersection I_P of C and D at P is equal to the sum of the orders of D at those places on C which have their centres at P.*

Proof. We choose a system $\mathscr{R}_A$ of affine coordinates X, Y such that (i) P is a finite point in the coordinate system $\mathscr{R}_A$; (ii) Y_∞ does not lie on C; (iii) no two intersections of C and D lie on the same ordinate $X = k$ ($k \in K$); and we suppose that the coordinates of P in $\mathscr{R}_A$ are (a, b), that the equations of C and D are $F(X, Y) = 0$ and $G(X, Y) = 0$, and that the Y-resultant of $F(X, Y)$ and $G(X, Y)$ is $R(X)$. Then, by Theorem 5 of Chapter II, the multiplicity of intersection I_P of C and D at P is the exponent of $X - a$ as a factor of $R(X)$.

Now, since Y_∞ is not on C, we may suppose (cf. p. 85) that

$$F(X, Y) = \prod_{i=1}^{m} (Y - P_i(X-a)),$$

where m is the order of C and $P_i(X-a) \in K^*\{X-a\}$. We have, further (cf. Appendix A, § 18),

$$R(X) = \prod_{i=1}^{m} G(X, P_i(X-a)). \tag{1}$$

Now each cycle Π_j in the set of m fractional power series $P_i(X-a)$ corresponds to a single place $\mathscr{P}_j$ on C at some point of the ordinate $X = a$; and we may suppose, in particular, that exactly p of the cycles, $\Pi_1, ..., \Pi_p$, correspond to places at P. Let Π_1 be the cycle $\{P_1, ..., P_\nu\}$. Then $P_1, ..., P_\nu$ can all be regarded as formal power series in $(X-a)^{1/\nu}$, with the same constant term b; and the order s_1 of D at $\mathscr{P}_1$ is equal to the common order in $(X-a)^{1/\nu}$ of $G(X, P_1), ..., G(X, P_\nu)$. Hence $\prod_{i=1}^{\nu} G(X, P_i)$ has order νs_1 in $(X-a)^{1/\nu}$, and therefore order s_1 in $X-a$. Similarly, the cycles $\Pi_2, ..., \Pi_p$ yield products $\prod G(X, P_i))$ of orders $s_2, ..., s_p$ respectively in $X-a$. If, however, $P_h(X-a)$ is one of the fractional power series which corresponds to a place $\mathscr{P}$ not at P, then its constant term is different from b, and the order in $X-a$ of $G(X, P_h)$ is accordingly zero. It now follows that the order in $X-a$ of $\prod_{i=1}^{m} G(X, P_i(X-a))$ is $s_1+...+s_p$. But we know that the multiplicity of intersection I_P is the exponent of $X-a$ as a factor of $R(X)$, i.e. of $\prod_{i=1}^{m} G(X, P_i(X-a))$; and therefore $I_P = s_1+...+s_p$, as is asserted by the theorem.

Combining the above theorem with Bézout's Theorem, we have the following corollary.

COROLLARY. *If $\sum_{\mathscr{P}}$ denotes summation over all places $\mathscr{P}$ on C, and $\sum_{\mathscr{Q}}$ denotes summation over all places $\mathscr{Q}$ on D, then*

$$\sum_{\mathscr{P}} O_{\mathscr{P}}(D) = \sum_{\mathscr{Q}} O_{\mathscr{Q}}(C) = mn,$$

where m and n are the orders of C and D.

If C is irreducible and has the homogeneous equation

$$f(x_0, x_1, x_2) = 0,$$

then any ratio $g(x_0, x_1, x_2)/h(x_0, x_1, x_2)$ of two K-forms $g(\mathbf{x})$ and $h(\mathbf{x})$ of the same degree defines a rational function χ on C, provided only that $h(\mathbf{x})$ is not divisible by $f(\mathbf{x})$ (cf. Chapter III, p. 58). We define the *order* $O_{\mathscr{P}}(\chi)$ *of the rational function* χ *at any place* $\mathscr{P}$ *on* C in the natural way as

$$O_{\mathscr{P}}(\chi) = O_{\mathscr{P}}(g) - O_{\mathscr{P}}(h);$$

and, with this definition, the above corollary leads at once to the following important property of irreducible algebraic curves.

THEOREM 6. *If* χ *is any rational function on an irreducible algebraic curve* C, *then the sum of the orders of* χ *at all places on* C *is zero, i.e.*

$$\sum_{\mathscr{P}} O_{\mathscr{P}}(\chi) = 0.$$

5. Zeuthen's rule

The interpretation of multiplicity of intersection which we obtained in the preceding section is so simple and so fully in accord with the conception of an algebraic curve that we have now been led to adopt, that we might perhaps be tempted to neglect other, somewhat differently oriented, approaches to the same problem that have also been devised. This would be unfortunate, and especially so in the case of the classical work of Zeuthen. Zeuthen's approach, which is a valuable complement to the one that we have chosen to use, was strongly conditioned by his primary interest in estimating the multiplicities of coincidences in correspondences associated with problems of enumerative geometry. We shall shortly give an interpretation, within our present order of ideas, of this alternative method of handling multiplicity of intersection; but first we look, in the simplest case, at the way in which the problem presented itself to Zeuthen, and the kind of solution that he obtained.

The simplest case of Zeuthen's problem is that of estimating the multiplicity of a coincidence (a, a) in a rational (m, n) correspondence between two complex variables X and Y. If the pairs (X, Y) of the correspondence are represented by the points of a curve $F(X, Y) = 0$ in S_2, the coincidences are mapped by the intersections of this curve with the line $X = Y$; and the stated multiplicity problem reduces to that of *finding the multiplicity of intersection of the curve* $F(X, Y) = 0$ *with the line* $X = Y$ *at the point* (a, a). The solution obtained by Zeuthen, which is particularly well adapted for use in the specialized problems of enumerative geometry, is as follows. We suppose that, as X approaches the value a, there are s of the corresponding values of Y, say $Y_1, \ldots, Y_s$, which tend to a. Then *the multiplicity of* a *as a coincidence is equal to the sum of the infinitesimal orders of* $Y_1-X,...,Y_s-X$, *relative to* $X-a$ *as an infinitesimal of order unity.*

For the wide range of applications which Zeuthen had in mind, his criterion had to be expressed in terms of orders of magnitude of a set of infinitesimal 'distances'; but we shall rather look, within our scheme of development, for an equivalent interpretation of multiplicity of intersection in terms of orders of formal power series. Suppose, then, that we are once again investigating the multiplicity of intersection of two curves C and D at a particular point P, but that we are now doing so in the context of a preassigned affine coordinate system (selected, perhaps, because it is related to the curves in some significant manner). Let the equations of the curves be

$$F(X, Y) \equiv a_0(X)Y^m + a_1(X)Y^{m-1} + ... + a_m(X) = 0, \qquad (1)$$

$$G(X, Y) \equiv b_0(X)Y^n + b_1(X)Y^{n-1} + ... + b_n(X) = 0, \qquad (2)$$

where $m, n > 0$; $a_i(X), b_i(X) \in K[X]$; $a_0(X) \neq 0$, $b_0(X) \neq 0$; and let the coordinates of P be (a, b). We suppose, as usual, that C and D have no common component, that neither of them has a line-component through P parallel to OY, and also (for convenience, although it is not strictly necessary) that neither curve has any multiple component. There is, however, no restriction now on the behaviour of C or D at Y_∞.

We suppose that C has p places $\mathscr{P}_1,...,\mathscr{P}_p$ and D has q places $\mathscr{Q}_1,...,\mathscr{Q}_q$ at P. In the fractional field $K^*|X-a|$, F and G have factorizations

$$F(X, Y) = a_0(X) \prod_{i=1}^{m} (Y-P_i), \qquad (3)$$

$$G(X, Y) = b_0(X) \prod_{j=1}^{n} (Y-Q_j), \qquad (4)$$

where the P_i and Q_j are elements of $K^*|X-a|$. Since neither curve has any multiple component, the P_i are all distinct, and so also are the Q_j. By Theorem 5, the multiplicity of intersection I_P of C and D at P is given by

$$I_P = \sum_{i=1}^{p} O_{\mathscr{P}_i}(D) = \sum_{i=1}^{p} O_{\mathscr{P}_i}(G(X, Y));$$

and this, as we showed in the course of the proof of Theorem 5, is the same as saying that

$$I_P = \sum_{i=1}^{p} O_{(X-a)}(G(X, P_1^{(i)})...G(X, P_{\nu_i}^{(i)})),$$

where $\{P_1^{(i)},..., P_{\nu_i}^{(i)}\}$ is the cycle of members of the set $\{P_1,..., P_m\}$ corresponding (cf. § 3.1) to the place $\mathscr{P}_i$, and the symbol $O_{(X-a)}$ means the order in $X-a$ of the relevant series. Hence

$$I_P = \sum_{i=1}^{p} O_{(X-a)}\Big(\prod_{h=1}^{\nu_i} G(X, P_h^{(i)})\Big)$$

$$= \sum_{i=1}^{p} \sum_{h=1}^{\nu_i} O_{(X-a)}(G(X, P_h^{(i)}))$$

$$= \sum_{i=1}^{p} \sum_{h=1}^{\nu_i} O_{(X-a)}\Big(b_0(X) \prod_{j=1}^{n} (P_h^{(i)}-Q_j)\Big).$$

Let us now evaluate the order $O^* \equiv O_{(X-a)}\Big(b_0(X) \prod_{j=1}^{n} (P^*-Q_j)\Big)$, where P^* denotes any one of the roots $P_1,..., P_m$ of (1) which corresponds to a place on C at P. The roots $Q_1,..., Q_n$ of (2) may be separated into three classes:

   (i) those which correspond to the places $\mathscr{Q}_1,..., \mathscr{Q}_q$ on D at P;

  (ii) those which correspond to places on D at finite points of the line $X = a$ which are distinct from P;

 (iii) those which correspond to places on D at Y_∞.

Each type of root Q_j makes its appropriate contribution to the order O^*.

Taking first the roots Q_j of type (iii), we can see that their combined contribution to O^* is zero. For these roots are all those of the Q_j which are of negative (fractional) order in $X-a$; and since $X-a$ is not a factor of $G(X, Y)$, it follows from (4) that the aggregate negative order of these Q_j is exactly counterbalanced by a positive power of $X-a$ as a factor of $b_0(X)$.

If, on the other hand, Q_j is of type (i) or type (ii), then it is an element of $K^*\{X-a\}$, and its constant term b_j is the ordinate of the centre of the corresponding place on D. Thus the order of P^*-Q_j is zero if Q_j is of type (ii) and a positive number if Q_j is of type (i). It now follows that

$$O^* = \sum_{j} O_{(X-a)}(P^*-Q_j),$$

summed over all those Q_j which correspond to places on D at P, and therefore

$$I_P = \sum_{i} \sum_{j} O_{(X-a)}(P_i-Q_j),$$

where the two summations are over the P_i and the Q_j which correspond to places at P on C and on D respectively. We have here the form of Zeuthen's rule that we have been seeking, and which, with a slight change of notation, we may enunciate formally as follows.

THEOREM 7 (*Zeuthen's Rule*). *Let $P(a, b)$ be an intersection of two algebraic curves, given by equations $F(X, Y) = 0$ and $G(X, Y) = 0$, these curves having no line component through P parallel to OY, no multiple component, and no common component. Further, in the field $K^*|X-a|$ of fractional power series let those of the roots of the equation $F(X, Y) = 0$ which are of non-negative order and which have the constant term b be $Y_1, ..., Y_M$; and let the roots of $G(X, Y) = 0$ with the same property be $Y'_1, ..., Y'_N$. Then the multiplicity of intersection I_P of the two curves at P is given by*

$$I_P = \sum_{i=1}^{M} \sum_{j=1}^{N} O_{(X-a)}(Y_i - Y'_j).$$

This rule of Zeuthen, together with the extensions and the broad geometrical expressions which he gave to it, was the essential basis of his theory of correspondences. Its immediate theoretical importance in our present system can be judged from the application that we make of it in the next two sections of this chapter.

6. The Basic Inequality

The characterizations of multiplicity of intersection that we have given in Theorems 5 and 7, though highly significant theoretically, are still cumbersome to apply to most individual cases, since they may require the solution in fractional power series of one or more equations $F(X, Y) = 0$, or at least the identification and representation by some means of all the places on a given curve at a given point. It is possible, however, from general considerations alone, to establish controlling inequalities, applicable in certain sets of circumstances, which often provide us immediately with as much information as we need. By far the simplest and most useful of these controls is that embodied in the following theorem.

THEOREM 8 (*The Basic Inequality*). *If P is an intersection of two curves C and D which is s-fold on C and t-fold on D, then the multiplicity of intersection I_P of C and D at P satisfies the inequality*

$$I_P \geqslant st;$$

and equality holds if and only if the tangents to the branches of C at P are all different from the tangents to the branches of D at P.

Proof. We may assume that C and D have no multiple component (a restriction that is easily removed subsequently) and also that they have no common component. Further, we shall suppose the affine coordinate system so chosen that P is at the origin O, and neither C nor D has any branch at O with OY as branch tangent. In these circumstances Zeuthen's rule (Theorem 7) applies; and if we adopt the notation of § 5, except that we now have $a = b = 0$, then

$$I_O = \sum_{i=1}^{M} \sum_{j=1}^{N} O_X(Y_i - Y_j'),$$

where the Y_i are the roots of $F(X, Y) = 0$ and the Y_j' are the roots of $G(X, Y) = 0$ that are of positive order in X.

By arranging that none of the branch tangents is along OY we have secured that every cycle of either of the sets $\{Y_i\}$ and $\{Y_j'\}$ corresponds to a place at O whose order is equal to the length of the cycle in question. For if such a place on C or D has a branch tangent $Y = aX$, distinct from $X = 0$, its canonical representation is of the form

$$X = u^\nu, \quad Y = au^\nu + a'u^{\nu'} + \dots \quad (\nu < \nu' < \dots),$$

and it arises from a cycle of ν roots, from the set $\{Y_i\}$ or the set $\{Y_j'\}$ as the case may be, of the form

$$Y = aX + a'X^{\nu'/\nu} + \dots .$$

The sum of the orders of the places on C at O is therefore equal to the number M of the roots Y_i, and the sum of the orders of the places on D at O is equal to the number N of the roots Y_j'. Hence, by Theorem 4, Corollary 1, $M = s$ and $N = t$.

If, now, T_i and T_j' denote the branch tangents at the places corresponding to Y_i and Y_j', we see that

$$O_X(Y_i - Y_j') \begin{cases} = 1 & \text{if } T_i \neq T_j', \\ > 1 & \text{if } T_i = T_j'. \end{cases}$$

It follows that $\sum_{i=1}^{M} \sum_{j=1}^{N} O_X(Y_i - Y_j')$ is equal to st if no T_i coincides with a T_j', and it is greater than st if there is at least one such coincidence. Theorem 8 is thus completely proved.

Controls of higher order than that given by the Basic Inequality depend on more detailed knowledge of the *structure* of C and D at the relevant point P, and also on knowledge of the 'points infinitely near to P' which the curves may have in common. These interesting concepts will form the subject of Chapter XI.

7. Multiplicity of intersection of branches

The multiplicity of intersection I_P of two curves at a given common point has already been defined in quite an elementary way in Chapter II, and in Theorem 5 of the present chapter we have a new and significant interpretation of the same multiplicity I_P in terms of the orders of D at the places on C with their centres at P. In this interpretation, however, one of the curves is resolved into branches while the other is treated as a whole; and we now ask whether our analysis of multiplicity of intersection cannot be carried a stage further, so that I_P may be expressed with complete symmetry as a sum of multiplicities of intersection, suitably defined, of all the individual branches of C at P with all those of D. More generally still, we may ask whether it is possible to define an *abstract* multiplicity of intersection of any two branches with the same centre P (whether these branches are algebraic or not) in such a way that, in the particular case which we here have in mind, I_P will admit of the symmetrical type of formulation just suggested.

To investigate this possibility, we begin by taking an arbitrary branch α, with centre at the origin and with fractional equation

$$Y = P(X^{1/\nu}).$$

If we put $\qquad P_i = P(\zeta^i X^{1/\nu}) \quad (i = 0,...,\nu-1),$

where ζ is a primitive νth root of unity, each of the ν fractional equations $Y = P_i$ equally represents α. If, now,

$$F(X, Y) \equiv \prod_{i=0}^{\nu-1} (Y - P_i), \tag{1}$$

$F(X, Y)$ is a polynomial of degree ν in Y, with coefficients in the ring $K\{X\}$; and we shall take the equation $F(X, Y) = 0$, or any equation equivalent to it in a sense to be defined, as the *formal equation of the branch* α. Then, proceeding in very much the same way as we did with curves, we shall define the multiplicity of intersection of α with any other branch β as the order of $F(X, Y)$ on β.

In taking such a step, we venture beyond the familiar algebraic territory of polynomials, and even beyond that of formal power series as we have understood these so far; and it will be necessary before we go any further for us to clarify certain points of algebra, connected with equations with their left-hand sides in the domain $K\{X\}[Y]$.

7.1. The rings $K\{X\}[Y]$ and $K\{X, Y\}$

We first establish a lemma which justifies our way of representing a branch by its formal equation, as defined in the preceding section.

LEMMA. *Any fractional power series* $P(X^{1/\nu})$ *in* $K^*\{X\}$ *satisfies a unique irreducible equation in* Y *of the form*

$$a_0(X)Y^\nu + \ldots + a_\nu(X) = 0, \tag{2}$$

with $a_i(X) \in K\{X\}$ $(i = 0, \ldots, \nu)$.

Conversely, if (2) *is an equation that is irreducible over* $K\{X\}$, *then its roots, in* $K^*\{X\}$, *form a single cycle*

$$P(X^{1/\nu}), \quad P(\zeta X^{1/\nu}), \quad \ldots, \quad P(\zeta^{\nu-1} X^{1/\nu}),$$

ζ *being a primitive ν-th root of unity.*

Proof. The series $P(X^{1/\nu})$ being given, let $F(X, Y)$ be the element of $K^*\{X\}[Y]$ defined by

$$F(X, Y) \equiv \prod_{i=0}^{\nu-1} (Y - P(\zeta^i X^{1/\nu})). \tag{3}$$

Any substitution $X^{1/\nu} \to \zeta^h X^{1/\nu}$ leaves the right-hand side of (3) invariant and thus leaves $F(X, Y)$ invariant. This means that $F(X, Y)$ belongs to $K\{X\}[Y]$; and therefore $P(X^{1/\nu})$ satisfies the equation $F(X, Y) = 0$ of the required form (2).

Now let $G(X, Y)$ be any element of $K\{X\}[Y]$ which is such that $G(X, P(X^{1/\nu})) = 0$. Then, if $G(X, P(X^{1/\nu}))$ is arranged as a power series $\sum_{i=0}^{\infty} c_i X^{i/\nu}$, every coefficient c_i is zero; and it follows from this that $G(X, P(\zeta^h X^{1/\nu})) = 0$ $(h = 0, \ldots, \nu-1)$, and consequently that $F(X, Y)$ is a factor of $G(X, Y)$ in $K\{X\}[Y]$. We may now infer at once that the polynomial $F(X, Y)$ in Y is irreducible over $K\{X\}$, and that $F(X, Y) = 0$ is the only irreducible $K\{X\}$-equation that is satisfied by $P(X^{1/\nu})$. If, finally, we take any given irreducible equation of type (2), it must coincide with the irreducible equation (3) determined by any one of its roots in $K^*\{X\}$; and this means that its set of roots constitutes a single cycle. The lemma is thus completely proved.

The lemma tells us, in particular, that the formal equation $F(X, Y) = 0$ of any branch α, that is to say the equation

$$\prod_{i=0}^{\nu-1} (Y - P(\zeta^i X^{1/\nu})) = 0$$

in the notation that we have been using, is always an *irreducible* $K\{X\}$-equation in Y.

For the further development of the treatment of branches that we now have in mind, we need to use, in addition to the ring $K\{X\}[Y]$ of expressions which are formal power series in X but only polynomials in Y, the more extensive ring $K\{X, Y\}$ of expressions which are formal power series in both X and Y. The elements of $K\{X, Y\}$ are all the formal expressions of the type

$$a_{00}+a_{10}X+a_{01}Y+a_{20}X^2+a_{11}XY+a_{02}Y^2+...,$$

with $a_{ik} \in K$ $(i,\ k = 0, 1,...)$. It will be sufficient simply to state here the properties of the ring $K\{X, Y\}$ that we shall require, indicating in Appendix A (§ 24) where proofs of them are to be found.

We define the *units* of the ring, in the usual way, as those of its elements which possess multiplicative inverses; and the units are, in fact, all those series which have their constant term a_{00} different from zero. Two elements of the ring are said to be *associated* if each is the product of the other by a unit.

The ring $K\{X, Y\}$, like the ring $K\{X\}[Y]$, possesses the property of uniqueness of factorization. By this we mean that every non-unit may be expressed as a product of a finite number of irreducible non-units, and the expression is unique to within replacement of the factors by associated elements of $K\{X, Y\}$.

Finally, we state a special case of the theorem known as *Weierstrass's Preparation Theorem*. If we regard polynomials as power series with only a finite number of non-zero coefficients, $K\{X\}[Y]$ is a subring of $K\{X, Y\}$; and the theorem which we now state asserts that every element of $K\{X, Y\}$ which satisfies a certain simple condition is associated with an element of $K\{X\}[Y]$.

THEOREM 9. *If $F(X, Y)$ is an element of the ring $K\{X, Y\}$ such that, for some positive integer n, Y^n occurs, multiplied only by an element of K, as a term in $F(X, Y)$, and if n is the smallest positive integer with this property, then $F(X, Y)$ can be expressed, in one and only one way, in the form*

$$F(X, Y) = U(X, Y)\overline{F}(X, Y),$$

where $U(X, Y)$ is a unit of $K\{X, Y\}$ and

$$\overline{F}(X, Y) = Y^n+a_1(X)Y^{n-1}+...+a_n(X),$$

with $a_i(X) \in K\{X\}$ $(i = 1,...,n)$.

7.2. Analytic curves of $S_2(K)$

Every branch α at the origin O has a formal equation $F(X, Y) = 0$, $F(X, Y)$ being an irreducible element of the polynomial ring $K\{X\}[Y]$; and, since any element of this ring can be resolved into a finite number of irreducible factors, every equation

$$G(X, Y) = 0 \quad (G(X, Y) \in K\{X\}[Y])$$

can be looked upon as representing a finite set of branches at O. We shall now show, with the help of Weierstrass's Preparation Theorem, that every equation $G(X, Y) = 0$ with its left-hand side in the wider ring $K\{X, Y\}$ likewise represents a finite set of branches at O or, as we shall now say, an *analytic curve* at O—the null analytic curve if $F(X, Y)$ is a unit of $K\{X, Y\}$. We shall be able, furthermore, to trace an analogy between such analytic curves at O and the familiar algebraic curves of S_2, represented by equations with their left-hand sides in $K[X, Y]$. The counterparts, in the new theory, of the irreducible curves of S_2 will be the branches at O.

Consider an arbitrarily given element $G(X, Y)$ of the ring $K\{X, Y\}$. $G(X, Y)$ may be written as a formal power series in X with coefficients in $K\{Y\}$:

$$\begin{aligned} G(X, Y) &= X^h a_h(Y) + X^{h+1} a_{h+1}(Y) + \cdots \\ &= X^h(a_h(Y) + X a_{h+1}(Y) + \cdots) \\ &= X^h H(X, Y), \end{aligned}$$

where $h \geqslant 0$, $a_i(Y) \in K\{Y\}$ $(i = h, h+1,\ldots)$, $a_h(Y) \neq 0$, and $H(X, Y) \in K\{X, Y\}$.

If $a_h(Y) \in K$, that is to say if Y does not occur in $a_h(Y)$, then $H(X, Y)$ is a unit of $K\{X, Y\}$. If $a_h(Y) \notin K$, then Theorem 9 applies to $H(X, Y)$, and therefore

$$H(X, Y) = U(X, Y)\bar{H}(X, Y),$$

where $U(X, Y)$ is a unit of $K\{X, Y\}$ and $\bar{H}(X, Y) \in K\{X\}[Y]$. Thus in any case we have a resolution of $G(X, Y)$ of the form

$$G(X, Y) = U(X, Y)X^h \bar{H}(X, Y),$$

where $U(X, Y)$ is a unit of $K\{X, Y\}$ and $\bar{H}(X, Y) \in K\{X\}[Y]$; and if we split $\bar{H}(X, Y)$ into its irreducible factors in $K\{X\}[Y]$ we have the more complete resolution

$$G(X, Y) = U(X, Y)X^h \prod_{i=1}^{s} (\bar{H}_i(X, Y))^{m_i},$$

where $m_1, ..., m_s$ are positive integers and h, s are non-negative integers.

If, now, $G(X, Y)$ is any non-unit of the ring $K\{X, Y\}$, we can show by factorizing $G(X, Y)$ in the manner just described that the equation $G(X, Y) = 0$ determines a finite set of branches with definite multiplicities—namely the line-branch along $X = 0$, counted h-fold, and the branch with formal equation $\bar{H}_i(X, Y) = 0$, counted m_i-fold $(i = 1, ..., s)$. We call any such set of branches an analytic curve at O.

DEFINITION. An *analytic curve* at O is a finite set of branches $\alpha_1, ..., \alpha_s$ at O, each branch α_i having a specified positive integer m_i as its multiplicity as a component of the analytic curve.

As we have just seen, every equation $G(X, Y) = 0$, in which $G(X, Y)$ is a non-unit of $K\{X, Y\}$, determines a well-defined analytic curve $\mathscr{A}$ at O. Conversely, every analytic curve at O can be represented by such an equation, built up out of the formal equations of its component branches; and two equations $G_1(X, Y) = 0$ and $G_2(X, Y) = 0$ represent the same analytic curve at O if and only if their left-hand sides are associated elements of the ring $K\{X, Y\}$.

THEOREM 10. *If $\mathscr{A}$ is an analytic curve at O, with equation $G(X, Y) = 0$ $(G(X, Y) \in K\{X, Y\})$, and α is a branch at O, with representation $(X(u), Y(u))$ $(X(u), Y(u) \in K\{u\})$, then α is a component of $\mathscr{A}$ if and only if $G(X(u), Y(u)) = 0$ in $K\{u\}$.*

Proof. Since α has its centre at the origin, the power series $X(u)$ is of positive order; and hence, by the properties of such series listed in Chapter IV, § 2, u can be expressed as a power series (possibly fractional) in X:
$$u = U(X) \quad (U(X) \in K^*\{X\}).$$
The branch therefore has a representation $(X, Y(U(X)))$, i.e. a representation $(X, P(X^{1/\nu}))$, where $P(X^{1/\nu}) = Y(U(X))$. It follows that α is a component of $\mathscr{A}$ if and only if
$$G(X, Y(U(X))) = 0,$$
that is to say if and only if
$$G(X(u), Y(u)) = 0.$$
We may note that since any affine transformation
$$\left. \begin{array}{l} X \to aX' + bY' \\ Y \to cX' + dY' \end{array} \right\} \quad (ad - bc \neq 0)$$

which leaves the origin unchanged transforms every element of $K\{X, Y\}$ into an element of $K\{X', Y'\}$—setting up an isomorphism between the two rings—the concept of an analytic curve at O, represented by an equation $G(X, Y) = 0$ with $G(X, Y)$ in $K\{X, Y\}$, is a local affine concept. On this concept is based the *affine* geometry of branches at a specified point O. We have already mentioned (p. 78) that a more general *analytic* theory of branches at O also exists. This is based on the wider group of local analytic transformations

$$\left.\begin{aligned} X &\to (aX'+bY')+V_2(X', Y')+V_3(X', Y')+\ldots \\ Y &\to (cX'+dY')+W_2(X', Y')+W_3(X', Y')+\ldots \end{aligned}\right\}$$

$(ad-bc \neq 0)$, $V_i(X', Y')$ and $W_i(X', Y')$ being forms of the ith degree, which also transform the elements of $K\{X, Y\}$ isomorphically into the elements of $K\{X', Y'\}$. The (local) affine group is plainly a subgroup of the local analytic group, so that all local analytic invariants are *a fortiori* local affine invariants.

We shall now direct our attention, more particularly, to a pair of branches α and β with the same centre O, and we shall suppose them to be represented, as analytic curves, by equations

$$F(X, Y) = 0 \quad \text{and} \quad G(X, Y) = 0,$$

which are irreducible in the sense previously indicated. We shall suppose also that both $F(X, Y)$ and $G(X, Y)$ effectively contain Y. The equations can then be reduced, by multiplication by units, to the forms

$$F(X, Y) \equiv (Y-P_1)\ldots(Y-P_\mu) = 0$$

and

$$G(X, Y) \equiv (Y-Q_1)\ldots(Y-Q_\nu) = 0,$$

where $\{P_1,\ldots,P_\mu\}$ is a complete cycle of elements of $K\{X^{1/\mu}\}$ and $\{Q_1,\ldots,Q_\nu\}$ is a complete cycle of elements of $K\{X^{1/\nu}\}$. We can then take $(u^\mu, P_i(u))$ and $(v^\nu, Q_j(v))$ as canonical (minimal) representations of α and β respectively. The order $O_\beta(\alpha)$ of α (as an analytic curve) on β (as a branch) is given by

$$O_\beta(\alpha) = O_v(F(v^\nu, Q_1(v))).$$

But, since each of the series $F(v^\nu, Q_j(v))$ $(j = 2,\ldots,\nu)$, is derivable from $F(v^\nu, Q_1(v))$ by a substitution $v \to \zeta^\rho v$, where $\zeta^\nu = 1$, the orders of the series are all equal to $O_\beta(\alpha)$; and we therefore have

$$O_\beta(\alpha) = \frac{1}{\nu} O_v\Big(\prod_{j=1}^{\nu} F(v^\nu, Q_j(v))\Big)$$

$$= O_X\Big(\prod_{j=1}^{\nu} F(X, Q_j(X^{1/\nu}))\Big).$$

Hence, since $F(X, Y) = (Y - P_1) \ldots (Y - P_\mu)$,

$$O_\beta(\alpha) = O_X\left(\prod_{j=1}^{\nu} \prod_{i=1}^{\mu} (Q_j - P_i)\right)$$

$$= \sum_{i=1}^{\mu} \sum_{j=1}^{\nu} O_X(P_i - Q_j).$$

Thus, by the symmetry of this expression, $O_\beta(\alpha) = O_\alpha(\beta)$; and we may now formulate the following definition of the multiplicity of intersection of an unordered pair of branches at O.

DEFINITION. If $Y = P_i(X^{1/\mu})$ $(i = 1, \ldots, \mu)$ and $Y = Q_j(X^{1/\nu})$ $(j = 1, \ldots, \nu)$ are the cycles of equivalent (minimal) fractional equations of any two branches α and β with the same centre O, then the *multiplicity of intersection $I_{\alpha,\beta}$ of α and β is* defined by the formula

$$I_{\alpha,\beta} = \sum_{i=1}^{\mu} \sum_{j=1}^{\nu} O_X(P_i - Q_j).$$

Theorem 5 can now be restated in the following symmetrical form.

THEOREM 11. *If P is any intersection of two algebraic curves C and D, with no common component, then the multiplicity of intersection I_P of C and D at P is the sum of the multiplicities of intersection of the branches of C at P with those of D at P.*

With this theorem we have at last achieved the fully satisfactory local characterization of multiplicity of intersection that was our primary objective in the foregoing investigation.

8. Applications

For the purpose of evaluating the multiplicity of intersection $I_{\alpha,\beta}$ for a given pair of branches, the fully resolved expression

$$I_{\alpha,\beta} = \sum_{i=1}^{\mu} \sum_{j=1}^{\nu} O_X(P_i - Q_j)$$

is more conveniently replaced by one or other of the equivalent expressions

$$I_{\alpha,\beta} = \mu \sum_{j=1}^{\nu} O_X(P_1 - Q_j) = \nu \sum_{i=1}^{\mu} O_X(P_i - Q_1),$$

which involve only one of the P_i or one of the Q_j. Even so, the evaluation of $I_{\alpha,\beta}$ for two arbitrary branches is quite a complicated matter. For the present, we shall postpone consideration of the general case to a later chapter (Chapter XI) and shall consider instead a few simple applications of the formulae just given.

Two linear branches. Let α and β be linear branches, with common centre O and with branch tangents not lying along OY.

$$\alpha:\ Y = P(X) = a_1 X + a_2 X^2 + ...,$$
$$\beta:\ Y = Q(X) = b_1 X + b_2 X^2 + ...$$

Then $I_{\alpha,\beta} = O_X(P-Q)$; and hence, if $a_i = b_i$ $(i = 1,...,n)$, but $a_{n+1} \neq b_{n+1}$, then $I_{\alpha,\beta} = n+1$. We say in this case that the branches have $(n+1)$-*point contact* (or *contact of order* n); and we shall see in Chapter XI that α and β can be regarded as having, after the origin O, n consecutive (infinitely near) points $O_1, O_2,..., O_n$ in common, each such point O_i being uniquely characterized by the set of coefficients $a_1, a_2,..., a_i$ in $P(X)$.

A linear and a non-linear branch. Let α again be linear, as before, but now let β be a branch of arbitrary order ν. If neither branch tangent lies along OY we have the equations:

$$\alpha:\ Y = P(X) = a_1 X + a_2 X^2 + ...,$$
$$\beta:\ Y = Q(X^{1/\nu}) = b_1 X + b_2 X^2 + ... + b_k X^k + \sum_{i=0}^{\infty} c_i X^{k+(\nu_1+i)/\nu},$$

where $c_0 \neq 0$ and $0 < \nu_1 < \nu$. Then $I_{\alpha,\beta} = \nu O_X(P-Q)$.

If $a_i = b_i$ $(i = 1,...,n)$, but $a_{n+1} \neq b_{n+1}$, where $n < k$, then $I_{\alpha,\beta} = (n+1)\nu$; and we shall see that this can be interpreted as meaning that β has each of the consecutive points $O, O_1,..., O_n$ on α, already referred to above, as a ν-fold point.

If $a_i = b_i$ $(i = 1,...,k)$, then $I_{\alpha,\beta} = k\nu + \nu_1$; and in this case β has ν-fold points at the points $O, O_1,..., O_{k-1}$ on α, and a ν_1-fold point at the next successive point O_k on α.

No choice of the coefficients a_i for the linear branch can make α intersect the given branch β with greater multiplicity than $k\nu + \nu_1$.

Cuspidal branches of any order. A branch β, with centre O and with branch tangent not along OY, is said to be a *simple cusp of order* ν if its equation takes the form

$$\beta:\ Y = Q(X^{1/\nu}) = aX + bX^{(\nu+1)/\nu} + \sum_{i=1}^{\infty} c_i X^{(\nu+1+i)/\nu};$$

with $b \neq 0$. The greatest multiplicity of intersection that such a branch can have with a linear branch α at O is $\nu+1$, and this maximum multiplicity is attained if and only if α has the same branch tangent as β. We say that β has a ν-fold point at O and a simple point at the consecutive point O_1 of any branch α with the same branch tangent as β.

Suppose that α, instead of being a linear branch, is itself a simple cuspidal branch, of order μ, with the same branch tangent as β:

$$\alpha: \; Y = P(X^{1/\mu}) = aX + b'X^{(\mu+1)/\mu} + \sum_{j=1}^{\infty} c_j' X^{(\mu+1+j)/\mu},$$

with $b' \neq 0$. In this case

$$I_{\alpha,\beta} = \mu \sum_{i=1}^{\nu} O_X(P-Q_i),$$

where

$$Q_i = Q(\zeta^{i-1}X^{1/\nu})$$
$$= aX + b\zeta^{i-1}X^{(\nu+1)/\nu} + \sum_{j=1}^{\infty} c_j \, \zeta^{(i-1)(j+1)} X^{(\nu+1+j)/\nu},$$

ζ being a primitive νth root of unity.

If $\mu < \nu$, then each $P-Q_i$ is of order $(\nu+1)/\nu$, so that

$$I_{\alpha,\beta} = \mu\nu + \mu;$$

and we shall interpret this result by saying that O is μ-fold for α and ν-fold for β, while α and β have μ further simple points in common.

If $\mu = \nu$ and $b' = b$ (or $b' = \zeta^{i-1}b$ for some i), then one of the differences $P-Q_i$ has higher order than $(\nu+1)/\nu$, while all the others are again of this order, and hence

$$I_{\alpha,\beta} > \nu^2 + \nu.$$

Thus, for example, two cuspidal branches of order 2 with the same cuspidal tangent have, in general, $I_{\alpha,\beta} = 6$; but if the coefficients of $X^{\frac{3}{2}}$ in their fractional equations are equal (or equal but opposed in sign) they will have $I_{\alpha,\beta} > 6$, the excess depending on what agreement there is between coefficients of subsequent terms in their equations.

These few examples will be sufficient for the moment to illustrate the application of the basic formula

$$I_{\alpha,\beta} = \sum_{i=1}^{\mu} \sum_{j=1}^{\nu} O_X(P_i - Q_j)$$

and to indicate the type of interpretation of the results deducible from this formula that we propose to discuss at a later stage.

NOTES AND EXERCISES ON CHAPTER V

1. *Places on the circle $X^2 + Y^2 = 1$.* To determine directly those places on the circle $X^2 + Y^2 = 1$ that have their centres on any given ordinate $X = a$, we first resolve $Y^2 + X^2 - 1$, in the field $K^*|(X-a)|$, into factors

$$Y^2 + X^2 - 1 = (Y - Q_1)(Y - Q_2),$$

where $\qquad Q_1, Q_2 = \pm\{(1-a^2) - 2a(X-a) - (X-a)^2\}^{\frac{1}{2}}.$

(i) Suppose $a^2 \neq 1$. In this case, expanding the left-hand side formally by the binomial theorem, we see that there are two places with centres on $X = a$, their equations being

$$Y = \pm\sqrt{(1-a^2)}\Big\{1-\frac{a}{1-a^2}(X-a)-\frac{1}{2(1-a^2)^2}(X-a)^2+...\Big\}.$$

(ii) Suppose $a = 1$. Then we may write

$$Q_1, Q_2 = \pm i(X-1)^{\frac{1}{2}}(2+(X-1))^{\frac{1}{2}} = \pm P\{(X-1)^{\frac{1}{2}}\},$$

and we now have the identity

$$Y^2+X^2-1 = [Y-P\{(X-1)^{\frac{1}{2}}\}][Y-P\{-(X-1)^{\frac{1}{2}}\}].$$

Thus Q_1, Q_2 in this case form a cycle of order 2, representing the single place with fractional equation

$$Y = i\sqrt{2}\{(X-1)^{\frac{1}{2}}+\tfrac{1}{4}(X-1)^{\frac{3}{2}}-\tfrac{1}{32}(X-1)^{\frac{5}{2}}+...\}.$$

Similarly, if $a = -1$.

A different representation of the (unique) place at any point $(\cos\alpha, \sin\alpha)$ of the circle can be obtained by writing

$$X = \cos\theta\cos\alpha-\sin\theta\sin\alpha, \qquad Y = \sin\theta\cos\alpha+\cos\theta\sin\alpha,$$

then putting $\sin\theta = 2t/(1+t^2)$, $\cos\theta = (1-t^2)/(1+t^2)$, and finally expanding $X(t)$ and $Y(t)$ in ascending powers of t.

The only places on the curve not included in the above are the two with centres I, J at infinity. These have representations

$$X = u^{-1}, \quad Y = \pm iu^{-1}(1-\tfrac{1}{2}u^2+...).$$

2. Show that the equation $Y^3-Y+(2u+u^2) = 0$ has roots of the form

$$Y_1 = 2u+u^2+8u^3+..., \quad Y_2 = 1-u-2u^2+..., \quad Y_3 = -1-u+u^2+...,$$

and deduce representations of the three places on the curve

$$Y^3+X^2 = Y+1$$

which have centres on the line $X = 1$.

3. Show that the cubic curve $Y^2 = X(X-1)^2$ has one place with finite centre on the line $X = 0$, two such places with the same centre on $X = 1$, and two such places with distinct centres on $X = 4$. Obtain parametric representations of all these places.

Show that the same curve has a single place at Y_∞, with parametric representation $X = u^{-2}$, $Y = u^{-3}-u^{-1}$; and show also that a normalized form for the representation of this place (in terms of homogeneous co-ordinates x, y, z such that $X = x/z$, $Y = y/z$) is

$$x = v, \quad y = 1, \quad z = v^3-2v^5+5v^7+....$$

4. Obtain an equation of the form $Y = P(X)$ $(P(X) \in K^*|X|)$, for each of the two places on the curve $X^3+Y^3 = XY$ at the origin.

5. Show that the curve $XY^2 = X^5+Y^5$ has three simple places (places of order 1) at O, of which one has OY as inflexional branch tangent, while the other two have OX as branch tangent. Show that the multiplicity of intersection of this curve at O with the parabola $Y = kX^2$ is 5 if $k \neq \pm 1$ and 10 if $k = \pm 1$.

6. Show that the place at the origin O on the conic with equation

$$Y = aX^2 + 2hXY + bY^2 \quad (a, h, b \in K, a \neq 0)$$

is represented by an equation of the form

$$Y = aX^2 + 2ahX^3 + a(4h^2 + ab)X^4 + \dots .$$

Deduce that if two conics k, k' touch at a point A, and if p is the line which forms with the common tangent at A a line-pair of the pencil defined by k, k', then the contact at A is two-point, three-point, or four-point according as p does not pass through A, passes through A, or coincides with the common tangent at A.

7. Show that the parabola $Y^2 = X$ is sextactic at the origin O to the cubic curve $Y^2 = X(1 - X^2)$.

8. Show that the curve $(X^2 + Y^2 - X)^2 = X^2 + Y^2$ has a simple cusp at the origin, and that its multiplicity of intersection at O with any circle through O is either 2 or 3. Show that its multiplicity of intersection with the curve $Y^2 = X^3$ at O is 6.

9. Show that the quartic curve with equation

$$X^2Y^2 - 3XY - X + 2 = 0$$

has two places at Y_∞, together constituting a tacnode with OY as tacnodal tangent; and that it has a cusp at X_∞ with OX as cuspidal tangent.

Show that the hyperbola $XY = \mu$, where μ is a parameter, has in general only one free intersection (not at Y_∞ or X_∞) with the curve; and hence obtain a parametric representation of the curve.

10. *Rational functions on C.* A place $\mathscr{P}$ on C is a *zero-place of order s* of a rational function χ on the curve if $O_{\mathscr{P}}(\chi) = s > 0$; and similarly $\mathscr{P}$ is a *pole-place of order s* of χ if $O_{\mathscr{P}}(\chi) = -s < 0$. By Theorem 6, the numbers of zero-places and pole-places of χ on C, weighted according to their orders, are equal. Thus, for example,

  (i) if χ is the rational function defined by x_1/x_2 on the conic $x_1^2 = x_0 x_2$, then χ has a zero-place of order 1 with centre $(0, 0, 1)$ and a pole-place of order 1 with centre $(1, 0, 0)$;

 (ii) if χ is the rational function defined by XY on the curve

$$Y^2 = X(X - 1)^2,$$

this being the same as that defined by $x_1 x_2/x_0^2$ on the curve

$$x_0 x_2^2 = x_1(x_1 - x_0)^2,$$

then χ has zero-places of orders 3 and 2, with centres $(0, 0)$ and $(1, 0)$ respectively, and a pole-place of order 5 with centre at Y_∞.

11. *Places at an s-fold point.* Let O be an s-fold point of C, and let there be p distinct places $\mathscr{P}_1, \dots, \mathscr{P}_p$ on C at O. Further, let it be supposed for convenience that the branch tangents at these places are all distinct from OY. In these circumstances, if $\mathscr{P}$ is any one of the p places in question, then the order ν of $\mathscr{P}$ is equal, in the notation of § 3, to the length of the cycle Π corresponding to $\mathscr{P}$; and if the branch-tangent of $\mathscr{P}$ is $Y = aX$, then each of the ν fractional power series in Π is of the form

$$P(X) = aX + a'X^{(\nu + \nu')/\nu} + \dots .$$

From this it follows readily that if, in the usual notation,

$$f(X, Y) = u_s(X, Y) + u_{s+1}(X, Y) + \ldots + u_n(X, Y),$$

then

$$u_s(X, Y) = k(Y - a_1 X)^{\nu_1} \ldots (Y - a_p X)^{\nu_p},$$

where k is a constant, ν_i is the order of $\mathscr{P}_i$, and $Y - a_i X = 0$ is the branch tangent of $\mathscr{P}_i$ $(i = 1, \ldots, p)$; this proves Corollary 1 of Theorem 4.

12. *Coincidences of an (m, n) correspondence.* Apply Theorem 7 to establish a direct algebraic equivalent of Zeuthen's rule (p. 91) for multiplicities of coincidences in a rational (m, n) correspondence between complex variables X, Y.

According to this rule, as may be noted, the multiplicity of a coincidence (a, a) may be greater than, equal to, or less than the number of values of Y corresponding to a given value of X that tend to a as X tends to a. Illustrate this by diagrams for a $(2, 2)$ correspondence.

13. If m, p are relatively prime integers, as are also n, q, and if $ab(a^m - b^n) \neq 0$, then the multiplicity of intersection I_O of the curves

$$Y^m = a^m X^p, \qquad Y^n = b^n X^q,$$

at the origin is given by Theorem 7 in the form

$$I_O = \sum_{i=1}^{m} \sum_{j=1}^{n} O_X(a\epsilon^i X^{p/m} - b\eta^j X^{q/n}),$$

where ϵ and η are primitive mth and nth roots of unity. Evaluate I_O in the two cases (a) when $p/m < q/n$, and (b) when $p/m = q/n$; and check your result by using a rational parametric representation of one of the two curves.

14. *Polar curves.* The results recorded in the discussions following Theorem 11 of Chapter I (p. 15) can now be newly interpreted by use of the Basic Inequality (p. 94) as follows: *If C has an s-fold point A $(s \geqslant 0)$, and if $C^{(1)}(P)$ is the first polar for C of a 'general' point P of the plane, then the multiplicity of intersection of C with $C^{(1)}(P)$ at A is at least $s(s-1)$; and the multiplicity is exactly $s(s-1)$ if and only if the s-fold point A is ordinary.*

The word 'general' is to be interpreted here, as in § 4.3 of Chapter I, as 'not lying on any one of the nodal tangents to C at A'.

15. *Hessian curve.* If C is an irreducible curve of order $n \geqslant 3$, and if $H(C)$ is its Hessian, show that

(i) C and $H(C)$ have multiplicity of intersection 6 at any *strictly ordinary* double† point of C, this being defined as an ordinary double point at which neither branch of C is inflexional, and

(ii) C and $H(C)$ have multiplicity of intersection 8 at any simple cusp† (cf. § 8, p. 103) of C.

In either case the point in question may be taken to be the origin O of an affine coordinate system. Then, if $f = 0$ and $h = 0$ are the equations of C and $H(C)$, the multiplicity of intersection at O will remain unaltered if h

† The equation of an (irreducible) curve with a strictly ordinary double point at O can be taken in the reduced form $0 = XY + (aX^3 + bY^3) + \ldots$ $(ab \neq 0)$; and that of a curve with a simple cusp at O in the reduced form

$$0 = Y^2 + cX^3 + \ldots \quad (c \neq 0).$$

is replaced by any polynomial $h' = h+fg$ $(g \in K[X,Y])$; and g can be so chosen in each case that the nodal tangents of $h' = 0$ at O are all distinct from those of C at O.

16. *Plücker formulae*. Let C be an irreducible plane curve of order n with δ strictly ordinary double points and κ simple cusps as its only multiple points. Let m be its class, defined here as the number of (proper) tangents to C that pass through a general point of S_2; and let ι be the number of its inflexions, which we suppose to be all of the regular 3-point contact type.

In Chapter I, § 4.3, we proved that all the intersections of C with the first polar $C^{(1)}(P)$ of a general point P of S_2 are either multiple points of C or points of contact of tangents from P; also that if T is any one of the latter, not being one of the points of contact of the ι inflexional tangents, then $C^{(1)}(P)$ passes simply through T and does not touch C there. Combining this result with Bézout's Theorem and with the result given above in Exercise 14, we derive the first Plücker formula

$$m = n(n-1)-2\delta-3\kappa$$

for the class m of C.

In the same way it can be shown that the Hessian $H(C)$ of C passes simply through each of the ι (ordinary) inflexions of C and does not touch C there; and from this, with Bézout's Theorem and the result given in Exercise 15, we deduce the second Plücker formula

$$\iota = 3n(n-2)-6\delta-8\kappa.$$

We shall return to some of these ideas and to other Plücker formulae in the exercises on Chapter VI.

17. As an example of Theorem 9, show that the analytic curve represented by the equation

$$0 = (X+Y)+(X^2+XY+Y^2)+(X^3+X^2Y+XY^2+Y^3)+\dots$$

is the linear branch with reduced equation

$$Y = -X-X^2-X^3-\dots.$$

[*Hint*. Multiply the right-hand side of the first equation by the unit $1-Y$.]

18. Show that the formal power series

$$f(X,Y) = (Y-X)^2+X^2(X-2Y)+X^3(X-2Y)+X^4(X-2Y)+\dots,$$

being irreducible in $K\{X,Y\}$, admits of factorization, as a quadratic polynomial in Y over $K^*|X|$, in the form

$$f(X,Y) = (Y-X-X^{\frac{3}{2}}-X^2-X^{\frac{5}{2}}-\dots)(Y-X+X^{\frac{3}{2}}-X^2+X^{\frac{5}{2}}-\dots);$$

and verify that the equation $f(X,Y) = 0$ represents an irreducible analytic curve subordinate to the cuspidal cubic $(Y-X)^2 = XY^2$.

19. Show that there exists a unit U of $K\{X,Y\}$ such that

$$X^2-2XY+Y^2-Y^3 = U(Y^2+A(X)Y+B(X)),$$

where

$$A(X) = -(2X+3X^2+10X^3+\dots), \qquad B(X) = X^2+2X^3+7X^4+\dots.$$

20. An analytic curve C at O has equation $Y^2-2P(X)Y+Q(X) = 0$, where the power series $P(X)$, $Q(X)$ and $(P(X))^2-Q(X)$ are of (finite) non-

negative orders p, q, and r. Show that (i) if $q = 0$, then C is the null analytic curve, (ii) if $p = 0$, $q > 0$, then C is a linear branch not directed along OY, and (iii) if $p > 0$, $q > 0$, then C is *either* a linear branch directed along OY if $q = 1$, *or* a pair of linear branches not along OY if r is even, *or* a single branch of order 2 if r is odd and $r > 1$.

21. If $a_i(X) \in K\{X\}$ and $O(a_i(X)) = \alpha_i$ ($i = 1,...,n$), show that precisely m roots of the equation

$$f(X, Y) \equiv Y^n + a_1(X)Y^{n-1} + ... + a_n(X) = 0$$

are of positive order if and only if

$$\alpha_n, \alpha_{n-1}, ..., \alpha_{n-m+1} > 0, \qquad \alpha_{n-m} = 0,$$

and hence that the analytic curve C with equation $f(X, Y) = 0$ can also be represented by an equivalent equation

$$g(X, Y) \equiv Y^m + b_1(X)Y^{m-1} + ... + b_m(X) = 0,$$

where the power series $b_j(X)$ ($j = 1,...,m$) are all of positive order. Show in this case that no component of C has branch tangent along OY if and only if $O(b_j(X)) \geqslant j$ ($j = 1,...,m$).

22. *The Newton diagram.* Let $f(X, Y) = \sum\limits_{p,q=0}^{\infty} c_{pq} X^p Y^q$, with $c_{00} = 0$, be any non-unit of $K\{X, Y\}$, and let us suppose for convenience that it has neither X nor Y as a factor. We define the *Newton diagram* of $f(X, Y)$ to be the array of integral lattice points (p, q) such that $c_{pq} \neq 0$; and we define a *barrier* of this diagram to be any line, other than an axis $p = 0$ or $q = 0$, which joins at least two points of the diagram and is such that no point of the diagram is on the same side of the line as the origin $(0, 0)$.

Consider any branch α at O which is a component of the analytic curve C with equation $f(X, Y) = 0$; and let us suppose that α admits of the parametric representation $X = u^\lambda U_1$, $Y = u^\mu U_2$, where λ, μ are positive integers and U_1, U_2 are units of $K\{u\}$. In order that the identity

$$\sum c_{pq}(U_1)^p(U_2)^q u^{\lambda p + \mu q} \equiv 0$$

may hold, there must be two or more terms in $f(X, Y)$ that give rise to terms of the same minimum order $h > 0$ on the left-hand side, all other terms in $f(X, Y)$ giving rise to terms of order $\lambda p + \mu q > h$. This means, however, that the line with equation $\lambda p + \mu q = h$ is a barrier in the Newton diagram of $f(X, Y)$, since it contains a set of s points $(p_1, q_1),...,(p_s, q_s)$ ($s \geqslant 2$) of the diagram, while all the remaining points of the latter lie on the side of the line remote from the origin $(0, 0)$.

For a branch α with branch tangent not along OX or OY (i.e. for which $\lambda = \mu$), the Newton diagram only tells us that the gradient m of the branch tangent must be a non-zero root of the equation

$$\sum_{i=1}^{s} c_{p_i q_i} m^{q_i} = 0.$$

But if α has branch tangent along OY, for example, its fractional equation being of the form $Y = mX^{\mu/\lambda} + ...$, then $-\lambda/\mu$ will be the gradient of the associated barrier, and m will again be a root of the above equation.

The principal value of the above analysis depends on the theorem that every barrier of the Newton diagram is associated with at least one place on C at O. This, however, is essentially what is established in the constructive proof of Theorem I of the present chapter (algebraic closure of $K^*|X|$) which is discussed in Appendix B.

23. To apply the methods of Exercise 22 to an analysis of the singularity at the origin of the curve C with equation

$$X^2Y^2(X+Y)-X^6-Y^7 = 0,$$

we note first that O is a five-fold point of C. The Newton diagram has three barriers corresponding respectively to the three pairs of terms $X^2Y^2(X+Y)$, $Y^3(X^2-Y^4)$, $X^3(Y^2-X^3)$ of the equation; and these indicate (i) a linear branch at O, with $X+Y = 0$ as branch tangent, (ii) two linear branches

$$X = Y^2+a_3Y^3+..., \qquad X = -Y^2+b_3Y^3+...,$$

each having OY as branch tangent, and (iii) a simple cuspidal branch $Y = X^{\frac{3}{2}}+...$ with OX as branch tangent. These constitute in all the singularity of order 5 of C at O.

CHAPTER VI

THE CLASS AND DEFICIENCY OF A PLANE CURVE

1. The theory of higher plane curves

In this chapter we shall be dealing in the main with traditional and comparatively elementary parts of the theory of plane algebraic curves, but by using some of the general ideas that we have introduced in previous chapters, and especially the idea of a generic point of a curve, we shall be able both to simplify the subject and to give it greater unity than would otherwise be possible. With the knowledge that we have gained in Chapter V of the principles that govern the proper assignment of multiplicities to the intersections of curves in S_2, we could now investigate in detail, if we should so wish, much of the projective geometry of algebraic plane curves. We do not propose, however, in the present chapter (nor indeed anywhere in this book) to embark upon a systematic exposition of that subject, but shall confine our attention to one or two particular aspects of it, concentrating mainly on results that we shall need in later chapters. The detailed study of the projective properties of algebraic curves in S_2, and especially of those of low order, is in itself a very large subject that was developed over a long period, mainly in the nineteenth century, under the general title of the theory of higher plane curves. Many good accounts of it are available,† and the reader may consult these for further information. Our chief concern here will be with certain properties of irreducible curves which depend only on the order of the curve concerned and its set of multiple points—in particular, with the properties connected with class and deficiency.

2. Transcendental lines and curves

The first of our main objectives in this chapter is to set up a direct connexion between algebraic curves, as so far considered, and algebraic envelopes, defined by K-equations $g(u_0, u_1, u_2) = 0$ in line-coordinates. In part to this end, but also with a less specific intention, we shall discuss first of all, as briefly as we can, a certain

† e.g. Salmon, *A Treatise on the Higher Plane Curves* (2nd edition, Dublin, 1873).

broad generalization of the simple concepts of line and curve that we have been working with so far. This generalization, which is analogous to our earlier enlargement of the concept of point so as to cover transcendental points as well as ground points, is brought about by permitting extension of the ground field from K to some wider field K'.

By the term 'curve' (or 'algebraic curve')—a term which covers 'line' as a curve of order unity—we have always meant up to now an entity, defined on pp. 4 and 6, which can be represented by a K-equation $f(x_0, x_1, x_2) = 0$; but we shall now refer to a curve in this strict sense as a *ground curve* of $S_2(K)$, in order to distinguish it from a *transcendental curve*, represented by an equation with coefficients in some proper extension of K. This idea of a transcendental curve cannot be wholly unfamiliar to the reader, since we are accustomed in elementary coordinate geometry to using equations of curves in which some or all of the coefficients are either parameters or functions of parameters, and these parameters are handled in practice in much the same way as indeterminates.

The simplest instance of a transcendental curve is a *transcendental line*, which can be represented by a linear equation

$$u_0 x_0 + u_1 x_1 + u_2 x_2 = 0$$

with coefficient ratios in some proper extension K' of the field K. The formal introduction of transcendental lines occasions us no difficulty, since we may think of any such line as specified by a coordinate triad $\mathbf{u}$, and the properties of transcendental lines are accordingly dual to the properties of transcendental points that we have already discussed in detail.

If a transcendental line has a coordinate representation $(1, u, v)$, where u and v are distinct indeterminates, it will be said to be a *generic line of S_2*. Dually, we shall sometimes refer to a point $(1, x, y)$, where x and y are distinct indeterminates, as a *generic point of S_2*.

DEFINITIONS. (i) Any algebraic equation $f(x_0, x_1, x_2) = 0$ with the ratios of its coefficients in some proper extension K' of K (but not all in K itself) will be said to define a *transcendental curve* of $S_2(K)$. The points of the curve are all those points—both ground points and transcendental points—which have coordinates that satisfy the equation.

(ii) If C is a transcendental curve of $S_2(K)$, its *coefficient field* is the extension of K that is generated by the ratios of the coefficients in the equation of C.

(iii) A curve C^* is said to be a *specialization over K†* of a curve C if the equations of C and C^* are of the same degree and every homogeneous K-equation that is satisfied by the coefficients c_λ in the equation of C is satisfied also by the corresponding coefficients c_λ^* in the equation of C^*.

We note that a curve of $S_2(K)$ is a ground curve if and only if its coefficient field is K itself. A transcendental line of $S_2(K)$, as already defined, is simply a transcendental curve which has an equation of the first degree; and every generic line of the plane is a transcendental line with coefficient field isormorphic over K to a field of the form $K(u, v)$, u and v being distinct indeterminates.

We may note further that every curve is a specialization of itself, and that the ground curves of $S_2(K)$ possess the property of having no specializations other than themselves.

A simple type of transcendental curve that we can usefully introduce, even in the context of a relatively elementary treatment of algebraic curves, is the generic curve of a linear system. Let us consider a linear system Λ, i.e. a system of curves (D) given, as in Chapter I, § 5, by an equation

$$f(\mathbf{x}; \boldsymbol{\lambda}) \equiv \sum_{i=0}^{r} \lambda_i f_i(\mathbf{x}) = 0$$

which involves $r+1$ undetermined parameters λ_i. If we now re-interpret the λ_i as $r+1$ independent indeterminates, we obtain, in place of a partially undetermined ground curve D of the linear system Λ, a transcendental curve $D(\boldsymbol{\lambda})$ with coefficient field $K(\lambda_1/\lambda_0,...,\lambda_r/\lambda_0)$. We say that $D(\boldsymbol{\lambda})$ is a *generic curve of the linear system* Λ; and it is clear that Λ consists of all ground curves which are specializations of the generic curve $D(\boldsymbol{\lambda})$. A generic line of S_2 is a generic curve, in this sense, of the net of all lines of the plane.

Introduction of generic curves of linear systems enables us to give precise meaning to what we often wish to think of as the behaviour of the curves of the system Λ 'in general', and also to express succinctly properties of the system as a whole. Thus a base point of the system Λ is simply a ground point of the transcendental curve

† Cf. the note on specialization on p. 134.

$D(\boldsymbol{\lambda})$, and its minimum multiplicity for the curves D of Λ is its actual multiplicity for $D(\boldsymbol{\lambda})$.

Further, if α is any branch of S_2, the minimum order on α of the curves of Λ is the order of $D(\boldsymbol{\lambda})$ on α, defined exactly as for ground curves.† From this, if we define the multiplicity of intersection of $D(\boldsymbol{\lambda})$ with any ground curve C at a point A to be the sum of the orders of $D(\boldsymbol{\lambda})$ at the places on C at A, we derive the following useful result.

If a point A of a (ground) curve C is a base point of the linear system Λ, then the minimum multiplicity of intersection of C with any curve D of Λ at A is equal to the multiplicity of intersection of C with $D(\boldsymbol{\lambda})$ at A.

2.1. Components of a transcendental curve

In the definitions on p. 112, we did not yet distinguish between reducible and irreducible transcendental curves. If $K' \supset K$ is the coefficient field of a curve C with equation $f(\mathbf{x}) = 0$, then the decomposition of $f(\mathbf{x})$ into factors that are irreducible over K' defines a primary (or relative) decomposition of C into components that are irreducible over K'; but now it may well happen that $f(\mathbf{x})$ admits of further decomposition in some extension K'' of K', so that some of the curves that are irreducible components of C over K' are reducible over K''. Nevertheless, it can be proved that every polynomial in any number of indeterminates over a field K' can be factorized over a suitably chosen extension of K' into *absolutely irreducible factors*, which remain irreducible for any further extension of the field. It would therefore be possible to make a distinction between transcendental curves which are absolutely irreducible and those which are not.‡

We may also note here that a transcendental curve, unlike a ground curve, may well contain a generic point of an irreducible ground curve C without having C as component. Thus, for example, the transcendental line $X = uY$ contains the generic point (u^2, u) of the parabola $Y^2 = X$, but, being of lower order than the parabola, cannot have it as a component.

---

† The indeterminate used in a representation of α must, however, be distinct from the indeterminates λ_i used in the definition of $D(\boldsymbol{\lambda})$. Thus, for example, the order of either of the transcendental lines $X \pm tY = 0$ at the place with centre O on the parabola $Y^2 = X$ can be found by substituting u^2 and u, but not t^2 and t, for X and Y in $X \pm tY$.

‡ On the subject of absolute irreducibility, see Hodge and Pedoe, *Methods of Algebraic Geometry*, ii, chapter x, § 11.

2.2. Intersections of transcendental curves

Just as any two ground curves of S_2 have in common a non-empty set of points, so also will the same be true of any two curves which may possibly be transcendental.

Some or all of the common points of such a pair of curves may, of course, be transcendental points. The common points of two curves are found by solving the equations of the curves simultaneously, and this can be done by eliminating one coordinate in order to obtain a single equation for the ratio of the remaining two coordinates. The only new feature that appears when the curves are not restricted to ground curves is that the equation $g(x_i/x_j) = 0$ for the ratio of coordinates may now have coefficients in an extension K' of K instead of K itself, and the field K' need not be algebraically closed. When this is the case, however, K' can certainly be extended to a field K'' which is such that the polynomial $g(X)$ splits completely into linear factors in $K''[X]$, so that the equation $g(x_i/x_j) = 0$ can be solved in this field. The extension K'' of K' is constructed for the particular polynomial $g(X)$ under consideration, and different K'-polynomials may lead to different extensions; but it is sufficient for our purpose that, for any K'-polynomial $g(X)$, there always exists a suitable extension K'' of K'. That this is the case is asserted by the following algebraic theorem.

THEOREM 1. *If $\mathcal{K}$ is any field and $P(X)$ is a polynomial*

$$P(X) \equiv a_0 X^n + a_1 X^{n-1} + \ldots + a_n \qquad (a_i \in \mathcal{K}, \ a_0 \neq 0)$$

in $\mathcal{K}[X]$, then there exists a minimum extension $\mathcal{K}'$ of $\mathcal{K}$, unique to within isomorphism over $\mathcal{K}$, such that $P(X)$ admits of complete decomposition in $\mathcal{K}'$:

$$P(X) \equiv a_0 (X - \alpha_1)(X - \alpha_2) \ldots (X - \alpha_n) \qquad (\alpha_i \in \mathcal{K}').$$

$\mathcal{K}'$ is called the *splitting field* of the polynomial $P(X)$. Proofs of Theorem 1 and full discussions of the related theory are to be found in the standard books on modern algebra, e.g. van der Waerden, *Modern Algebra*, chapter v (§ 35, 2nd edition).

By use of Theorem 1 we could extend the main results of Chapters I and II, in so far as they deal with the intersections of a pair of curves, to the case in which the curves may be transcendental. We shall not need this general theory here, however, and so we confine the following discussion to the one case that is essential for the setting up of the connexion already alluded to between curves and envelopes. This is the case in which one of the intersecting curves is a ground curve and the other is a transcendental line.

3. The intersections of a ground curve with a transcendental line

In Chapter I, p. 7, we set up an equation

$$J(\lambda, \mu) \equiv f(\lambda a_0 + \mu b_0,\ \lambda a_1 + \mu b_1,\ \lambda a_2 + \mu b_2) = 0$$

to determine the points of intersection of a ground line L, fixed by two points $\mathbf{a}$ and $\mathbf{b}$, and a ground curve C, given by its equation $f(x_0, x_1, x_2) = 0$; and from this equation we were able to infer a number of basic facts concerning the tangents and the singular or multiple points of C. We shall now show that this theory can be extended to transcendental lines as well as ground lines.

THEOREM 2. *No ground curve can have a transcendental line as a component. If C is a ground curve of order n and L is a transcendental line, the number of intersections of C with L, when properly counted, is n.*

Proof. Let C be a given ground curve of order n and L an arbitrary transcendental line. We show first of all that L is not a component of C, and to this end we suppose that a triangle of reference has been selected in such a way that none of its vertices lies on C. Then C has an equation $f(x_0, x_1, x_2) = 0$, of degree n, such that x_0, x_1, x_2 all actually occur in the K-polynomial $f(x_0, x_1, x_2)$. We may assume, without loss of generality, that the equation of L can be written in the form $x_0 - px_1 - qx_2 = 0$, where not both of p and q are in K. Then, at the points of intersection of C with L,

$$f(px_1 + qx_2,\ x_1,\ x_2) = 0.$$

If L were a component of C, this equation would be identically satisfied, and we should have, in particular, $f(p, 1, 0) = 0$ and $f(q, 0, 1) = 0$; i.e. p and q would be algebraic over K and therefore, since K is algebraically closed, p and q would be elements of K. This is contrary to hypothesis; and therefore L cannot be a component of C.

Now suppose that we take two points $\mathbf{a}$ and $\mathbf{b}$ of L, with coordinates in $K(p, q)$, which are not points of C. Then the equation

$$J(\theta) \equiv f(a_0 + \theta b_0,\ a_1 + \theta b_1,\ a_2 + \theta b_2) = 0 \tag{1}$$

is of degree n in θ, and its roots determine the points of C which lie on L. Equation (1) has coefficients in $K' \equiv K(p, q)$ and, by

Theorem 1, there exists a splitting field K'', unique to within isomorphism over K', in which the polynomial $J(\theta)$ can be resolved into n linear factors. The n roots of equation (1) then define precisely n intersections, properly counted, of C with L; and the fact that K'' is unique to within isomorphism over K' means that the set of intersections in question is uniquely defined to within isomorphic equivalence over K' (cf. p. 47). This proves the theorem.

EXAMPLE. Let C be the circle $X^2+Y^2 = 1$ and let L be the transcendental line $Y = mX$, m being an indeterminate. Then C meets L in the two transcendental points $(\mu^{-1}, m\mu^{-1})$ and $(-\mu^{-1}, -m\mu^{-1})$, where $\mu = \sqrt{(1+m^2)}$. In this case $K' = K(m)$; and the equation $(1+m^2)X^2 = 1$ for the abscissae of the points of intersection is resolved in the splitting field

$$K'' = K'(\mu) = K(m, \sqrt{(1+m^2)}).$$

Note. We have shown in Theorem 2 only that a ground curve cannot have a transcendental *line* as component, but it can be proved more generally that a ground curve cannot have any transcendental curve at all as component. Any ground curve, in fact, can be resolved into its irreducible components over K, and since K is algebraically closed, these components are absolutely irreducible (by a theorem to be found in Hodge and Pedoe, *Methods*, ii, p. 76).

Using Theorem 2, we can now extend considerably the elementary theory of plane algebraic curves worked out in Chapter I. In that chapter the only points considered were ground points, but it is evident that much of what was said there admits of immediate generalization. We have already seen how to extend the range of application of the Joachimsthal equation $J(\theta) = 0$, and in this way we can define the polar curves for a given curve C of transcendental points of the plane, the multiplicity of a generic point of C, the tangent to C at a generic point, and so on. It will be left to the reader to supply and justify such generalizations wherever they are required in the discussion which follows.

THEOREM 3. *Every generic point ξ of an irreducible ground curve C is a simple point of C, and C has a well-defined tangent line at ξ.*

Proof. Let the equation of C be $f(x_0, x_1, x_2) = 0$, and let the value of the partial derivative $\partial f/\partial x_i$ at ξ be τ_i $(i = 0, 1, 2)$. Then $\tau_i \in K_\xi \cong K_C$. If ξ were a singular point of C, $\partial f/\partial x_i$ would be zero at ξ $(i = 0, 1, 2)$; and since every K-equation that is satisfied by the generic point ξ of C is satisfied by every ground point of C, the derivatives would be zero at all points of the curve. This would mean, however, that every ground point of C was a singular point, which we know to be impossible (p. 10). The point ξ is therefore a simple point of C; and there is a unique tangent line to C at ξ which meets C more than once there, namely the line τ.

THEOREM 4. *The tangent line to an irreducible ground curve C at any generic point ξ is a transcendental line of the first kind, except only in the case in which C is a line, when the tangent is this same ground line.*

Proof. We should expect the coordinates τ_i of the tangent at ξ to be algebraically dependent over K, since elimination of ξ_0, ξ_1, ξ_2 between the four equations $\partial f(\xi)/\partial \xi_i = \tau_i$ $(i = 0, 1, 2)$ and $f(\xi) = 0$ should yield an algebraic relation between them. The existence of such a relation can be inferred formally in the following way. The τ_i all belong to the minimum field of definition K_ξ of ξ, which is isomorphic over K with the field K_C. But any two elements of K_C are algebraically dependent over K (cf. p. 151), and unless τ is a ground line this must be true of two of the ratios τ_i/τ_k. If τ is a ground line, the ratios of the $\partial f(\xi)/\partial \xi_i$ are all in K, so that, say,

$$\partial f/\partial x_i - c_{ik}\, \partial f/\partial x_k = 0 \quad (i, k = 0, 1, 2)$$

when $\mathbf{x} = \xi$, where the c_{ik} are elements of K. But then, since ξ is generic for C, the same equations must be satisfied by every ground point of C, from which it follows that C is a ground line. We have, in fact, $f(\mathbf{x}) = \dfrac{1}{n} \displaystyle\sum_{i=0}^{2} x_i \dfrac{\partial f}{\partial x_i} = \dfrac{1}{n}(x_0 + c_{10} x_1 + c_{20} x_2)\dfrac{\partial f}{\partial x_0}$; and, by hypothesis, $f(\mathbf{x})$ is irreducible. In this case the tangent to C at any of its points coincides with C itself. The proof of the theorem is now complete.

Theorem 4 permits us to extend to irreducible plane curves in general the dual concepts of envelope and line-equation that are already familiar from the more elementary theory of the proper conic, but we shall not go into the discussion of tangent envelopes and their properties until the next section, § 4.

Before leaving the present subject of generic points, we take the opportunity of anticipating certain misunderstandings that may easily arise. The assertion made in Theorem 3, that every generic point of an irreducible curve C is a simple point of C, may be puzzling at first sight, especially if we think of a generic point which happens to be a formal transcendental point of order greater than unity, such as the point (u^2, u^3) on the semicubical parabola $Y^2 = X^3$. In fact, however, it is only the *centre* of the transcendental point, i.e. a ground point of C, that can be multiple on the curve. A formal transcendental point P itself, which we may think of intuitively as a general parametric point in the neighbourhood of its centre P_0, is always simple. A line L through P (which is necessarily transcendental unless C is a line) need not contain P_0 at all, for we know nothing about it beyond the fact that one of the n points in which it meets C is the transcendental point P. The remaining $n-1$ points of intersection, some of which may be transcendental points and some ground points, may include P_0 but need not do so. Thus, for example, the transcendental line $X = uY$ meets the parabola $Y^2 = X$ in two points, of which one is the generic point (u^2, u) and the other is the centre of this formal transcendental point; but the transcendental line $X+uY-2u^2 = 0$ meets the parabola in two transcendental points (u^2, u) and $(4u^2, -2u)$ with the same centre $(0, 0)$.

Since any place $\mathscr{P}$ on a curve C is simply a formal transcendental point of the curve which is defined to within substitution for the parameter, what we have been saying about tangents at generic points can be expressed in terms of tangents at places; and then, since we have already associated a tangent with each place on C in a different way, there is a possibility of confusion. We now need to distinguish carefully, in fact, between (*a*) the *tangent to C at $\mathscr{P}$*, which is transcendental except when C is a line, and (*b*) the *branch tangent of the place $\mathscr{P}$* on C (i.e. the tangent to $\mathscr{P}$ as a branch, in accordance with the definition on p. 75), which is always a ground line. The branch tangent of $\mathscr{P}$ can be obtained from the (transcendental) tangent to the curve at $\mathscr{P}$ by specializing the parameter suitably, namely by substituting 0 for u after putting the representation $\boldsymbol{\tau}$ of the tangent into standard form.

EXAMPLE. The tangent to the curve $y^2z = x^3$ at the place $(u^2, u^3, 1)$ has coordinate vector

$$(y\dot{z}-\dot{y}z,\ z\dot{x}-\dot{z}x,\ x\dot{y}-\dot{x}y) \equiv (-3u^2,\ 2u,\ u^4);$$

and, putting $u = 0$ in the standard representation $(-3u,\ 2,\ u^3)$, we obtain a set of coordinates $(0, 2, 0)$ of the cuspidal tangent $y = 0$.

THEOREM 5. *Any irreducible ground curve C is met by any generic line L of S_2 in n distinct generic points $\xi^{(i)}$ ($i = 1,...,n$) of C.*

Proof. Let L be any generic line of S_2 (p. 112). The equation of L can be written as $x_0 + u_1 x_1 + u_2 x_2 = 0$, u_1 and u_2 being distinct indeterminates. It then follows from Theorem 2 that, since this equation cannot be satisfied by the coordinates of any ground point whatever, L must meet C in n transcendental points $\xi^{(i)}$. But any transcendental point of C is generic for C (Theorem 3, p. 61), and the $\xi^{(i)}$ are consequently n generic points of C. They must be distinct, since otherwise the generic line L would be the tangent to C at one of them at least, and this is impossible by Theorem 4. Theorem 5 is accordingly established.

4. The tangent envelope of an irreducible algebraic curve

The dual of an algebraic curve is an algebraic envelope, and just as an irreducible curve may be defined as the totality of points which satisfy a fixed irreducible K-equation in x_0, x_1, x_2 so an irreducible envelope may be defined as the totality of lines which satisfy a fixed irreducible K-equation in the line-coordinates u_0, u_1, u_2. All the foregoing theory of algebraic curves can be duplicated for algebraic envelopes, and, in particular, generic points of curves have their dual counterparts in generic lines of envelopes.

Suppose, now, that C is a given irreducible algebraic curve, with equation $f(x_0, x_1, x_2) = 0$. We shall show, using Theorem 4 of the previous section, that the tangents to C are the lines of an irreducible algebraic envelope, the tangent τ at a generic point ξ of C being a generic line of this envelope. Except in the one trivial case in which C is a line, τ is a transcendental line of the first kind, and therefore (by the dual of Theorem 2, p. 60) a generic line of a unique irreducible algebraic envelope E, with equation $\phi(u_0, u_1, u_2) = 0$, say. This envelope, moreover, is associated with the curve C itself, being independent of the choice of a particular generic point ξ. For the relation $\phi(\tau_0, \tau_1, \tau_2) = 0$ may be written as a K-equation in ξ, namely $\phi(\partial f(\xi)/\partial \xi_0, \partial f(\xi)/\partial \xi_1, \partial f(\xi)/\partial \xi_2) = 0$; and it follows that any such relation which holds for one generic point of C holds for every such generic point. In the exceptional case of a curve C which is a line, τ is a ground line and not a generic line of an envelope at all, so that the envelope E derived from C is illusory in this case.

The envelope E determined by C in the way just explained is called the *tangent envelope* of C. The equation $\phi(u_0, u_1, u_2) = 0$ is called the *line-equation* of the envelope (or of C). The degree of the line-equation, which is plainly a projective invariant of C, is referred to as the *class* of C. The order n and the class m of an irreducible algebraic curve are dual characters of it, and it is to be expected that the number m will play an important role in the geometry of the curve. Before going on to establish the basic connexion between order and class, we first prove a fundamental theorem on the geometrical relationship between the associated manifolds C and E.

THEOREM 6. *If C is an irreducible algebraic curve, ξ is a generic point of C, and τ is the tangent to C at this transcendental point, the correspondence $\xi \leftrightarrow \tau$ between a generic point of the curve C and a generic line of its tangent envelope E defines a birational correspondence between C and E.*

Proof. We may take as the generic point ξ a place $\mathscr{P}$, with minimal representation $\xi(u)$ in $K\{u\}$. Then

$$f(\xi_0(u), \xi_1(u), \xi_2(u)) = 0,$$

and hence

$$\sum_{i=0}^{2} \frac{\partial f(\xi(u))}{\partial \xi_i} \frac{d\xi_i}{du} = 0,$$

i.e.

$$\sum_{i=0}^{2} \tau_i \dot{\xi}_i = 0 \quad (\tau_i(u) = \partial f(\xi(u))/\partial \xi_i, \ \dot{\xi}_i = d\xi_i/du).$$

But we also have, by Euler's Theorem on homogeneous functions,

$$\sum_{i=0}^{2} \tau_i \xi_i = 0,$$

and therefore

$$\tau_0 : \tau_1 : \tau_2 = \xi_1 \dot{\xi}_2 - \dot{\xi}_1 \xi_2 : \xi_2 \dot{\xi}_0 - \dot{\xi}_2 \xi_0 : \xi_0 \dot{\xi}_1 - \dot{\xi}_0 \xi_1,$$

i.e. in vector notation,

$$\left(\frac{\partial f}{\partial \xi_i}\right) = \tau = \rho \xi \wedge \dot{\xi}. \tag{1}$$

In exactly the same way, it follows from the relation

$$\phi(\tau_0(u), \tau_1(u), \tau_2(u)) = 0$$

that

$$\left(\frac{\partial \phi}{\partial \tau_i}\right) = \sigma \tau \wedge \dot{\tau}. \tag{2}$$

But, by (1),

$$\tau \wedge \dot{\tau} = \rho^2(\xi \wedge \dot{\xi}) \wedge (\dot{\xi} \wedge \dot{\xi} + \xi \wedge \ddot{\xi})$$
$$= \rho^2 |\xi \ \dot{\xi} \ \ddot{\xi}| \xi$$
$$= \lambda \xi, \tag{3}$$

say; and from (2) and (3)

$$\left(\frac{\partial \phi}{\partial \tau_i}\right) = \sigma \lambda \boldsymbol{\xi}.$$

We now have

$$\tau_0 : \tau_1 : \tau_2 = \frac{\partial f(\boldsymbol{\xi})}{\partial \xi_0} : \frac{\partial f(\boldsymbol{\xi})}{\partial \xi_1} : \frac{\partial f(\boldsymbol{\xi})}{\partial \xi_2}$$

and

$$\xi_0 : \xi_1 : \xi_2 = \frac{\partial \phi(\boldsymbol{\tau})}{\partial \tau_0} : \frac{\partial \phi(\boldsymbol{\tau})}{\partial \tau_1} : \frac{\partial \phi(\boldsymbol{\tau})}{\partial \tau_2},$$

so that each of the two sets of ratios $\xi_0 : \xi_1 : \xi_2$ and $\tau_0 : \tau_1 : \tau_2$ is expressed rationally in terms of the other set; and this is what we mean by the statement that $\boldsymbol{\xi} \leftrightarrow \boldsymbol{\tau}$ defines a birational correspondence[†] between the curve C and its tangent envelope E.

COROLLARY. *If $\boldsymbol{\xi}(u)$ is a minimal representation of a place $\mathscr{P}$ on an irreducible curve C with equation $f(\mathbf{x}) = 0$, and if*

$$\tau_i(u) = [\partial f / \partial x_i]_{\mathbf{x} = \boldsymbol{\xi}(u)} \qquad (i = 0, 1, 2),$$

then $\boldsymbol{\tau}(u)$ is a minimal representation of the tangent to C at $\mathscr{P}$.

The fact that evaluation of the partial derivatives $\partial f / \partial x_i$ for $\mathbf{x} = \boldsymbol{\xi}(u)$ yields a *minimal* representation of the tangent at $\mathscr{P}$ is of great importance, since the use that we make in our treatment of algebraic curves of the orders of formal power series makes it imperative that we should be able to produce minimal representations of places and dual places when we require them. It may be remarked, however, that even though $\boldsymbol{\xi}(u)$ may be a standard representation of $\mathscr{P}$, the derived representation $\boldsymbol{\tau}(u)$ of the dual place that is associated with $\mathscr{P}$ need not be in standard form.

The birational correspondence $\boldsymbol{\xi} \leftrightarrow \boldsymbol{\tau}$ is a one-one correspondence between places on C and dual places on E. It gives rise (cf. p. 153) to a one-one correspondence between the ground points of C and the tangents at these points; but there may be a finite number of points and a finite number of tangents for which the uniqueness of the correspondence fails, namely certain singular points of C or singular lines of E. At a node of C, for example, there are two distinct tangents, one for each of the two places at the node.

We now turn to the relation that holds between the order n and the class m of any irreducible curve C, a relation which we can investigate in the following way. Consider an undetermined line $\mathbf{u}$ of S_2, i.e. a line for which u_0, u_1, u_2, are undetermined elements

† For a general discussion of birational correspondence see Chapter VII, § 4.

of K. This contains, in particular, the two ground points $(u_1, -u_0, 0)$ and $(u_2, 0, -u_0)$; and the points in which it is met by C are determined by the equation

$$J(\theta) \equiv f(u_1 + \theta u_2, -u_0, -\theta u_0) = 0.$$

This equation for θ will have at least two of its roots coincident if and only if $D(u_0, u_1, u_2) = 0$, where $D(\mathbf{u})$ is the discriminant of $J(\theta)$. Now there are precisely two ways in which this can come about: (i) when the line $\mathbf{u}$ is a tangent to C, (ii) when the line passes through a multiple point of C. It follows that, if the multiple points of C are $\mathbf{b}^{(i)}$ $(i = 1,...,s)$, the resolution of $D(\mathbf{u})$, with the numbers u_0, u_1, u_2 re-interpreted as indeterminates, into its irreducible factors in $K[u_0, u_1, u_2]$ must be of the form

$$D(u_0, u_1, u_2) = [\phi(u_0, u_1, u_2)]^p \prod_{i=1}^{s} (b_0^{(i)} u_0 + b_1^{(i)} u_1 + b_2^{(i)} u_2)^{q_i},$$

where $p, q_1,..., q_s$ are all positive integers. Since $D(u_0, u_1, u_2)$ is a form of degree $n(n-1)$ in u_0, u_1, u_2, we can at once deduce the inequality $m \leqslant n(n-1)$. If C possess any multiple points at all, we can make the stronger assertion $m < n(n-1)$. We shall be able to show below (p. 125) by a different argument that the value of the exponent p of $\phi(u_0, u_1, u_2)$ as a factor of $D(u_0, u_1, u_2)$ is in fact 1.

It may be remarked that the above reasoning does not exclude the possibility that a line may be both a line of the tangent envelope E and also a line through a multiple point of C (i.e. that its coordinates may annul both $\phi(\mathbf{u})$ and one of the linear factors of $D(\mathbf{u})$). The nodal tangents at the multiple points of C, for example, have this property, and in fact any ground line of E, being a specialization of the tangent to C at a generic point $\boldsymbol{\xi}$, must be either a proper tangent to C or a nodal tangent at a multiple point of C. It follows from this that, if a point P does not lie on any of the nodal tangents, then the lines of E that pass through it are all proper tangents of C, and their number, properly counted, is m. Further, by dualizing the argument used immediately above, we see that the m tangents through P are distinct provided only that P is further restricted not to lie on a certain curve with equation $D(x) = 0$, where $D(x)$ is the discriminant of the polynomial $J(\theta) \equiv \phi(x_1 + \theta x_2, -x_0, -\theta x_0)$.

From the dual of Theorem 5 and the above argument, we now have the following theorem.

THEOREM 7. *The class m of an irreducible curve C is equal on the one hand to the number of (necessarily transcendental) tangents of C that pass through a generic point of S_2, and on the other hand to the number of tangents of C (proper ground tangents) that pass through a ground point of prescribed generality of S_2 (not lying on a certain composite algebraic curve).*

Either part of this theorem provides us with a means of computing the class m of a curve C when we know the order of C and the composition of its singularities. The computation based on the second part is the more elementary in conception, and we shall now carry it out for a curve of order n with multiple points $O_1, ..., O_s$ of multiplicities $k_1, ..., k_s$.

We suppose, then, that P is a ground point of S_2, chosen as indicated in Theorem 7 so that the m lines of E that pass through it are distinct proper tangents of C (none passing through a multiple point O_i). The points of contact $T_1, ..., T_m$ of these tangents are then also distinct. By Theorem 11 on p. 15, the first polar $C^{(1)}(P)$ of P with respect to C, which is a curve of order $n-1$, meets C only at $T_1, ..., T_m$ and $O_1, ..., O_s$. Further, by the additional result given on p. 16, each point T_i is a simple intersection of $C^{(1)}(P)$ with C, provided only that the tangent PT_i is not inflexional.

We now observe that C can have only a finite number of inflexional tangents. For a direct calculation (cf. Exercise 9 at the end of the chapter) shows that the tangent line at an inflexion of a curve C (not itself a line) is a singular line of the associated tangent envelope of C, and the number of such singular lines is finite by the dual of the corollary to Theorem 6, Chapter I. Thus by imposing on P the further restriction that it does not lie on any inflexional tangent of C we ensure that precisely m of the $n(n-1)$ intersections of C with $C^{(1)}(P)$ fall at $T_1, ..., T_m$, and the rest at $O_1, ..., O_s$.

Now consider the intersections at $O_1, ..., O_s$, and let the minimum multiplicity of intersection of C at O_i with curves of the net of first polars of all points of S_2 with respect to C be δ_i (in other words, let δ_i be the multiplicity of intersection of C at O_i with the generic curve of this net). Any curve $C^{(1)}(P)$ of the net in question, as is easily seen, will only have a multiplicity of intersection greater than δ_i with C at O_i if the coordinates of P satisfy a certain algebraic relation; and we may therefore choose P so that its coordinates satisfy no such relation corresponding to any of the points O_i and still conform to all the restrictions previously imposed. Thus, in brief, P can be so chosen that precisely δ_i of the intersections of $C^{(1)}(P)$ with C fall at O_i $(i = 1,...,s)$ and only one such intersection falls at each of $T_1,..., T_m$; and we therefore have the general formula

$$m = n(n-1) - \sum_{i=1}^{s} \delta_i$$

for the class of C. As regards the values of the δ_i, we only know in general that O_i is a point of multiplicity k_i-1 on $C^{(1)}(P)$ (p. 14); and hence, by the Basic Inequality (p. 94), $\delta_i \geqslant k_i(k_i-1)$. We have therefore the inequality

$$m \leqslant n(n-1) - \sum_{i=1}^{s} k_i(k_i-1)$$

for the class of C. If O_i is an ordinary multiple point of C, we know (p. 15) that the k_i-1 nodal tangents of $C^{(1)}(P)$ at O_i are all distinct from the k_i nodal tangents of C at O_i, and it follows that in this case $\delta_i = k_i(k_i-1)$. We can accordingly formulate the following theorem.

THEOREM 8. *If the only multiple points of an irreducible curve C of order n are s ordinary multiple points $O_1,..., O_s$, of multiplicities $k_1,..., k_s$ respectively, then the class m of C is given by the formula*

$$m = n(n-1) - \sum_{i=1}^{s} k_i(k_i-1).$$

Theorem 8 gives the only general formula for class that we shall obtain. Formulae for special types of curve can be worked out whenever the relevant multiplicities δ_i can be evaluated, and this is possible in a number of simple cases. Suppose, for example, that C has a simple cusp (p. 77) at O_i. We find then that $\delta_i = 3$; and this result gives at once the so-called *Plücker formula*

$$m = n(n-1) - 2\delta - 3\kappa$$

for the class of a curve of order n with δ nodes (ordinary double points) and κ simple cusps as its only singularities.

EXERCISE. Show that if a linear system Λ has no unassigned base points, no base point multiplicities exceeding those that are assigned, and no fixed branch tangents at the base points, the class m of its generic curve is given, in the notation of Chapter I, § 5, by $m = 2n + 2\gamma - 2r$.

5. The deficiency of a curve

We now introduce a further important numerical character of an irreducible curve.

DEFINITION. The *deficiency* (or *quasi-genus*) of an irreducible curve C of order n is the number D given by the formula

$$D = \tfrac{1}{2}(n-1)(n-2) - \tfrac{1}{2}\sum_{i=1}^{s} k_i(k_i-1),$$

where the k_i ($i = 1,...,s$) are the multiplicities of all the multiple points of C.

If the multiple points of C are all ordinary, the value of the deficiency is the same as that of the *genus p* of C—the most fundamental of all the numerical characters of the curve, which will be defined on p. 268 below—and in this case we sometimes refer to D as the genus of C. The term 'deficiency' is used because, as we shall see shortly, D is a measure of the extent to which the actual set of multiple points of C falls short of the maximum possible number of double points for a curve of the same order. The traditional way of establishing the properties of D is by considering a certain linear system of curves, defined in terms of the multiple points of the curve C under consideration. These curves are known as the sub-adjoints of C.

DEFINITION. If C is a given irreducible curve, a curve of order N is called a *sub-adjoint A^N* of C if its multiplicity at each multiple point O_i of C is not less than k_i-1, where k_i is the multiplicity of C at O_i.

A given curve C has sub-adjoints A^N for all values of N great enough to permit the necessary singularities. The first use that we shall make of these associated curves of a given curve C is in establishing the fact that the deficiency of C cannot be negative. From this basic property can at once be deduced, as we shall see, a sharp limitation on the sets of multiple points that are possible for an irreducible curve of any given order.

THEOREM 9. *The deficiency of any irreducible curve is greater than or equal to zero.*

Proof. Let the given curve C be of order n, and let its multiple points be $O_1,..., O_s$ with multiplicities $k_1,..., k_s$ respectively. Then the sub-adjoints A^N of C of any given order N form a linear system (A^N) that is complete with respect to the assigned base $O_1^{k_1-1},..., O_s^{k_s-1}$. We shall consider, in particular, the system (A^{n-1}). This system contains (p. 15) the net of first polar curves $C^{(1)}(P)$ of all ground points P of S_2, and (A^{n-1}) can therefore have no base points on C

other than the O_i, and its effective base-point multiplicity at each point O_i is precisely k_i-1. If, now, r is the freedom and ϵ the super-abundance of (A^{n-1}) with respect to the assigned base, we have

$$r = \tfrac{1}{2}(n-1)(n+2) - \tfrac{1}{2}\sum_{i=1}^{s} k_i(k_i-1) + \epsilon,$$

whence we obtain the relation

$$r = D + 2n - 2 + \epsilon.$$

On the other hand, the multiplicity of intersection of every curve of (A^{n-1}) with C at O_i is at least $k_i(k_i-1)$; and since C is irreducible the curve cannot be a component of C. It follows, therefore, that every A^{n-1} meets C in at most $n(n-1) - \sum_{i=1}^{s} k_i(k_i-1)$ points remote from the O_i. Thus, if N_0 is the maximum number of intersections of any A^{n-1} with C, remote from the O_i,

$$N_0 = n(n-1) - \sum_{i=1}^{s} k_i(k_i-1) - \sigma, \quad \sigma \geqslant 0;$$

and therefore $\qquad\qquad N_0 = 2D + 2n - 2 - \sigma.$

Plainly, however, since there exists at least one A^{n-1} through any r given points, we must have $N_0 \geqslant r$; and this gives

$$2D + 2n - 2 - \sigma \geqslant D + 2n - 2 + \epsilon,$$

i.e. $\qquad\qquad\qquad D \geqslant \sigma + \epsilon \geqslant 0.$

The theorem is accordingly proved.

When the only multiple points of C are d double points (ordinary or non-ordinary) the theorem tells us that $\tfrac{1}{2}(n-1)(n-2) - d \geqslant 0$, and so gives an upper bound for d.

    COROLLARY. *No irreducible curve of order n can have more than* $\tfrac{1}{2}(n-1)(n-2)$ *double points.*

It can be shown that this upper bound for the number of double points is attained in the case of a curve which is a general plane projection of a rational normal curve $C^{(n)}$ in S_n, with parametric representation $(\theta^n, \theta^{n-1},..., 1)$. Thus *the deficiency D of an irreducible curve C of order n with no singularities except double points is the actual deficiency of the number of its double points as compared with the maximum number $\tfrac{1}{2}(n-1)(n-2)$ possible for an irreducible curve of order n.*

5.1. Curves of deficiency zero

Since zero is the lowest possible value for the deficiency of an irreducible curve, we naturally ask what special property attaches to those curves for which this minimum value of D is attained.

THEOREM 10. *Every curve of deficiency zero is rational.*

Proof. Let C be an irreducible curve of order n and deficiency 0, given by an equation $f(\mathbf{x}) = 0$. The method by which we show that C is rational (and which gives us a means of determining effectively a rational parametric representation of C) depends on the construction of what is known as a *rationalizing pencil of curves* for C. This means a pencil Λ which is such that (i) a generic curve of the pencil meets C in one and only one point not common to all curves of the pencil, and (ii) a generic point of C lies on one and only one curve of the pencil. When the equation $f(\mathbf{x}) = 0$ of C and the equation $F(\mathbf{x})+\lambda G(\mathbf{x}) = 0$ of a generic curve of Λ are solved simultaneously for the ratios $x_0:x_1:x_2$ in a suitable extension of $K(\lambda)$, one and only one of the points so obtained will depend effectively on λ; i.e. there will be one transcendental point only, and all the other points will be ground points of C. It follows from this that the coordinates of the transcendental point (which is necessarily a generic point of C) will be rational functions of λ over K.

The last statement can be justified in the following way. Elimination of x_2 between the equations $f(\mathbf{x}) = 0$ and $F(\mathbf{x})+\lambda G(\mathbf{x}) = 0$ yields an equation for $x_0:x_1$ of the form

$$a_0(\lambda)x_0^p+a_1(\lambda)x_0^{p-1}x_1+\ldots+a_p(\lambda)x_1^p = 0 \qquad (a_i(\lambda) \in K[\lambda]);$$

and this equation must be equivalent to

$$a_0(\lambda)(x_0-\alpha_1 x_1) \ldots (x_0-\alpha_{p-1} x_1)(x_0-\alpha'_p x_1) = 0,$$

where $\alpha_1,\ldots,\alpha_{p-1}$ are in K and α'_p is in some suitable extension of $K(\lambda)$. But then, since at least one of the ratios $a_i(\lambda)/a_0(\lambda)$ is different from zero, we can express α'_p rationally in terms of λ by comparing suitable coefficients in the two equations. Thus for the transcendental point required, $x_0:x_1$ (and similarly also $x_0:x_2$) is a rational function of λ over K.

Any rationalizing pencil, then, leads to a rational parametric representation of C. The representation, furthermore, is proper (cf. p. 24), and C is accordingly a rational curve.

In pursuance of the plan that we have outlined, we consider first of all the linear system (A^{n-2}) of sub-adjoints of order $n-2$ of the given curve C. Whatever may be the value of D, we find easily, as in the preceding section, that the freedom r of (A^{n-2}) is given by

$$r = n-2+D+\epsilon \quad (\epsilon \geqslant 0); \tag{1}$$

and we infer from this that, if $D = 0$ and $n > 2$, then (A^{n-2}) certainly exists and has positive freedom. Similarly, for the maximum number N_0 of intersections of a curve of the system (A^{n-2}) with C at points remote from the multiple points of C, we obtain an expression

$$N_0 = n-2+2D-\sigma \quad (\sigma \geqslant 0). \tag{2}$$

Putting $D = 0$ in (1) and (2), and using the fact that r cannot exceed N_0, we obtain the inequality

$$n-2+\epsilon \leqslant n-2-\sigma,$$

i.e. $$\sigma+\epsilon \leqslant 0.$$

But σ and ϵ are both non-negative, and therefore $\sigma = \epsilon = 0$. Thus when $D = 0$ the sub-adjoint curves A^{n-2} have effective freedom $n-2$, and a generic curve of the system (A^{n-2}) meets C in precisely $n-2$ points remote from the multiple points. If, now, we select $n-3$ points of C, remote from the multiple points, which impose linearly independent conditions on a sub-adjoint A^{n-2} required to contain them, the aggregate of sub-adjoints A^{n-2} through these $n-3$ points as additional base points will be a rationalizing pencil for C. The existence of such a pencil proves that C is a rational curve.

Remarks. (i) It should be noted carefully that $D = 0$ is only a *sufficient* condition for C to be rational. Curves may possess concealed 'infinitely near' multiple points in addition to their overt singularities, as will be explained in Chapter XI; and such a curve may be rational even though its deficiency (which takes account only of the overt singularities) is greater than zero.

(ii) By a method analogous to that used in the proof of Theorem 10 (again using the sub-adjoints A^{n-2}) it can be shown that any curve for which $D = 1$ can be transformed birationally into a plane cubic curve—a non-singular cubic if the original curve is not rational, and a singular cubic otherwise. See, for example, Semple and Roth, *Introduction to Algebraic Geometry*, p. 36.

6. Noether's transformation

The importance of the deficiency D as a character of an irreducible curve C depends on two facts: (i) D is directly computable in terms of the order of C and the multiplicities of its singular points, and (ii) D has the fundamental property of being non-negative. In this section we shall make use of this latter property in order to prove a notable result which represents an essential simplification of the subsequent theory. The theorem in question, due originally to Max Noether, asserts that any irreducible curve C in S_2, however complicated may be its singularities, can always be transformed by a finite series of standard quadratic transformations of S_2 into a curve $\bar{C}$ with only *ordinary* multiple points. The superiority of $\bar{C}$ over C, from the point of view of general theory, resides in the fact that its places are all of order unity, and therefore easy to handle in relation to the intersections of $\bar{C}$ with other curves.

We shall begin by enumerating briefly the elementary properties of a standard quadratic transformation, assuming that the reader is already familiar with some at least of these, and that he will have no difficulty in verifying the others.†

6.1. Properties of the standard quadratic transformation

A standard quadratic transformation T is a self-transformation of S_2, based on a triangle XYZ, and such that, when XYZ is taken as triangle of reference and the unit point is suitably chosen, the equations of T take the form

$$x' : y' : z' = yz : zx : xy \quad (= 1/x : 1/y : 1/z).$$

Plainly, T is self-inverse. The vertices and sides of the triangle XYZ are exceptional for the transformation, and we call them the *fundamental points* and *fundamental lines* of T.

The properties of T that we require may be listed as follows.

(i) T is *regular* at any pair of corresponding points P, P' which are remote from the fundamental lines. In particular, it transforms every branch at either of these points into a unique branch of the same order at the other, establishing a homographic correspondence between directions at P and directions at P'.

(ii) If C is any irreducible curve of the type $C^n(X^\alpha, Y^\beta, Z^\gamma)$, but not a fundamental line, then the irreducible transform C' of C

---

† For an introductory treatment of the subject, see Semple and Kneebone, *Algebraic Projective Geometry*, chapter ix, § 3.

(obtained by discarding any factors x, y, or z in the transformed equation) is a curve of the type $C^{2n-\alpha-\beta-\gamma}(X^{n-\beta-\gamma}, Y^{n-\gamma-\alpha}, Z^{n-\alpha-\beta})$.

(iii) T sets up a homographic correspondence between directions λ at any fundamental point, X say, and points L of the opposite fundamental line YZ, in such a way that branches at X with branch tangent λ (excluding only the actual lines XY and XZ) are transformed into branches at the corresponding point L; and conversely, provided only that L is not Y or Z, all branches (excluding the line YZ) with centre at L are transforms of branches at X with λ as branch tangent.

(iv) If L is a point of YZ, remote from Y and Z, every *linear* branch at L with branch tangent not along YZ is the transform of a linear branch at X with branch tangent in the associated direction λ.

6.2. Resolutions

We now consider an arbitrarily given irreducible curve C, of order n, in S_2, and we suppose that O is a singular point of multiplicity s of C. By a *standard resolution of the singular point O of C* we shall understand any standard quadratic transformation T such that

(a) O is a fundamental point of T, and the two remaining fundamental points A and B of T do not lie on C;

(b) OA and OB each meet C in $n-s$ distinct points remote from O;

(c) AB meets C in n distinct points.

Let the multiple points of C other than O be $O^{(1)},..., O^{(\mu)}$, of multiplicities $k_1,..., k_\mu$; and let us now consider the transform C' of C by T.

Every place $\mathscr{P}$ on C, with centre at a point P not on OA, OB, or AB, transforms in accordance with (i) into a place $\mathscr{P}'$ on C', of the same order as $\mathscr{P}$, with centre at the transform P' of P; and the branch tangents correspond in the fixed homography between directions at P and directions at P'. Hence *if P is any point of C, not on OA, OB, or AB, and if P is of multiplicity $k \geqslant 1$, then its transform P' is a point of multiplicity k on C', and the sets of nodal tangents at P and P' are projectively equivalent.*

Next, by (ii), we see that C' is a curve $C^{2n-s}(O^n, A^{n-s}, B^{n-s})$. Since C meets AB in n distinct points remote from A and B (and therefore none of the tangents at these points can coincide with AB) it follows by (iv) that the n-fold point of C' at O is ordinary.

Similarly, since C meets each of OA and OB (without contact) in $n-s$ points, all remote from fundamental points, it follows that the $(n-s)$-fold points of C' at A and B are also ordinary. Thus *the transform C' of C is of order $2n-s$, and it has ordinary multiple (or simple) points of multiplicities n, $n-s$, $n-s$ at O, A, B respectively.*

We now note that neither OA nor OB can have any intersection with C' that is not at O or at A or B. Of the $2n-s$ intersections of C' with AB, however, we know that exactly $n-s$ fall at each of A and B; for if C' had AB as a branch tangent at either A or B then one of the branch tangents of C at O would be along OB or OA, and this is ruled out by condition (*b*). Thus precisely s of the intersections of C' with AB must fall at points remote from A and B Let these points be denoted by $L_1,..., L_m$ $(1 \leqslant m \leqslant s)$. Each L_i corresponds to a direction λ_i at O, not along OA or OB, and these directions must be those of the branch tangents of C at O. Those branches of C at O which have their branch tangent in the direction λ_i will be transformed by T into branches of C' with centre at L_i. Hence *precisely s of the intersections of AB with C' are remote from A and B, and they fall at a set of points $L_1,..., L_m$ $(1 \leqslant m \leqslant s)$, which correspond to the distinct nodal tangents of C at O.* These points $L_1,..., L_m$ are sometimes referred to as the transforms by T of points $O_1,..., O_m$, infinitely near to O on C. (Cf. Chapter V, § 8, and Chapter XI, § 6.)

Suppose, then, that the multiplicities of $L_1,..., L_m$ as points of C' are $s_1,..., s_m$, and that their multiplicities as intersections of AB with C' are $\sigma_1,..., \sigma_m$. It follows that

$$s = \sum_{i=1}^{m} \sigma_i,$$

where $\qquad 1 \leqslant s_i \leqslant \sigma_i \quad (i = 1,..., m),$

and hence $\qquad 1 \leqslant m \leqslant \sum_{i=1}^{m} s_i \leqslant s.$

The most extreme cases are as follows:

(i) $m = s$, $s_i = \sigma_i = 1$ $(i = 1,..., m)$: O is an ordinary s-fold point of C which is resolved by T into s simple points of C';

(ii) $m = 1$, $s_1 = 1$, $\sigma_1 = s$: C has a single branch of order s at O which is resolved into a linear branch having s-point contact with AB at L_1;

(iii) $m = 1$, $s_1 = \sigma_1 = s$: C has again a single branch of order s at O, but this is now resolved into a branch of C' of the same order s at L_1 (with branch tangent not along AB).

There are, of course, many intermediate possibilities.

We can now compare the deficiencies D and D' of the two curves C and C'. These are given by the respective formulae:

$$D = \tfrac{1}{2}(n-1)(n-2) - \tfrac{1}{2}s(s-1) - \tfrac{1}{2}\sum_{i=1}^{\mu} k_i(k_i-1),$$

$$D' = \tfrac{1}{2}(2n-s-1)(2n-s-2) - \tfrac{1}{2}\sum_{i=1}^{m} s_i(s_i-1) - \tfrac{1}{2}\sum_{i=1}^{\mu} k_i(k_i-1)$$
$$- \tfrac{1}{2}n(n-1) - 2\cdot\tfrac{1}{2}(n-s)(n-s-1);$$

and on reduction of these we obtain the equation

$$D' = D - \tfrac{1}{2}\sum_{i=1}^{m} s_i(s_i-1).$$

We thus have the following result.

Any standard resolution of an s-fold point of C yields a transformed curve C' whose deficiency is reduced, as compared with that of C, by an amount $\tfrac{1}{2}\sum_{i=1}^{m} s_i(s_i-1)$, where $s_1,...,s_m$ are the multiplicities of the points of C' that arise from the neighbourhood of the s-fold point of C.

It follows, in particular, that $D' < D$ if and only if one, at least, of the points $L_1,...,L_m$ is multiple on C'

6.3. Noether's Theorem

We are now in a position to prove the fundamental theorem to which we have already alluded.

THEOREM 11 (*Noether's Theorem*). *Every irreducible curve C of S_2 can be transformed, by a finite sequence of standard quadratic transformations of the plane into itself, into an irreducible curve $\bar{C}$ with only ordinary singularities.*

Proof. If C has at least one non-ordinary multiple point, we select some one such point O and apply a standard resolution to it, transforming C into a curve C'. Then we know that either the deficiency D' of C' is less than the deficiency D of C, or the multiple point O of C is resolved into a set of simple points of C'. Further, every multiple point of C' which does not arise from a point of C in the neighbourhood of O is either ordinary or else it arises from a point of C of the same multiplicity as itself and with a projectively equivalent set of nodal tangents.

If $D' < D$, and if C' has any non-ordinary multiple point O_1 that arises from the neighbourhood of O, we may apply a standard resolution to O_1, transforming C' into a curve C'' of deficiency D''; and now either $D'' < D'$ or O_1 is completely resolved. Since deficiency is non-negative, we must be able, by a finite number of successive resolutions, to transform O into a set of simple or ordinary multiple points. Having done so, we can deal similarly with every other non-ordinary multiple point that C may possess (all such points having retained their projective character through the sequence of transformations already applied) and we shall finally arrive at a transform $\bar{C}$ of C with only ordinary multiple points. This proves the theorem.

We mention in conclusion, as typical examples of the resolution of singularities, the following simple results.

(i) Resolution of an ordinary double point (node) O of C gives rise to two simple intersections of C' with AB, remote from A and B.

(ii) Resolution of a simple cusp of C at O gives rise to a linear branch of C' which touches AB at a point L_1.

(iii) Resolution of a common tacnode of C at O gives rise to an ordinary double point of C' at a point L_1 of AB, with neither tangent at L_1 along AB.

(iv) Resolution of a double cusp of C at O gives rise to a simple cusp of C' at L_1 on AB, with cuspidal tangent distinct from AB. In this case a further resolution of type (ii) is needed to complete the process.

The reader will easily be able to construct further examples for himself.

NOTES AND EXERCISES ON CHAPTER VI

[In some of the following exercises we use affine line coordinates U, W in conjunction with affine point coordinates X, Y, the standard equation of a line being taken for this purpose in the form $Y + UX + W = 0$. The line $(0, 0)$ is thus the axis OX, and the unrepresented lines are all those through Y_∞. If apologies are necessary for the unsymmetrical choice of U, W as affine line coordinates, it may be emphasized that this is very much an *ad hoc* expedient for having a finite line OX as the dual origin $(0, 0)$.]

1. *Note on specialization.* In amplification of the term 'specialization over K' which we have used in § 2, we may give the following extended definition: If $\mathbf{z} = (z_1, ..., z_r)$ and $\boldsymbol{\zeta} = (\zeta_1, ..., \zeta_r)$ are any two sets of r elements from

the same or different extension fields of K, then we say that $\mathbf{z}$ is a *specialization of* ζ *over* K if its elements satisfy every K-equation $F(X_1, ..., X_r) = 0$ that is satisfied by those of ζ.

This idea is already familiar in so far as a generic point of an irreducible curve (or generic line of an irreducible envelope) was defined to be such that *every* point of the curve (or line of the envelope) is a specialization of it over K; but the concept of specialization has very much wider applications (cf. Chapter IX, p. 211). We only note here that every set such as ζ is a specialization of itself over K, and if $\zeta_1, ..., \zeta_r$ are all elements of K, then ζ has no other specialization over K.

The concept of specialization, as above defined, largely takes the place, in a purely algebraic development of geometry, of the concept of continuous variation (with approach to a limit) in analytic theory.

2. Show directly that the branch tangent at any place on an irreducible curve C is a specialization of the tangent to C at a generic point.

3. If u, v are distinct indeterminates, show that every pair of ground points of the parabola $Y^2 = X$ is a specialization over K of the pair (u^2, u), (v^2, v) and also a specialization over K of the pair (u^2, u), (e^{2u}, e^u), but not a specialization over K of the pair (u^2, u), $(u^2, -u)$.

4. The envelope defined by the parabola $Y^2 = X$ has the generic line $(U, W) = (-\frac{1}{2}t^{-1}, -\frac{1}{2}t)$, this being the tangent at the generic point (t^2, t); and its equation, therefore, is $4WU = 1$.

Verify the curve-envelope relation for each of the pairs of equations:

(i)	$X^2 + Y^2 = 1$,	$W^2 - U^2 = 1$;
(ii)	$Y^2 = X^3$,	$4U^3 + 27W = 0$;
(iii)	$X^3 + Y^3 = XY$,	$(9W^2 - U)^2 = 4(1 - 3UW)(U^2 - 3W)$;
(iv)	$X^3 + Y^3 = 1$,	$(U^3 + W^3)^2 = 2U^3 - 2W^3 - 1$.

5. Find a rational parametric representation of the envelope with equation $W^2 = U^2(1 - U)$, and hence or otherwise find the equation of its associated curve. Show that the latter is a tricuspidal quartic (with concurrent cuspidal tangents).

6. If Θ is a quantity, algebraic over $K(U, W)$, such that $\Theta^2 = 1 - 4UW$, show that the intersections of the parabola $Y^2 = X$ with the generic line $Y + UX + W = 0$ of S_2 are the points

$$(\tfrac{1}{4}(\Theta \mp 1)^2 U^{-2}, \tfrac{1}{2}(\pm \Theta - 1) U^{-1}) \tag{1}$$

with coordinates in $K(U, \Theta)$.

Show that the pair of coincident points obtained by replacing Θ by 0 in the pair (1) is a specialization over K of this pair.

7. If t is an indeterminate, show that the line $Y = tX$ meets the curve $Y^2 = X^3$ in the ground point O counted twice and in a further generic point. Show also that the line $3tX - 2Y - t^3 = 0$ touches the curve at one generic point and meets it again in another generic point, that it has the cuspidal tangent as a specialization, and that the inflexion of the curve counted twice is a specialization over K of the pair of generic points in question.

8. *Curve-branches and envelope-branches.* In dealing with branches α, as defined in Chapter IV, and their duals β, each of which has a line as centre, it

is sometimes convenient to refer to the former as *curve-branches* and to the latter as *envelope-branches*. A pair of branches α, β of the two kinds will be said to be *duals of each other*—a relation expressed symbolically by writing $\beta = \bar{\alpha}$ or $\alpha = \bar{\beta}$—if *they are projectively equivalent* together to a pair of branches of the form $\mathbf{x} = \mathbf{a}(t)$, $\mathbf{u} = \mathbf{a}(t)$ for some choice of a vector function $\mathbf{a}(t)$.

Apart from this general duality correspondence, however, every curve-branch α not contained in a line defines a unique *associated envelope-branch* $\beta = \alpha^*$, and similarly every envelope-branch β not contained in a point (as envelope) defines a unique *associated curve-branch* $\alpha = \beta^*$. Thus, if $\mathbf{x} = \mathbf{a}(t)$ is any representation of α, then α^* may be defined to be the envelope-branch with equation $\mathbf{u} = \mathbf{b}(t)$, where

$$\mathbf{b}(t) = \mathbf{a}(t) \wedge \dot{\mathbf{a}}(t),$$

the dot denoting differentiation with respect to t; and it is then seen at once that α^* is independent of the choice of representation $\mathbf{a}(t)$ for α. The definition of β^* is similar. It now follows (cf. p. 121) that $\alpha^{**} = \alpha$ and $\beta^{**} = \beta$.

Finally we may say that two curve-branches α_1 and α_2 are *dualized associates of each other* if $\alpha_2 = \bar{\alpha}_1^*$, the order of performance of the operations denoted by the star and bar being immaterial, and the relation between α_1 and α_2 being symmetrical.

9. *Characteristic numbers of dual branches.* If β is an envelope-branch dual to the curve-branch α, then the characteristic numbers m, n of α (cf. Chapter IV, § 4.1) can immediately be interpreted, by duality, as characteristic numbers also of β. On the other hand, if another curve-branch α' is a dualized associate $\bar{\alpha}^*$ of α, the relation between the characteristic numbers m, n of α and the corresponding numbers m', n' of α' has to be found by computation. Taking the equations of α in the reduced form (cf. p. 77)

$$x_0 : x_1 : x_2 = 1 : t^m : c_1 t^{m_1} + c_2 t^{m_2} + \ldots \quad (c_i \neq 0,\ i = 1, 2, \ldots),$$

where $m_1 = m+n$, we find easily that the equations of α' can be written in the form

$$\left.\begin{array}{l} x_0' = \left(\dfrac{m_1}{m} - 1\right) c_1 t^{m_1} + \left(\dfrac{m_2}{m} - 1\right) c_2 t^{m_2} + \ldots \\[2mm] x_1' = -\dfrac{m_1}{m} c_1 t^{m_1-m} - \dfrac{m_2}{m} c_2 t^{m_2-m} + \ldots \\[2mm] x_2' = 1 \end{array}\right\},$$

from which it follows that $m' = n$ and $n' = m$. Hence:

If α has characteristic numbers m, n, then any dualized associate α' of α has characteristic numbers n, m.

From this and the table in Chapter IV, § 4.2, we deduce in particular that

   (i) *any dualized associate of a non-inflexional linear branch is a non-inflexional linear branch* ($m = n = 1$); and

   (ii) *any dualized associate of a simple cuspidal branch* ($m = 2$, $n = 1$) *is a simple inflexional branch* ($m = 1$, $n = 2$), *and conversely.*

The reader should examine for himself the dualized associates of the other branches listed in the above-mentioned table.

10. *Plücker curves and Plücker's equations.* An irreducible curve C, not a line, together with its associated envelope E can be regarded in combination as a *complete curve* (C, E), having a finite number of point singularities (multiple points of C) and line singularities (multiple lines of E). The dual of (C, E) is then another complete curve $(\overline{E}, \overline{C})$, where $\overline{C}$ is the ordinary dual of C, and $\overline{E}$ is the associated locus of $\overline{C}$ (dual also to E). The point and line singularities of $(\overline{E}, \overline{C})$ will correspond by duality to the line and point singularities of (C, E).

The simplest general class of irreducible curves C such that the dual $C' = \overline{E}$ of the associated envelope E of any one of its members is also a member of the class—the class being thus invariant under duality—is that of the so-called *Plücker curves*. These are defined by the conditions that

(i) the only point singularities of C are strictly ordinary double points (cf. Exercise 15, p. 107) and simple cusps; and

(ii) the only line singularities of C are strictly ordinary double tangents and simple inflexions.

The fact that the aggregate of Plücker curves, as so defined, is invariant under duality follows at once from the results given in the preceding note of this set.

The *characters of a Plücker curve* C are n, m, δ, κ, τ, ι, denoting respectively the order, class, and numbers of double points, cusps, double tangents, and inflexions of C; and those of its dual C', in the same order, are m, n, τ, ι, δ, κ. The advantage of restricting ourselves to the self-dual class of Plücker curves is that any general relation connecting the six characters above defined implies at once the dual relation defined by the substitution

$$\begin{pmatrix} n & m & \delta & \kappa & \tau & \iota \\ m & n & \tau & \iota & \delta & \kappa \end{pmatrix}.$$

Thus from the two relations already recorded (Chapter V, Exercise 16, p. 108), namely

$$m = n(n-1) - 2\delta - 3\kappa \tag{1}$$

and

$$\iota = 3n(n-2) - 6\delta - 8\kappa, \tag{2}$$

we can derive the dual relations

$$n = m(m-1) - 2\tau - 3\iota \tag{3}$$

and

$$\kappa = 3m(m-2) - 6\tau - 8\iota. \tag{4}$$

Of these four relations, however, only three are independent, as the reader should verify for himself. It is in fact the case that the six Plücker characters are reducible to three independent ones, in the sense that there is no fixed relation between these three (as, for example, n, δ, κ), while the remaining three can be expressed in terms of them.

From (1),...,(4) we may deduce in particular the relation

$$\tfrac{1}{2}(n-1)(n-2) - \delta - \kappa = \tfrac{1}{2}(m-1)(m-2) - \tau - \iota = p, \quad \text{say}, \tag{5}$$

which expresses the fact that *the deficiencies of C, as a curve and as an envelope, are equal.* Also, in terms of this common deficiency (in fact the genus), we find that

$$m = 2n + 2p - 2 - \kappa \quad \text{and} \quad n = 2m + 2p - 2 - \iota, \tag{6}$$

and hence

$$3(m-n) = \iota - \kappa. \tag{7}$$

11. Show that every irreducible cubic curve is a Plücker curve. Show also that the dual of a non-singular cubic is a 9-cuspidal sextic; that the dual of a nodal cubic is a tricuspidal quartic; and that the cuspidal cubic is a self-dual species.

12. Enumerate all the species of Plücker quartic curves, showing in particular that one such species is self-dual.

13. Show that the quartic curve C with equation $y^2z^2+z^2x^2+x^2y^2 = 0$ has flecnodes (cf. Chapter I, Exercise 15, p. 28) at each of X, Y, Z so that it is *not* a Plücker curve. Verify that its Hessian is a sextic having multiplicity of intersection 8 (instead of 6) with C at each of X, Y, Z, so that C has no proper inflexions. [In an obvious sense, however, one may regard the curve as having two (improper) inflexions at each of X, Y, Z.]

14. If a Plücker curve has $\frac{1}{2}(n-1)(n-2)$ double points, show that it is rational and that it has no cusps. Show then that its class is $2n-2$ and that it has $3n-6$ inflexions (cf. Chapter I, § 6). Show further that the number of its double tangents is $2(n-2)(n-3)$.

15. Show that the curve C with equation $(x^2+y^2-zx)^2 = z^2(x^2+y^2)$ is of deficiency 0, and verify that the conics of the pencil $x^2+y^2 = \lambda yz$ have one free intersection with C. Hence or otherwise obtain a rational parametric representation of C.

16. Show that the curve with equation $(Y-X^2)^2 = XY^2$ is of deficiency 1.

By applying to it the special quadratic transformation $X = X', Y = X'Y'$, show that it is nevertheless rational, and obtain a rational parametric representation of it.

Show that the curve has a single place at the origin and obtain a standard representation of this place.

17. Show that the curve with equation $x^2y^2+2z^4 = 3xyz^2+xz^3$ has a tacnode and a cusp, and that the conics touching the tacnodal tangent at the former and the cuspidal tangent at the latter form a rationalizing pencil. Find the resulting rational parametric representation of the curve.

18. *Curves of deficiency* 1. If $f(x,y,z) = 0$ is the equation of a curve C of deficiency 1, show that it is always possible to find a linear net of sub-adjoints A^{n-2} of C such that the curves of this net have three free intersections with C. If the equation of such a net is $\lambda F+\mu G+\nu H = 0$, show that the equations $x':y':z' = F:G:H$ transform the points (or places) on C into the points (or places) on a cubic curve C'.

If C is the curve $z^3(x+y) = x^2y^2$, show that the equation

$$\lambda yz+\mu zx+\nu xy = 0$$

defines a net of the kind in question; and that the resulting transform C' of C has equation $z'^3 = x'y'(x'+y')$.

19. *Resolution of a branch*. If α is any branch of order ν, with centre at the reference point Z and branch tangent not along ZX or ZY, show that the transformation $(x,y,z) \to (1/x, 1/y, 1/z)$ carries α into a branch α' of order $\nu' \leqslant \nu$, with centre on YZ, and that the branch tangent of α' does or does not lie along YZ according as $\nu' < \nu$ or $\nu' = \nu$.

[*Note*. If α is algebraic (a place on an algebraic curve), then the argument leading to Theorem 11 shows that a finite number of successive resolutions such as the above will transform α ultimately into a linear branch. We shall see in Chapter XI that every branch has this property, whether it is algebraic or not.]

20. Apply a standard quadratic transformation to analyse the singularity at Z of the curve $z(x-y)(x^2-y^2) = x^4$.

21. *Multiplicity of intersection.* If O is a common point of the curves C_1, C_2, then it is always possible to choose points A, B so that (i) no intersection of C_1, C_2 other than O lies on any of OA, OB, AB, and (ii) the quadratic transformation based on O, A, B is a standard resolution of O for both curves. Show that, in such case, if the multiplicities of O for C_1 and C_2 are s_1 and s_2, then the multiplicity of intersection of C_1 and C_2 at O exceeds $s_1 s_2$ by the sum of the multiplicities of intersection of the resolved curves C_1' and C_2' at any points on AB, other than A and B, which they may have in common. [Use the fact that the multiplicity of intersection of two concentric branches (cf. Chapter, V, § 7.2) is an analytic invariant.]

Deduce from the above a precise meaning for the statement that *the multiplicity of intersection of C_1, C_2 at O is equal to the sum of products of the multiplicities of these curves at O and at common points in the neighbourhood of O* (*as defined by any particular sequence of standard resolutions*).

22. If a standard quadratic transformation carries any irreducible curve C whose multiple points are all ordinary into another such curve C', show that the deficiencies (genera) of C and C' are equal.

23. *Use of the special quadratic transformations.* If quadratic transformations are to be used for the express purpose of identifying the separate places on C at a multiple point O (more rapidly than by the original identification of cycles of roots of an equation for Y, as in Chapter V), then the *special quadratic transformation* $(X, Y) \to (X, Y/X)$, with inverse $(X, Y) \to (X, XY)$, together with its counterpart obtained by interchanging the roles of X and Y, are much more convenient to use than standard quadratic transformations. Detailed properties of these special transformations are set out in Chapter XI, § 3.2.

Use special quadratic transformations to investigate the singularities at the origin of the curves (i) $(Y-aX^2)^2 = X^5$, (ii) $Y^3 = X^4$, (iii) $Y^2(Y-aX) = X^4$, (iv) $(Y-aX^2)(Y-bX^2)(Y-cX^2) = X^7$.

24. *Use of another quadratic transformation.* Discuss in detail the properties of the transformation

$$X = X'/(X'+a), \quad Y = Y'/(X'+a)^2 \quad (a \neq 0).$$

Obtain, in particular, the equations of the reverse transformation, and describe the systems of curves which arise from lines by the direct and reverse transformations.

Show that the above transformation carries the tacnodal quartic $Y^2 = (1-X^2)(1-k^2X^2)$ into a cubic curve which is in general non-singular, and prove that any general tacnodal quartic can be transformed into a cubic by a transformation of the above type.

CHAPTER VII

THE THEORY OF THE FUNCTION FIELD

1. Review

BEFORE we go on to further important developments, it may be useful to review briefly the progress that we have made so far, and the stage in our inquiry to which it has brought us.

In Chapter I we were concerned mainly with the primary concept of a plane algebraic curve, which we considered in relation to the ground points of the curve, the intersections of the curve with lines, its simple and multiple points, and its tangents. In Chapter II we learned how to handle sets of ground points in the plane, and more particularly sets of intersections of pairs of curves, by means of equations set up in an appropriate way; and we were able to assign to every common point of a C^m and a C^n (with no common component) a definite *multiplicity* as an intersection of the curves, in such a way that the total number of intersections of two curves, when properly counted, is always equal to the product of the orders of the curves.

In Chapter III we no longer confined our attention exclusively to the ground points of the plane, but went on to define and discuss the properties of *transcendental points*. A transcendental point has coordinates in an extension field K' of K; and it is said to be of the first or the second kind according as these coordinates do or do not satisfy some algebraic equation with coefficients in K. The points of $S_2(K)$ now fall into three classes: (i) ground points; (ii) transcendental points of the first kind, each of which belongs to a unique irreducible algebraic curve; and (iii) transcendental points of the second kind, which do not belong to any algebraic curves at all. Any transcendental point of the first kind is a *generic point* of the algebraic curve which it determines; and if two points α and β are generic points of the same curve then they correspond in a K-isomorphism of their minimum fields of definition. In Chapter III also, we constructed the function field K_C of any irreducible algebraic curve C (i.e. the field of rational functions on C) and with its aid we were able to prove that (i) every irreducible curve C possesses a generic point, and (ii) the minimum field of definition of every generic point of C is isomorphic over K with K_C.

In Chapter IV we were largely concerned with transcendental points of one particular type, namely with *formal transcendental points*, which have coordinates in $K|u|$, the field of extended formal power series in an indeterminate u. We began by defining a new class of geometric objects, the *quasi-branches* of S_2. These were essentially formal transcendental points, defined only to within regular transformation of the parameter; and we were concerned more particularly with *minimal quasi-branches*, i.e. formal transcendental points which are not derivable from other such points by substitution of index greater than unity. All those quasi-branches that can be obtained from a given minimal quasi-branch $\tilde{\alpha}$ by substitutions of any index whatever are said to constitute a *branch* α. A branch, like the transcendental points inherent in it, is either of the first kind (*algebraic*) or of the second kind (*non-algebraic*). An algebraic branch is termed a *place* on the unique irreducible algebraic curve C to which it belongs; and we saw in Chapter V that every ground point P of an irreducible algebraic curve C is the centre of one or more places on C, and the sum of the orders of these places is equal to the multiplicity of P as a point of C. And lastly in this connexion, we defined the order of any algebraic curve C' on any branch α not contained in C' (this order being zero unless C' passes through the centre of α), and we proved that the multiplicity of intersection of two curves C and C' at any isolated common point P is equal to the sum of the orders of C' at the places on C with centre P, i.e. on the branches of C which have P as centre. This result was of cardinal importance in relation to the proper interpretation and use of the theorem of Bézout for curves in the plane. At the end of Chapter V we introduced the new local concept of an *analytic curve* at a point O of the plane, and this enabled us to express the multiplicity of intersection of any two algebraic curves C and D at a common point P symmetrically as the sum of the multiplicities of intersection of the branches of either curve at P with those of the other curve at P.

Throughout the first six chapters, we have not deviated in principle from our original limited objective, which was the study of plane algebraic curves, conceived of as consisting either of aggregates of ground points satisfying irreducible K-equations in the coordinates, or of formal combinations of such aggregates. The general conception of transcendental point, and the ideas of branches in the plane and places on a curve, were introduced with the primary object of enabling us to handle difficult questions about multiplicity of intersection, and also questions concerned with the analysis of singularities. But out of the innovations which we have made for these limited purposes, new conceptions have emerged, with possible implications extending far beyond the original objective. Thus we have already seen that an irreducible algebraic curve can be envisaged not merely as a locus of ground points but also as a totality of places, each place having a ground point of the curve as its centre, and each such ground point being the centre, usually of one, but possibly of several, of the places. Each individual place (unlike a ground point of the curve) is sufficient by itself to determine the entire curve.

Again, we have seen that every irreducible algebraic curve C defines, to within isomorphism over K, an associated extension field of K, its function field K_C, which is such that every transcendental point of C generates, over K, a field isomorphic with K_C. A new question that now forces itself urgently upon our attention is the following: 'Which of the properties of an irreducible curve C depend only on the structure of the function field K_C of the curve?' In other words, we must ask what it is possible to say about the whole family of curves C' with function fields isomorphic with K_C. In formulating such a question we are, of course, allowing the curve C to be displaced from the centre of the picture by the type of function field to which it gives rise; and indeed, if Σ is any field which can occur as the function field of a curve, we are proposing to look upon all curves C with $K_C \cong \Sigma$ as geometrical *representations* or *models* of Σ. Such a study of fields Σ in relation to their geometrical models is known as the *invariantive* or *birational* geometry of algebraic curves. It will appear, in due course, that in this invariantive geometry the concept of a curve as an aggregate of places has a meaning, but the concept of a curve as an aggregate of ground points has not, since only the first of the two concepts possesses the requisite invariance.

2. The basic algebra

The general theory of the structure of the function field of an arbitrary irreducible algebraic curve and of the relationship between the curve and the field is made to depend, in the treatment which we shall adopt, on the conception of algebraic extension of a field; and we shall first of all discuss this notion briefly from the

point of view of pure algebra. We have already met the general
logical idea of an extension field in Chapter III, where we defined
several types of extension of the ground field K, but we have not so
far mentioned the more specific idea of *algebraic* extension. The
procedure of algebraic extension, which has many applications in
various branches of mathematics, is of fundamental importance
throughout the whole of modern algebraic geometry.

2.1. Simple algebraic extension of a field

In this section we shall use the symbol $\mathscr{K}$ to denote an arbitrary
field, in order to keep the reader aware that we are not at present
limiting the argument to our usual ground field K of the complex
numbers.

If $\mathscr{K}$ and $\mathscr{K}'$ are two fields such that $\mathscr{K}$ is a subfield of $\mathscr{K}'$ we
describe $\mathscr{K}'$ as an *extension* of $\mathscr{K}$. If, now, $\mathscr{S}$ is any subset of $\mathscr{K}'$,
there is a smallest extension of $\mathscr{K}$ which contains every element of
$\mathscr{S}$ (namely the intersection of all the subfields of $\mathscr{K}'$ in which
$\mathscr{K} \cup \mathscr{S}$ is included). We say that this smallest extension of $\mathscr{K}$ is
the *extension generated by* $\mathscr{S}$, and we denote it by $\mathscr{K}(\mathscr{S})$. According
to the particular choice of $\mathscr{S}$, $\mathscr{K}(\mathscr{S})$ may reduce to $\mathscr{K}$, or comprise
the whole of $\mathscr{K}'$ or it may be a field intermediate between $\mathscr{K}$ and $\mathscr{K}'$.

In a similar way, if $\mathscr{R}$ and $\mathscr{R}'$ are rings, $\mathscr{R}$ being a subring of $\mathscr{R}'$,
and if $\mathscr{S}$ is any subset of $\mathscr{R}'$, we shall use the symbol $\mathscr{R}[\mathscr{S}]$ to denote
the smallest subring of $\mathscr{R}'$ which contains $\mathscr{R} \cup \mathscr{S}$.

Now it is possible to extend a field $\mathscr{K}$, not only by adjoining to
it one or more elements of an existing extension field $\mathscr{K}'$, but also
by *constructing* a larger field in which $\mathscr{K}$ is contained. We had
examples of this procedure in the discussion of symbolic adjunction
in Chapter III; and a further example is provided by the method of
algebraic extension now to be outlined. We shall begin by taking
a field $\mathscr{K}$ (which will be subject to no restriction whatever) and a
polynomial $f(X)$, of degree $n \geqslant 1$, in a single indeterminate X,
with coefficients in $\mathscr{K}$, which is irreducible over $\mathscr{K}$. Our aim is to
extend $\mathscr{K}$ by adjoining to it a root of the equation $f(X) = 0$, i.e. *to
construct an extension $\mathscr{K}'$ of $\mathscr{K}$ such that the equation $f(X) = 0$ has
a root in $\mathscr{K}'$*. The standard way of doing this, which had been used
already by Dedekind,† is to show that the residue classes modulo

---

† R. Dedekind and H. Weber, 'Theorie der algebraischen Funktionen einer
Veränderlichen', *J. reine angew. Math.* **92** (1882), 181–290; reprinted in Dedekind's
Werke, i. 238–350.

$f(X)$ in the ring $\mathscr{K}[X]$ constitute such a field (actually the smallest such field). We shall not, however, adopt quite this procedure, as we wish to bring out as clearly as possible the fact that the general method by which we now generate an algebraic extension of $\mathscr{K}$ is a direct generalization of the method (in which each step had an intuitive interpretation) which we used in Chapter III to form the function field K_C of a curve C. Nevertheless, the results which we shall obtain in the end are precisely the same as those reached in Dedekind's theory.

We begin by taking an indeterminate X and forming the ring $\mathscr{K}[X]$ of polynomials in X with coefficients in $\mathscr{K}$. This ring, being an integral domain, has a field of quotients, which is the field $\mathscr{K}(X)$. The elements of this field are the rational functions of X, and each of them may be written as a fraction $g(X)/h(X)$, where $g(X)$ and $h(X)$ are elements of $\mathscr{K}[X]$ with no common factor involving X, and $h(X) \neq 0$. In the ring $\mathscr{K}[X]$, the irreducible polynomial $f(X)$ with which we began defines a relation of congruence

$$g_1(X) \equiv g_2(X) \pmod{f(X)},$$

which holds if and only if the difference $g_1(X) - g_2(X)$ is divisible by $f(X)$; and we can extend this relation in $\mathscr{K}[X]$ to a corresponding relation in $\mathscr{K}(X)$ (cf. p. 58) by putting

$$g_1(X)/h_1(X) \sim g_2(X)/h_2(X) \pmod{f(X)}$$

whenever

$$g_1(X)h_2(X) - g_2(X)h_1(X) \equiv 0 \pmod{f(X)}$$

in $\mathscr{K}[X]$. If, now, we identify every element of $\mathscr{K}[X]$ that can be written in the form $g(X)/1$ with the corresponding element $g(X)$ of $\mathscr{K}[X]$, then $\mathscr{K}[X]$ becomes a subring of $\mathscr{K}(X)$; and since the two relations

$$g_1(X) \equiv g_2(X) \pmod{f(X)} \quad \text{in } \mathscr{K}[X]$$

and

$$g_1(X)/1 \sim g_2(X)/1 \pmod{f(X)} \quad \text{in } \mathscr{K}(X)$$

are equivalent, the extended definition of congruence modulo $f(X)$ does not conflict with the original one.

Now the relation of congruence modulo $f(X)$ in $\mathscr{K}(X)$ is an equivalence relation, and it therefore brings about a separation of $\mathscr{K}(X)$ into disjoint *congruence classes*, every rational function $g(X)/h(X)$ determining a well-defined congruence class $\{g(X)/h(X)\}$ $(\mathrm{mod}\, f(X))$, which we shall usually denote simply by $\{g/h\}$. Since, moreover, the four rational operations, applied to the elements g/h of $\mathscr{K}(X)$, are compatible with the relation $g_1/h_1 \sim g_2/h_2$, they may be carried over to the congruence classes $\{g/h\}$; and, when this is done, the set of congruence classes becomes a field $\mathscr{K}'$. $\mathscr{K}'$ may then be interpreted as an extension of $\mathscr{K}$ by the familiar device of identifying $\mathscr{K}$ (element by element) with the isomorphic subfield of $\mathscr{K}'$ that consists of all elements of the form $\{k/1\}$, $k \in \mathscr{K}$. We shall say that $\mathscr{K}'$ is the *simple algebraic extension of $\mathscr{K}$ generated by the irreducible polynomial $f(X)$*.

The extension is said to be *simple* because it can be obtained by adjoining to $\mathscr{K}$ a single element η—so that we may write $\mathscr{K}' = \mathscr{K}(\eta)$. We may, for example, choose as η the particular element $\{X/1\}$ $(\bmod f(X))$ of $\mathscr{K}'$. Then, if we take the set consisting of the single element η as the set $\mathscr{S}$ on p. 143, $\mathscr{K}(\mathscr{S})$ becomes the subfield $\mathscr{K}(\eta)$ of $\mathscr{K}'$ which consists of all elements of $\mathscr{K}'$ which are expressible rationally over $\mathscr{K}$ in terms of η, i.e. all elements of the form $g(\eta)/h(\eta)$ where $g(X)$, $h(X) \in \mathscr{K}[X]$ and $h(\eta) \neq 0$. But

$$g(\eta)/h(\eta) = g(\{X\})/h(\{X\})$$
$$= \{g(X)\}/\{h(X)\}$$
$$= \{g(X)/h(X)\},$$

and therefore $\mathscr{K}(\eta)$ is the same as $\mathscr{K}'$.

Since, in particular,

$$f(\eta) = \{f(X)\} \quad (\bmod f(X))$$
$$= 0 \quad \text{in } \mathscr{K}',$$

the field $\mathscr{K}(\eta)$ that we have constructed contains a root η of the equation $f(X) = 0$ with which we began.

The particular element $\eta = \{X\}$ $(\bmod f(X))$ of $\mathscr{K}'$ is by no means the only one that can be taken as generating element. If η' is any element of $\mathscr{K}'$ of the form

$$\eta' = \frac{a\eta + b}{c\eta + d} \quad (a, b, c, d \in \mathscr{K}; \quad ad - bc \neq 0),$$

then plainly $\mathscr{K}(\eta') = \mathscr{K}(\eta) = \mathscr{K}'$.

We now sum up the main results of the foregoing argument in a theorem.

THEOREM 1. *If $\mathscr{K}$ is any field whatever, then every non-constant irreducible polynomial $f(X)$ of $\mathscr{K}[X]$ determines a simple algebraic extension $\mathscr{K}'$ of $\mathscr{K}$. There are infinitely many possible choices of a generating element in $\mathscr{K}'$; and, in particular, there exists a generating element which satisfies the equation $f(X) = 0$.*

In the special case in which the polynomial $f(X)$ is of the first degree, $\mathscr{K}'$ coincides with $\mathscr{K}$. For if $f(X) = aX+b$, $a \neq 0$, then $X \sim -b/a \pmod{f(X)}$, and therefore $\eta = \{X\} = \{-b/a\} \in \mathscr{K}$. It follows that when the field $\mathscr{K}$ is algebraically closed the concept of algebraic extension is nugatory.

One of the simplest non-trivial cases of algebraic extension is obtained, as we shall see, by taking for $\mathscr{K}$ the field $K(X)$ of rational functions in an indeterminate X with coefficients in the complex field K and adjoining to $K(X)$ a root η of an irreducible equation in Y, $f(X, Y) = 0$. We shall show, in fact, that the simple algebraic extension of $K(X)$ so constructed is the function field K_C of the irreducible algebraic curve whose equation is $f(X, Y) = 0$.

2.2. Properties of the typical extension field $\mathscr{K}(\eta)$

We shall now establish, still without imposing any restriction upon $\mathscr{K}$, certain basic properties of the typical simple algebraic extension $\mathscr{K}'$ of $\mathscr{K}$ which is determined by an irreducible equation $f(X) = 0$, of degree n. We shall continue to use the notation of the previous section, and, in particular, the symbol η will be reserved for the generating element $\{X\}$ $(\operatorname{mod} f(X))$ of $\mathscr{K}'$.

PROPERTY 1. *Every element of $\mathscr{K}'$ has a unique representation of the form*
$$a_0+a_1\eta+\ldots+a_{n-1}\eta^{n-1} \quad (a_i \in \mathscr{K}), \tag{1}$$
as a $\mathscr{K}$-polynomial in η of degree not exceeding $n-1$.

Proof. Since $\mathscr{K}' = \mathscr{K}(\eta)$, every element of $\mathscr{K}'$ can be written as a rational function $g(\eta)$ of η. If this rational function happens to be a polynomial, we need only divide $f(X)$ into $g(X)$, leaving a remainder $r(X)$. Then
$$g(X) = f(X)q(X)+r(X),$$
say, and hence
$$g(\eta) = 0 . q(\eta)+r(\eta);$$
and since $r(\eta)$ is of the form (1) we have expressed $g(\eta)$ in the required manner.

Now suppose $g(\eta)$ is the reciprocal of a polynomial, i.e. $g(\eta) = 1/h(\eta)$, where $h(\eta) \neq 0$. Then, since $f(X)$ is irreducible, the highest common factor of $h(X)$ and $f(X)$ is 1, and there accordingly exist polynomials $p(X)$ and $q(X)$ such that
$$p(X)f(X)+q(X)h(X) = 1.$$

Hence
$$p(\eta).0 + q(\eta)h(\eta) = 1,$$
i.e.
$$1/h(\eta) = q(\eta).$$

Thus the present case has been made to depend on the one already considered; and by combining the two cases we can now extend to any rational function $g(\eta)$ the possibility of reduction to the form (1).

The uniqueness of the representation follows from the fact that if, for some element $g(\eta)$ of $\mathscr{K}'$, we had two different representations

$$g(\eta) = a_0 + a_1\eta + ... + a_{n-1}\eta^{n-1},$$

and
$$g(\eta) = b_0 + b_1\eta + ... + b_{n-1}\eta^{n-1},$$

then η would satisfy the non-trivial equation

$$(a_0 - b_0) + (a_1 - b_1)X + ... + (a_{n-1} - b_{n-1})X^{n-1} = 0,$$

of degree less than n.

DEFINITIONS. (i) An *element ζ of an extension* of a field $\mathscr{K}$ is said to be *algebraic over $\mathscr{K}$* if it satisfies an algebraic equation with coefficients in $\mathscr{K}$.

(ii) An *extension field* of $\mathscr{K}$ is said to be *algebraic over $\mathscr{K}$* if all its elements are algebraic over $\mathscr{K}$.

If an element ζ is algebraic over $\mathscr{K}$, there exists at least one $\mathscr{K}$-polynomial $g(X)$ such that $g(\zeta) = 0$. The set of all K-polynomials with this property is an ideal in $\mathscr{K}[X]$; and, since every polynomial-ring over a field is a principal ideal ring (cf. Appendix A, § 6), the polynomials in question are all the multiples of a certain polynomial $m(X)$. This polynomial, which is unique to within a factor in $\mathscr{K}$, is irreducible over $\mathscr{K}$; and since it has the minimum degree for all polynomials in the ideal it is called the *minimum polynomial of ζ over $\mathscr{K}$*.

PROPERTY 2. *Every element of the extension field $\mathscr{K}(\eta)$ is algebraic over $\mathscr{K}$, and the degree of its minimum polynomial is at most n.*

Proof. Let ζ be any element of $\mathscr{K}(\eta)$. Then $\zeta, \zeta\eta, ..., \zeta\eta^{n-1}$ are all elements of $\mathscr{K}(\eta)$ and are therefore all expressible in the form (1). We can accordingly write

$$\zeta\eta^i = \sum_{j=0}^{n-1} a_{ij}\eta^j \quad (i = 0, ..., n-1);$$

that is,†
$$\sum_{j=0}^{n-1} (a_{ij} - \delta_{ij}\zeta)\eta^j = 0 \quad (i = 0, ..., n-1).$$

† The Kronecker symbol δ_{ij} has the value 1 if $i = j$ and the value 0 if $i \neq j$.

It follows that $\qquad |a_{rs}-\delta_{rs}\zeta| = 0,$

that is, ζ satisfies the determinantal equation

$$|a_{rs}-\delta_{rs}X| = 0,$$

which is a $\mathscr{K}$-equation of degree n. Thus ζ is algebraic over $\mathscr{K}$, and the degree of its minimum equation is at most n.

It follows as a corollary to the result just proved that if, in place of η, we take any other generating element η' of $\mathscr{K}(\eta)$, the degree of the irreducible equation satisfied by η' is again n. It will be appreciated already that the degree of the minimum polynomial of an element is a very important number in the theory of algebraic extensions; and we now adopt the following formal definitions.

DEFINITIONS. (i) If an element of an extension field of $\mathscr{K}$ is algebraic over $\mathscr{K}$, the degree of its minimum polynomial is called the *degree of the element over* $\mathscr{K}$.

(ii) The *degree of a simple algebraic extension $\mathscr{K}'$ of $\mathscr{K}$* is the common degree of all its generating elements; and this degree is denoted by $\mathscr{K}':\mathscr{K}$.

PROPERTY 3. *If $\mathscr{K},\mathscr{K}_1,...,\mathscr{K}_s$ is a sequence of fields with the property that each field after the first is a simple algebraic extension of its immediate predecessor, then $\mathscr{K}_s$ is algebraic over $\mathscr{K}$.*

Proof. For convenience, we shall denote $\mathscr{K}$ here by $\mathscr{K}_0$. We may then suppose that

$$\mathscr{K}_i = \mathscr{K}_{i-1}(\eta_i), \qquad \mathscr{K}_i:\mathscr{K}_{i-1} = m_i \quad (i = 1,...,s).$$

We require to show that any element ζ of $\mathscr{K}_s$ is algebraic over $\mathscr{K}_0$. Now ζ is a linear combination, over $\mathscr{K}_{s-1}$, of $1, \eta_s,..., \eta_s^{m_s-1}$; each of the coefficients in the linear expression is itself a linear combination, over $\mathscr{K}_{s-2}$, of $1, \eta_{s-1},..., \eta_{s-1}^{m_{s-1}-1}$; and so on. Thus ζ is ultimately expressible as a linear combination, over $\mathscr{K}_0$, of the $N = m_1 m_2 ... m_s$ elements

$$\eta_1^{q_1} \eta_2^{q_2} ... \eta_s^{q_s} \quad (0 \leqslant q_i \leqslant m_i-1; \ i = 1,...,s). \tag{2}$$

By the same argument, the $N+1$ elements $1, \zeta,..., \zeta^N$ of $\mathscr{K}_s$ are each linearly dependent on the N elements (2), and they therefore form a set of elements linearly dependent over $\mathscr{K}_0$. Thus ζ satisfies an equation with coefficients in $\mathscr{K}_0$, and it is accordingly algebraic over $\mathscr{K}_0$.

Whereas Properties 1 to 3 are valid for every possible choice of the field $\mathscr{K}$, the last property that we shall establish has not this unrestricted validity, and we shall only prove that it holds for fields of characteristic zero. We shall show that, for such fields, adjunction of a finite number of elements is equivalent to the single adjunction of an appropriately chosen linear combination of the elements in question.

PROPERTY 4. *If $\mathscr{K}$ is a field of characteristic zero, and if $\eta_1,...,\eta_s$ are all algebraic over $\mathscr{K}$, then there exists a linear combination θ of $\eta_1,...,\eta_s$ with coefficients in $\mathscr{K}$ (or even in any prescribed infinite subset of $\mathscr{K}$) such that $\mathscr{K}(\eta_1,...,\eta_s) = \mathscr{K}(\theta)$.*

Proof. It is plainly sufficient to prove the theorem in the simplest case $s = 2$, for the general result can then be inferred by induction with respect to s. We shall show that, if η_1 and η_2 are both algebraic over $\mathscr{K}$, then there exists an element k of $\mathscr{K}$ such that

$$\mathscr{K}(\eta_1, \eta_2) = \mathscr{K}(\theta),$$

where $\theta = \eta_1 + k\eta_2$.

Let η_1 and η_2 satisfy the irreducible $\mathscr{K}$-equations $f(X) = 0$ and $g(X) = 0$ respectively, where $f(X) = (X-\alpha_1)...(X-\alpha_p)$ and $g(X) = (X-\beta_1)...(X-\beta_q)$ in some extension $\mathscr{K}'$ of $\mathscr{K}$.† Then, since $f(X)$ and $g(X)$ are irreducible and $\mathscr{K}$ is of characteristic zero, $\alpha_1,...,\alpha_p$ are all different‡ and so are $\beta_1,...,\beta_q$. Let $\alpha_1 = \eta_1$ and $\beta_1 = \eta_2$. Since each of the equations

$$\alpha_i + y\beta_j = \alpha_1 + y\beta_1 \quad (i = 1,...,p; \; j = 2,...,q)$$

has at most one root for y in $\mathscr{K}$, we may choose an element k in $\mathscr{K}$ (or in any given infinite subset of $\mathscr{K}$) such that

$$\alpha_i + k\beta_j \neq \alpha_1 + k\beta_1$$

for any $i = 1,...,p$, $j = 2,...,q$; and we then put

$$\theta = \alpha_1 + k\beta_1 = \eta_1 + k\eta_2.$$

Since $g(\beta_1) = 0$ and $f(\theta - k\beta_1) = f(\alpha_1) = 0$, β_1 satisfies the equations $g(X) = 0$ and $f(\theta - kX) = 0$, with coefficients in $\mathscr{K}(\theta)$; so that $g(X)$ and $f(\theta - kX)$ have $X - \beta_1$ as a common factor in $\mathscr{K}'(\theta)[X]$. But since none of the other roots β_j of $g(X) = 0$ is a root of $f(\theta - kX) = 0$, this is their highest common factor, and it there-

† Such a field $\mathscr{K}'$ certainly exists, since we may adjoin all the roots of $f(X) = 0$ and then all the roots of $g(X) = 0$ to $\mathscr{K}$ by a finite succession of simple algebraic extensions.

‡ If an equation $f(X) = 0$ with coefficients in a field $\mathscr{K}$ of characteristic zero is irreducible, then its roots (in a suitable extension of $\mathscr{K}$) are all distinct; for otherwise $f(X)$ and its derivative $f'(X)$ would have a non-constant common factor in $\mathscr{K}[X]$, thus contradicting the irreducibility of $f(X)$.

fore belongs to $\mathscr{K}(\theta)[X]$. Thus $\beta_1 \in \mathscr{K}(\theta)$, i.e. $\eta_2 \in \mathscr{K}(\theta)$. But then $\eta_1 = \theta - k\eta_2 \in \mathscr{K}(\theta)$; and therefore $\mathscr{K}(\eta_1, \eta_2) \subset \mathscr{K}(\theta)$. On the other hand, since $\theta = \eta_1 + k\eta_2$, $\theta \in \mathscr{K}(\eta_1, \eta_2)$; and therefore $\mathscr{K}(\theta) \subset \mathscr{K}(\eta_1, \eta_2)$. The two fields $\mathscr{K}(\theta)$ and $\mathscr{K}(\eta_1, \eta_2)$ are accordingly the same, and this proves the required result.

3. The function field K_C of an irreducible curve C

We now return to the geometry of $S_2(K)$, with the complex field as ground field; and once again we denote by C an irreducible curve with equation $f(X, Y) = 0$. The function field K_C of the curve has already been defined in Chapter III, § 2.4, its elements being the classes $\{F/G\}$ of rational functions of X and Y which are all congruent modulo $f(X, Y)$ in the sense there defined. We have seen, moreover, that if ξ and η denote the particular congruence classes $\{X\}$ and $\{Y\}$, then $f(\xi, \eta) = 0$, and (ξ, η) is a transcendental (generic) point of C. This last result is of great importance, for it links the concept of the function field of a curve to the abstract theory of algebraic extension of fields outlined in § 2.1 of the present chapter, thus enabling us to apply powerful algebraic methods in a very direct way to the invariantive geometry of algebraic curves.

One, at least, of ξ and η must be transcendental over K, since ξ and η generate the function field as an extension of K, and we shall suppose that ξ is transcendental. This means simply that we assume that C is not a line $X = c$. Then η is a root of the equation $f(\xi, Y) = 0$ for Y, and it is therefore algebraic over $K(\xi)$. But since every element of K_C is a rational function of ξ and η over K, and therefore equally a rational function of η over $K(\xi)$, we now have exactly the situation presupposed in Theorem 1, with $K(\xi)$ as $\mathscr{K}$ and K_C as the extension field $\mathscr{K}(\eta)$. Furthermore, since ξ is transcendental over K, and therefore behaves in the same way as an indeterminate, $K(\xi)$ is isomorphic with the field of all rational functions in a single indeterminate with complex coefficients. The structure of the function field K_C may accordingly be described in the following terms.

THEOREM 2. *The function field K_C of any irreducible algebraic curve C, given by an equation $f(X, Y) = 0$ which is not of the form $X - c = 0$, is isomorphic over K with the simple algebraic extension $K(\xi, \eta)$, determined by the equation $f(\xi, Y) = 0$, of the field $K(\xi)$ of rational functions over K in a single indeterminate ξ.*

Adopting the convenient model $K(\xi, \eta)$ of K_C, where ξ, η are the rational functions $\{X\}$, $\{Y\}$ on C, we can readily infer a number of important properties of the function field.

By § 2.2, Property 1, it follows that *if the degree of $f(X, Y)$ in Y is n, then every element ζ of $K(\xi, \eta)$ has a unique representation of the form*

$$\zeta = a_0(\xi) + a_1(\xi)\eta + \ldots + a_{n-1}(\xi)\eta^{n-1},$$

where the $a_i(\xi)$ are all in $K(\xi)$.

By § 2.2, Property 2, it follows that *every element ζ of $K(\xi, \eta)$ is algebraic over $K(\xi)$ and satisfies a unique irreducible K-equation $g(\xi, \zeta) = 0$, of degree at most n in ζ.* This last result may also be expressed by saying that ξ and ζ are algebraically dependent over K. We say, generally, that *two elements α and β of an extension of $\mathcal{K}$ are algebraically dependent over $\mathcal{K}$* if and only if there exists a $\mathcal{K}$-polynomial $g(X, Y)$ such that $g(\alpha, \beta) = 0$. If one such polynomial exists, then, provided that α and β are not both in $\mathcal{K}$, there is an irreducible $\mathcal{K}$-polynomial, unique to within a factor in $\mathcal{K}$, with the same property; and every $\mathcal{K}$-polynomial $g(X, Y)$ such that $g(\alpha, \beta) = 0$ has this polynomial as a factor. (Cf. Theorem 2, p. 60.)

THEOREM 3. *If ξ' and η' are any two elements of a simple algebraic extension $K(\xi, \eta)$ of the field $K(\xi)$, where ξ is an indeterminate, then ξ' and η' are algebraically dependent over K.*

Proof. By the result just inferred from Property 2, there exist unique irreducible K-polynomials $F(X, X')$ and $G(X, Y')$, in the indeterminates X, X', Y', such that

$$F(\xi, \xi') = 0 \quad \text{and} \quad G(\xi, \eta') = 0. \tag{1}$$

Now $F(X, X')$ and $G(X, Y')$ have no non-constant common factor in $K[X, X', Y']$; and also (if we exclude the trivial case in which ξ' or η' is an element of K) the two polynomials are each of positive degree in X, so that their X-resultant is a non-zero polynomial $g(X', Y')$ in X' and Y'. In virtue of (1), however, $F(X, \xi')$ and $G(X, \eta')$ have a common factor $X - \xi$; and therefore $g(\xi', \eta') = 0$. Thus ξ' and η' are algebraically dependent over K.

COROLLARY 1. *If one, at least, of ξ' and η' is transcendental over K, then ξ' and η' satisfy a unique irreducible K-equation $h(X', Y') = 0$.*

COROLLARY 2. *In the case specified in Corollary 1, the subfield $K(\xi', \eta')$ of $K(\xi, \eta)$ is isomorphic over K with the function field $K_{C'}$ of the curve C' for which (ξ', η') is a generic point.*

This follows from Theorem 5, p. 63.

4. Birational correspondence

Up to the present we have been looking upon the curve C as the datum, and the field K_C as an algebraic adjunct to the curve. But now that we have seen how to characterize the algebraic structure of K_C in a simple and yet general manner, by establishing an isomorphism between K_C and an extension $K(\xi, \eta)$ of K such that ξ is transcendental over K while ξ and η satisfy the equation $f(X, Y) = 0$ of C, we are ready to carry out the programme, already outlined in § 1 of this chapter, of treating the field itself as the datum and every curve for which it is the function field as a geometrical model of it. In order to emphasize the primacy of the field over all the individual curves which represent it, we shall now denote it by a neutral symbol Σ.

The same field Σ has infinitely many pairs of generators (ξ, η) over K, each pair corresponding to a curve of the field, and in this section we shall discuss the geometrical relationship between any two curves obtained from the field in this way.

Let us therefore take a field Σ which is the function field K_C of some irreducible curve C, given by an equation $f(X, Y) = 0$. Then $\Sigma = K(\xi, \eta)$, where (ξ, η) is a generic point of C. If (ξ', η') is any other pair of generators of Σ over K, one at least of these must be transcendental. Thus, by Theorem 3 and its corollaries, ξ' and η' are algebraically dependent over K, and (ξ', η') is a generic point of a curve C' with function field $K_{C'}$ isomorphic with Σ. As we shall see shortly, different pairs of generators of Σ do not necessarily yield different curves, but nevertheless we do obtain infinitely many curves, all belonging to the field Σ, and we shall refer to these curves as the *curves of Σ* or the *projective models of Σ*. Any one of the curves can be taken as the initial curve C which determines the field, to within isomorphism over K, and so determines the entire family of curves.

Now suppose that C and C' are any two curves of Σ, with equations $f(X, Y) = 0$ and $f'(X, Y) = 0$ and generic points (ξ, η) and (ξ', η') respectively, ξ and ξ' each being transcendental over K. Since $K(\xi, \eta) = K(\xi', \eta')$, we have the relations

$$\xi' = \phi(\xi, \eta), \quad \eta' = \psi(\xi, \eta), \tag{1}$$

and
$$\xi = \phi'(\xi', \eta'), \quad \eta = \psi'(\xi', \eta'), \tag{2}$$

where ϕ, ψ, ϕ', ψ' are all rational functions over K. Furthermore,

$\Sigma \cong K_C$ and $\Sigma \cong K_{C'}$, by the correspondences defined by $\xi \leftrightarrow \{X\}$, $\eta \leftrightarrow \{Y\}$ on C and $\xi' \leftrightarrow \{X\}$, $\eta' \leftrightarrow \{Y\}$ on C' respectively.

Suppose next that $\mathscr{P}$ is any place on C, represented by a transcendental point $(X(u), Y(u))$ with coordinates in $K|u|$. Then this point has a minimum field of definition

$$H_u = K(X(u), Y(u)) \subset K|u|;$$

and, since (ξ, η) and $(X(u), Y(u))$ are both generic points for C, there exists (by Theorem 4, p. 62) an isomorphism τ between Σ and H_u such that $\xi \leftrightarrow X(u)$ and $\eta \leftrightarrow Y(u)$. To the elements ξ' and η' of Σ there will now correspond, in this isomorphism, elements $X'(u)$ and $Y'(u)$ of H_u such that

$$X'(u) = \phi(X(u), Y(u)), \qquad Y'(u) = \psi(X(u), Y(u)), \qquad (3)$$

and $\quad X(u) = \phi'(X'(u), Y'(u)), \qquad Y(u) = \psi'(X'(u), Y'(u)); \qquad (4)$

and since $f'(\xi', \eta') = 0$, we also have $f'(X'(u), Y'(u)) = 0$. Thus any place $\mathscr{P}$ on C, given by $(X(u), Y(u))$, gives rise to a unique place $\mathscr{P}'$ on C', given by $(X'(u), Y'(u))$; and in the same way $\mathscr{P}'$ on C' gives rise to $\mathscr{P}$ on C. We therefore have a $(1, 1)$ correspondence, given by equations (3) and (4), between the places on C and those on C'. Such a $(1, 1)$ correspondence, representable in terms of rational functions, is said to be a *birational correspondence*. We note, incidentally, that the subfields $H_u = K(X(u), Y(u))$ and $H'_u = K(X'(u), Y'(u))$ of $K|u|$ are identical by virtue of equations (3) and (4).

We now sum up the conclusions reached so far in a theorem.

THEOREM 4. *If C and C' are any two irreducible plane curves with the same function field Σ (or with function fields that are isomorphic over K) then there exists a birational correspondence, given by equations of the form (3) and (4), between the curves which makes every place on either of them correspond to a unique place on the other.*

By putting $u = 0$ in equations (3) and (4), we see that the birational correspondence between C and C' possesses a secondary interpretation as a correspondence between ground points, since the centres P, P' of any two corresponding places $\mathscr{P}$, $\mathscr{P}'$ are connected by the equations

$$X' = \phi(X, Y), \qquad Y' = \psi(X, Y), \qquad (5)$$

and $\quad X = \phi'(X', Y'), \qquad Y = \psi'(X', Y'). \qquad (6)$

Unlike the correspondence between places, however, the correspondence between ground points is only $(1, 1)$ *in general.* If P is an s-fold point of C ($s > 1$) there may be as many as s places on C at P. These places may all transform into places on C' with the same centre P' (in which case P and P' are corresponding points of the curves) or they may transform into places some of which have different centres. In the latter case there is clearly no single point of C' which corresponds to P on C. The transform of a point (X, Y) of C can, of course, only fail to be uniquely determined when the rational functions ϕ and ψ in equations (5) both assume the indeterminate form $0/0$ at the point in question.

The equations $f(X, Y) = 0$ and $f'(X, Y) = 0$ of C and C' are evidently transformed into each other by the substitutions (5) and (6).

All the curves of a given field Σ being birationally equivalent, we now look upon Σ (defined to within isomorphism over K) as defining an *aggregate of birationally equivalent curves*. Now the field Σ that we have been considering so far was introduced as the function field K_C of some curve C, and it is evident that we cannot take for Σ a completely arbitrary field. Σ must, in fact, be an extension of the ground field K which possesses at least one pair of generators (ξ, η) such that ξ is transcendental over K and η is algebraic over $K(\xi)$; and it follows from what has been said above that every field which satisfies this condition defines an aggregate of curves. We shall say that any such field is a *one-dimensional algebraic function field*, or a field of the type $\mathscr{A}_1(K)$. An extreme case of the algebraic function field is $K(\xi)$ itself, for every element of $K(\xi)$ is algebraic over $K(\xi)$; and we shall see that this field defines a particularly important aggregate of birationally equivalent curves, namely the aggregate of *rational curves*.

If Σ is a field $\mathscr{A}_1(K)$, every pair of generators (ξ, η) of Σ over K yields a generic point (ξ, η) of a curve of the field. We must now ask whether it is possible for Σ to possess two pairs of generators (ξ, η) and (ξ', η') which determine generic points of the same curve C of Σ. For this to be possible, Σ must possess an automorphism over K, namely the self-correspondence given by $\xi \leftrightarrow \xi'$, $\eta \leftrightarrow \eta'$. This follows from Theorem 4, p. 62. Conversely, if Σ has an automorphism over K, then every curve of C possesses a corresponding birational self-transformation. As it happens, function fields for which there exists a non-identical automorphism over K are exceptional—though the exceptions are both interesting and important—and this means that only curves of certain special types admit of non-identical birational transformation into themselves. Plainly, the field $K(\xi)$ of rational functions in an indeterminate ξ possesses a triple infinity of automorphisms σ, arising from the homographic substitutions

$$\xi \to \frac{a\xi+b}{c\xi+d} \quad (a,b,c,d \in K; \; ad-bc \neq 0);$$

and the curves with function fields isomorphic with $K(\xi)$—the rational curves—each possess a triple infinity of birational self-transformations. For the moment, this rather extreme case of a field Σ with automorphisms over K may serve to illustrate the particular point which we have in mind.

5. Parametrizations of the field Σ

Suppose, now, that we take some field $\mathscr{A}_1(K)$, which we denote once again by Σ, and that $[C]$ is the aggregate of (irreducible) curves C of S_2 which have function fields isomorphic with Σ.

DEFINITION. By a *parametrization of* Σ we understand a mapping, isomorphic over K, of Σ on to a subfield H_u of the field $K|u|$ of formal power series in u, this subfield being required to be *minimal* in the sense that it cannot be derived from any other subfield $\bar{H}_u$ by a substitution $u \to \phi(u)$ of index greater than unity.

Plainly, if $(X(u), Y(u))$ is a generating pair of elements of H_u, and if C is the curve of Σ with $(X(u), Y(u))$ as a generic point, then $(X(u), Y(u))$ is a representation of a definite place $\mathscr{P}$ on C; and conversely, if $(X(u), Y(u))$ is any minimal representation† of a place $\mathscr{P}$ on any curve C of Σ, then the correspondence between elements of Σ and rational functions on C (evaluated for $X = X(u)$, $Y = Y(u)$) yields a parametrization of Σ.

If Σ possesses no non-identical automorphism over K, then a parametrization τ of Σ evidently determines a unique place $\mathscr{P}$ on each curve C of the field, and in fact it can be thought of in this case as a *place on the aggregate of curves* $[C]$ or a *place on* Σ. In the contrary case, however, in which the correspondence between generating pairs of elements of Σ and curves C is not one-one, the parametrization τ only determines a unique place on a particular curve C when we prescribe a definite choice of the isomorphic mapping of Σ on to the function field K_C, that is to say a definite choice of ξ and η in Σ for a generic point (ξ, η) of C.

† By a 'minimal representation of a place' we mean, of course, a minimal quasi-branch $\bar{\alpha}^{(1)}$; cf. p. 69.

Now that we have introduced the idea of a parametrization of the field Σ we are able to associate an *order* with every element of Σ, and so bring to bear on the present discussion of the function field the important theorems on orders of power series already proved in earlier chapters.

DEFINITION. The *order* of any element ζ of Σ, relative to a minimal parametrization τ, is the order of the power series in H_u that corresponds to ζ.

THEOREM 5. *Let C be any curve of the field Σ, and (if Σ possesses non-trivial automorphisms over K) let a particular isomorphism between Σ and K_C be prescribed. Then any minimal parametrization τ of Σ defines a unique place $\mathscr{P}$ on C; and the order of any element ζ of Σ with respect to τ is equal to the order of the corresponding rational function on C at the place $\mathscr{P}$.*

Proof. It only remains for us to prove the last statement about the two orders. Consider, then, a curve C of the set $[C]$, with a generic point (ξ, η) such that the (prescribed) isomorphic mapping of Σ on to K_C maps ξ on $\{X\}$ and η on $\{Y\}$. If $\zeta = \chi(\xi, \eta)$, then ζ is mapped on $\{\chi(X, Y)\}$. Now the parametrization τ determines a unique place $\mathscr{P} = (X(u), Y(u))$ on C, and the order of the rational function $\{\chi(X, Y)\}$ at the place $\mathscr{P}$ is $O(\chi(X(u), Y(u)))$, in accordance with the definition on p. 91. But $O(\chi(X(u), Y(u)))$ is also the order of $\zeta = \chi(\xi, \eta)$ relative to τ, as defined above; and the theorem is accordingly proved.

The order of an element ζ of Σ was defined above as its order relative to a minimal parametrization of Σ; but since selecting such a parametrization amounts to the same thing as determining a place $\mathscr{P}$ on any chosen curve C of Σ, we can refer equally well to the *order of ζ at a place $\mathscr{P}$ on a curve C of Σ*—and this is the mode of expression that we shall usually adopt. We may note, further, that the order of ζ at $\mathscr{P}$ on C is the same as the order of ζ at the place $\mathscr{P}'$ corresponding to $\mathscr{P}$ on any birational transform of C (which may possibly be C itself). This is so because the correspondence $\mathscr{P} \leftrightarrow \mathscr{P}'$ was defined, in § 4, by reference to a single parametrization of the field Σ.

We proved in an earlier chapter (Theorem 6, p. 91) that, if χ is any rational function on an irreducible curve C, then $\sum_{\mathscr{P}} O_{\mathscr{P}}(\chi) = 0$, the summation extending over all places $\mathscr{P}$ on C. It is convenient here to reformulate this same result in slightly different terms.

COROLLARY. *If C is any curve of the field Σ, then the sum of the orders of any element ζ of Σ at all places on C is zero: in symbols,*
$$\sum_{\mathscr{P}} O_{\mathscr{P}}(\zeta) = 0.$$

Note. Throughout the present section we have allowed for the possibility that, when C is a curve of Σ, there may exist more than one isomorphism between Σ and K_C. Since the intervention of automorphisms of the field Σ may at first seem confusing, it may help to clarify the situation if we take a simple example. Suppose, then, that C is the curve $Y^2 = X^3$. This curve is rational, and Σ can be taken to be the field $K(t)$ of all rational functions in an indeterminate t. One mapping of Σ on K_C is obtained by making $\xi = t^2$ and $\eta = t^3$ correspond to the rational functions $\{X\}$ and $\{Y\}$ on C, and another one is obtained by making $\xi' = (t+1)^2$ and $\eta' = (t+1)^3$ correspond to $\{X\}$ and $\{Y\}$. The associated automorphism of Σ is, of course, that defined by $t \longleftrightarrow t+1$. The element $\zeta = t$ of Σ corresponds in the first case to $\{Y/X\}$ and in the second case to $\{(Y-X)/X\}$. One parametrization of Σ is defined by replacing t by u in each element $f(t)$ of Σ and then expanding the rational function $f(u)$ as a formal power series $\bar{f}(u)$. In the first mapping, this parametrization determines the place (u^2, u^3) on C, with centre $(0, 0)$; and in the second, it determines the place $((1+u)^2, (1+u)^3)$, with centre $(1, 1)$. At each of these places, ζ has the same order 1.

6. Unirational correspondence

If Σ is a field $\mathscr{A}_1(K)$, and ξ and η are any two elements of Σ which generate this field over K, then, as we have seen, the point (ξ, η) defines a curve C of Σ. But now suppose that instead of a pair of generators of Σ we take an arbitrary pair of elements ξ' and η' of Σ, subject only to the restriction that at least one of them is transcendental over K. These elements generate a subfield $\Sigma' \equiv K(\xi', \eta')$ of Σ which may or may not be Σ itself. Since $K \subset \Sigma' \subset \Sigma$, and the degree of transcendence (see Appendix A, § 11) of Σ over K, and also that of Σ' over K, is unity, it follows that Σ is algebraic over Σ'. Also $\Sigma = K(\xi, \eta) = \Sigma'(\xi, \eta)$, and therefore, by Property 4 of § 2.2, Σ is a simple algebraic extension of Σ'. We denote $\Sigma : \Sigma'$ by m.

Since $\Sigma' \equiv K(\xi', \eta')$ is an $\mathscr{A}_1(K)$, (ξ', η') is a generic point of an irreducible curve C' which has Σ' as its function field. We say that this curve C' is *subordinate to the field* Σ; and our next task will be to investigate more closely the nature of the relationship which exists between any two curves such as C and C'.

We note, first of all, that the relationship in question can be described in a somewhat less abstract manner. Since

$$\xi', \eta' \in \Sigma = K(\xi, \eta),$$

there exist relations

$$\xi' = \phi(\xi, \eta), \quad \eta' = \psi(\xi, \eta), \tag{1}$$

where ϕ and ψ are rational functions over K; and we may accordingly say that C' is derived from C by the *unirational transformation*

$$X' = \phi(X, Y), \quad Y' = \psi(X, Y), \tag{2}$$

or that equations (2) define a *unirational correspondence* between C and C'. A useful example to bear in mind during the discussion which follows is that in which $\xi' = \xi$, $\eta' = 0$; for in this case the correspondence amounts simply to projection of C on to the axis OX from Y_∞. Then, if C is a curve of order n which does not pass through Y_∞, each point of C has a unique image point on OX, while each point of OX (with a finite number of exceptions) has n distinct image points on C.

Unirational transformations, like the birational transformations already considered in § 4, are best thought of as being primarily transformations of places into places. It is immediately apparent that, if we substitute for X and Y in equations (2) the power series $X(u)$ and $Y(u)$ which occur in a representation of any place $\mathscr{P}$ on C, we obtain a representation $(X'(u), Y'(u))$ of a uniquely defined place $\mathscr{P}'$ on C'; and the centres of the places (which we may assume to be finite points) then correspond also by equations (2). But since we do not have in the present case, as we did for the birational transformation, an explicit inverse of the forward transformation (2), it is by no means obvious how many places $\mathscr{P}$ will be transformed into any prescribed place $\mathscr{P}'$, or even that there will always be such places. What can in fact be shown to happen is that, for every choice of $\mathscr{P}'$, there is a set of m places $\mathscr{P}$, distinct or otherwise, which are transformed into $\mathscr{P}'$. In other words, *the unirational transformation* (1) *of C into C' determines an* $(m, 1)$ *correspondence* $\mathscr{P} \leftrightarrow \mathscr{P}'$ *between places on the two curves, m being the degree of K_C over $K_{C'}$*. There is also an $(m, 1)$ correspondence $P \leftrightarrow P'$ between ground points of C and C', but this correspondence, as is evident from what we already know about the particular case of the birational transformation (i.e. the case $m = 1$ of the unirational transformation) is only $(m, 1)$ *in general*.

EXERCISE. Verify that the above conception of a correspondence between places is legitimate, by showing that substitutionally equivalent representations correspond, in both directions, to substitutionally equivalent representations.

We shall now examine the nature of the correspondence $\mathscr{P} \leftrightarrow \mathscr{P}'$ in some detail. The central problem is, of course, to find a way of determining all the places $\mathscr{P}$ on C which transform into any given place $\mathscr{P}'$ on C'.

Let us suppose, then, that the place $\mathscr{P}'$ has been fixed, and that a definite minimal representation $(X'(u), Y'(u))$ of it has been selected. We shall show first of all that a place $\mathscr{P}$ transforms into $\mathscr{P}'$ if and only if it has a representation, which may be fractional,† which is carried by the transformation (2) into the particular integral representation $(X'(u), Y'(u))$ of $\mathscr{P}'$. To do so, we consider a place $\mathscr{P}$ on C, given by a minimal (integral) representation $(X(u), Y(u))$. The representation determined by (2) is then $(\phi(X(u), Y(u)), \psi(X(u), Y(u)))$, and it represents $\mathscr{P}'$ if and only if there exists a regular substitution $u \to s(u)$ and a positive integer r such that

$$\phi(X(s(u)), Y(s(u))) = X'(u^r),$$
and
$$\psi(X(s(u)), Y(s(u))) = Y'(u^r).$$

$\mathscr{P}$ therefore transforms into $\mathscr{P}'$ if and only if it has a representation, namely $(X(s(u^{1/r})), Y(s(u^{1/r})))$, which is transformed by (2) into $(X'(u), Y'(u))$.

Our problem is now reduced to that of finding all the representations $(X(u), Y(u))$, fractional as well as integral, such that

$$\phi(X(u), Y(u)) = X'(u) \quad \text{and} \quad \psi(X(u), Y(u)) = Y'(u),$$

where $(X'(u), Y'(u))$ is a given minimal representation; and we shall next show that this problem has precisely m solutions.

Since $(X(u), Y(u))$ and $(X'(u), Y'(u))$ are transcendental points of C and C' respectively, we have the following isomorphisms over K:

$$\Sigma = K(\xi, \eta) \cong K(X(u), Y(u)) = H_u$$
and
$$\Sigma' = K(\xi', \eta') \cong K(X'(u), Y'(u)) = H'_u.$$

We already know that Σ is a simple algebraic extension, of degree m, of Σ'; and in order to determine the unknown transcendental point $(X(u), Y(u))$ we need to extend the isomorphism $\Sigma' \cong H'_u$ to an isomorphism between Σ and a suitably constructed simple algebraic extension H_u of H'_u. As H'_u is a subfield of the algebraically closed field $K^*|u|$, any desired algebraic extension of it

---

† By contrast with birational transformations of one curve into another (cf. p. 122), the theory of unirational transformations involves the systematic use of redundant place representations, and, as a counterpart to this, the use also of fractional place representations in $K^*|u|$. The significance of the latter will be apparent from the context.

may be carried out within $K^*|u|$; and we shall now show that there are just m extensions that satisfy the requirements of the problem, and that each of them leads to a place $\mathscr{P}$ which is transformed into $\mathscr{P}'$.

Since Σ is a simple algebraic extension of Σ' of degree m, it possesses a generating element ζ over Σ' which satisfies a minimum equation

$$G(\xi', \eta'; z) \equiv \sum_{i=0}^{m} C_i(\xi', \eta')z^i = 0, \qquad (3)$$

where $C_i(\xi', \eta') \in K(\xi', \eta')$ $(i = 0, 1, ..., m)$ and $C_m(\xi', \eta') \neq 0$. Every element χ of Σ can be expressed, in one and only one way, in the form

$$\chi = \sum_{i=0}^{m-1} Q_i(\xi', \eta')\zeta^i, \quad Q_i(\xi', \eta') \in K(\xi', \eta'). \qquad (4)$$

In particular,

$$\xi = \sum_{i=0}^{m-1} A_i(\xi', \eta')\zeta^i \quad \text{and} \quad \eta = \sum_{i=0}^{m-1} B_i(\xi', \eta')\zeta^i.$$

Since equation (3) is irreducible over Σ', it follows, by the isomorphism $\Sigma' \cong H'_u$, that the equation

$$G(X'(u), Y'(u); z) \equiv \sum_{i=0}^{m} C_i(X'(u), Y'(u))z^i = 0 \qquad (5)$$

is irreducible over H'_u. The required extension of the isomorphism $\Sigma' \cong H'_u$ to $\Sigma \cong H_u$ can be effected by taking for H_u any field $H'_u(Z(u))$, where $Z(u)$ is a root, in $K^*|u|$, of equation (5); and it can only be effected in this way. Equation (5) has m roots $Z_j(u)$ $(j = 1, ..., m)$, and each of these defines a field $H_u^{(j)} = H'_u(Z_j(u))$ which is isomorphic with Σ in such a way that any element χ of Σ, given by (4), corresponds to the element of $H_u^{(j)}$ given by

$$\sum_{i=0}^{m-1} Q_i(X'(u), Y'(u))(Z_j(u))^i.$$

In this isomorphism, ξ and η will correspond respectively to elements

$$X_j(u) = \sum_{i=0}^{m-1} A_i(X'(u), Y'(u))(Z_j(u))^i$$

and

$$Y_j(u) = \sum_{i=0}^{m-1} B_i(X'(u), Y'(u))(Z_j(u))^i.$$

Since $f(\xi, \eta) = 0$, it follows that $f(X_j(u), Y_j(u)) = 0$, so that $(X_j(u), Y_j(u))$ represents a place $\mathscr{P}_j$ on C. And further, from the relations

$$\xi' = \phi(\xi, \eta) \quad \text{and} \quad \eta' = \psi(\xi, \eta)$$

we can infer that

$$X'(u) = \phi(X_j(u), Y_j(u)) \quad \text{and} \quad Y'(u) = \psi(X_j(u), Y_j(u)),$$

i.e. that each of the places $\mathscr{P}_j$ on C transforms into $\mathscr{P}'$ on C'.

The m representations $(X_j(u), Y_j(u))$ derived from the representation $(X'(u), Y'(u))$ by the above procedure are necessarily all different. Since $\Sigma = \Sigma'(\zeta) = K(\xi, \eta)$, ζ is expressible as a rational function over K of ξ and η; and therefore $Z_j(u)$ is expressible as a rational function over K of $X_j(u)$ and $Y_j(u)$. If, now, we had $X_j(u) = X_k(u)$ and $Y_j(u) = Y_k(u)$, it would follow that

$$Z_j(u) = Z_k(u);$$

and this is impossible since equation (5), being irreducible over H'_u, must have distinct roots.

But although the m representations $(X_j(u), Y_j(u))$ are all different, it still does not follow that the places $\mathscr{P}_j$ on C which they determine are all distinct, for two or more of the representations might be substitutionally equivalent. We shall prove first of all in this connexion that *the set of places $\mathscr{P}'$ for which the m associated places $\mathscr{P}_1, ..., \mathscr{P}_m$ are not all different is certainly finite*; and we shall do so by showing that, except possibly for a finite number of places $\mathscr{P}'$, the m places $\mathscr{P}_j$ have distinct centres.

In equation (3), which determines Σ as an extension of Σ', the coefficients $C_i(\xi', \eta')$ are rational functions over K of ξ' and η'; but we can clearly arrange matters, by multiplying the equation by a suitably chosen factor in $K[\xi', \eta']$, so that these coefficients are K-polynomials in ξ' and η'. Then the discriminant of (3) is also a K-polynomial in ξ' and η', $D(\xi', \eta')$ say; and, since (3) is irreducible, $D(\xi', \eta') \neq 0$. The discriminant $D(X'(u), Y'(u))$ of equation (5) is likewise different from zero.

Now
$$\sum_{i=0}^{m} C_i(X'(u), Y'(u))(Z_j(u))^i = 0 \quad (j = 1, ..., m),$$

and the C_i are all polynomials. It follows that, as long as the centre (a', b') of $\mathscr{P}'$ is a finite point, we may substitute 0 for u in this equation, thus obtaining a relation

$$\sum_{i=0}^{m} C_i(a', b')(c_j)^i = 0 \quad (j = 1, ..., m),$$

where $c_j = Z_j(0)$.

Suppose, then, that $\mathscr{P}'$ is chosen on C' in such a way that (i) it has a finite centre, and (ii) its centre does not lie on the curve

$D(X, Y) = 0$. Then the discriminant of the equation $G(a', b'; z) = 0$ is different from zero, and consequently the coefficient $C_0(a', b')$, which is a factor of the discriminant, is also different from zero. The equation therefore has m distinct finite roots $c_1, ..., c_m$. These roots, by what we have shown immediately above, are the initial terms of the series $Z_1(u), ..., Z_m(u)$ in $K^*|u|$.

If, now, two of the places $\mathscr{P}_j$ corresponding to $\mathscr{P}'$ were to coincide, two of the representations $(X_j(u), Y_j(u))$ would be substitutionally equivalent; and since each $Z_j(u)$ is the same rational function over K of $X_j(u)$ and $Y_j(u)$, two of the series $Z_1(u), ..., Z_m(u)$ would be substitutionally equivalent and would, in particular, have the same initial term. With our choice of $\mathscr{P}'$ this is impossible; and it is readily seen that at most a finite number of choices for $\mathscr{P}'$ on C' have been excluded. There are, in fact, only a finite number of places at infinity on C', and there are also only a finite number of places on C' with centres on the curve $D(X, Y) = 0$, since we know that $D(\xi', \eta') \neq 0$ and C' is therefore not a component of $D(X, Y) = 0$.

We have now shown that to every place $\mathscr{P}'$ on C' there corresponds a set of m places $\{\mathscr{P}_1, ..., \mathscr{P}_m\}$ on C, these places being distinct for all except possibly a finite number of choices of $\mathscr{P}'$. Before stating this conclusion as a formal theorem, we shall make it more precise in one further particular, by establishing a rule which determines the multiplicity of any place $\mathscr{P}$ on C in the set $\{\mathscr{P}_1, ..., \mathscr{P}_m\}$ to which it belongs. We shall show that *if a minimal representation of $\mathscr{P}$ is transformed by the unirational transformation into a representation of redundancy $r \geqslant 1$ of a place on C', then $\mathscr{P}$ is to be counted r times in the set of m places to which it belongs.* In order to do this we shall have to look more closely into the way in which substitutionally equivalent representations can occur in the set $\{(X_j(u), Y_j(u))\}$.

Suppose that two of the m representations which arise from a certain place $\mathscr{P}'$ on C' are equivalent. We may assume, without loss of generality, that $\mathscr{P}'$ has a finite centre and also that its representation is taken in the canonical form

$$(a' + u^\mu, \ b' + b''u^\nu + b'''u^{\nu'} + ...),$$

where $0 < \mu$, $0 < \nu < \nu' < ...$; $b'', b''', ... \neq 0$. We assume further that the equivalent representations are $(X_1(u), Y_1(u))$ and $(X_2(u), Y_2(u))$, arising respectively from roots $Z_1(u)$ and $Z_2(u)$ of equation (5) which are of indices p and q. Then there exists a substitution for the parameter which transforms $(X_1(u), Y_1(u))$ into $(X_2(u), Y_2(u))$, and it must be of the form

$$u^{1/p} \to d_1 u^{1/q} + d_2 u^{2/q} + \ldots \quad (d_1 \neq 0). \tag{6}$$

Since this substitution leaves $(X'(u), Y'(u))$ invariant we have, in the first place,

$$a' + (d_1 u^{1/q} + d_2 u^{2/q} + \ldots)^{p\mu} = a' + u^\mu,$$

that is, $\qquad a' + d_1^{p\mu} u^{p\mu/q} + \text{higher terms} = a' + u^\mu.$

Hence $p\mu/q = \mu$ and $d_1^{p\mu} = 1$, so that $p = q$ and $d_1 = \delta$, where δ is a $p\mu$th root of unity. We have further

$$(\delta u^{1/p} + d_2 u^{2/p} + \ldots)^{p\mu} = u^\mu,$$

that is, $\qquad \delta u^{1/p} + d_2 u^{2/p} + \ldots = \delta' u^{1/p},$

where δ' is also a $p\mu$th root of unity. Hence $\delta' = \delta$ and $d_i = 0$ $(i = 2, 3, \ldots)$. The substitution (6) accordingly has the form

$$u^{1/p} \to \delta u^{1/p} \quad (\delta^{p\mu} = 1).$$

This substitution has to leave $Y'(u)$ invariant as well as $X'(u)$, which means that

$$b' + b'' \delta^{pv} u^v + b''' \delta^{pv'} u^{v'} + \ldots = b' + b'' u^v + b''' u^{v'} + \ldots,$$

that is, $\qquad \delta^{pv} = \delta^{pv'} = \ldots = 1.$

Now, since the representation $(X'(u), Y'(u))$ is proper, the integers $\mu, v, v', \ldots$ have no common factor other than 1; and the equations $\delta^{p\mu} = 1$, $\delta^{pv} = 1$, $\delta^{pv'} = 1, \ldots$ can only be satisfied for $\delta \neq 1$ if $p > 1$ and δ (which we know to be a $p\mu$th root of unity) is in fact a pth root of unity. In this way we obtain p and only p substitutions

$$u^{1/p} \to \delta u^{1/p} \quad (\delta^p = 1)$$

which leave the representation $(X'(u), Y'(u))$ invariant; and from these substitutions we derive a complete cycle of p fractional representations

$$X_h(u) = a + P_h(u^{1/p}), \qquad Y_h(u) = b + Q_h(u^{1/p}) \quad (h = 1, \ldots, p),$$

all corresponding to a single place $\mathscr{P}$ on C. Thus $\mathscr{P}$ accounts for p of the m places $\mathscr{P}_1, \ldots, \mathscr{P}_m$ which transform into $\mathscr{P}'$. But since we have, by the given unirational transformation,

$$(a + P_h(u^{1/p}), \, b + Q_h(u^{1/p})) \to (X'(u), Y'(u)),$$

where the left-hand representation would be made integral by the substitution $u^{1/p} \to u$† and the right-hand representation is already integral, we have equally well

$$(a+P_h(u),\ b+Q_h(u)) \to (X'(u^p),\ Y'(u^p));$$

and in the latter instance the left-hand representation is minimal and the right-hand one is of redundancy p. This is sufficient to complete the identification of the multiplicity of $\mathscr{P}$ in the set $\{\mathscr{P}_1,...,\mathscr{P}_m\}$ with the redundancy of any representation of $\mathscr{P}'$ that is derived by the transformation (2) from a minimal representation of $\mathscr{P}$.

We now bring together in a comprehensive theorem the various important results that have been established in the course of the discussion which occupies the preceding seven pages.

THEOREM 6 (*The Unirational Transformation Theorem*). *Any unirational transformation of an irreducible curve C into another irreducible curve C' sets up an $(m, 1)$ correspondence $\mathscr{P} \leftrightarrow \mathscr{P}'$ between C and C', m being the degree $K_C : K_{C'}$ of the function field of C over that of C'. More precisely, the correspondence has the following properties*:

(i) *To every place $\mathscr{P}$ on C there corresponds a unique place $\mathscr{P}'$ on C'.*

(ii) *To every place $\mathscr{P}'$ on C' there correspond m places $\mathscr{P}$, distinct or otherwise, on C.*

(iii) *For all but possibly a finite number of the places $\mathscr{P}'$ on C', the m corresponding places $\mathscr{P}$ on C are distinct.*

(iv) *If a place $\mathscr{P}$ on C has a minimal integral representation $(X(u), Y(u))$, and if the representation of $\mathscr{P}'$ derived from this by the equations of the unirational transformation is $(X'(u), Y'(u))$, then the multiplicity of the place $\mathscr{P}$ in the set of m places corresponding to $\mathscr{P}'$ is equal to the redundancy of $(X'(u), Y'(u))$ as a representation of $\mathscr{P}'$.*

7. Irreducible (m, n) correspondences between curves

The full and meticulous proof which we have given of Theorem 6 is amply justified by the fact that this theorem is fundamental to the whole theory of algebraic correspondences between curves. It is essential in particular, as we shall shortly see, to the development of the theory of algebraic curves in spaces of arbitrary

---

† Since $Z_h(u) \in K(X_h(u), Y_h(u))$ and $X_h(u),\ Y_h(u) \in H'_u(Z_h(u))$, it may readily be seen that the index of the representation $(X_h(u), Y_h(u))$ is equal to the index of the element $Z_h(u)$ of $K^*|u|$, i.e. the least positive integer p for which $Z_h(u)$ can be written as a power series in $u^{1/p}$.

dimensionality. For the present we only need to explain its relation to the theory of correspondences in general, and to introduce in this connexion the basic technical terms.

The unirational correspondence between C and C' described in Theorem 6 is an instance of what is known as an (*irreducible*) *algebraic* $(m, 1)$ *correspondence* between the two curves or, more precisely, between the places on the curves. A place $\mathscr{P}'$ on C' which is such that the m corresponding places on C are not all distinct is called a *branch place* on C' of the correspondence; and a place $\mathscr{P}$ on C that counts more than once in the set of m such places that correspond to the same place on C' is called a *coincidence place* on C. A branch place $\mathscr{P}'$ is *simple* if only two of the corresponding places $\mathscr{P}$ are coincident. If it is not simple its constitution is defined by the multiplicities of the places that correspond to it.

We may now extend these considerations to the more general concept of an (m, n) correspondence by treating any such correspondence between two curves C and D as the 'product' of a $(1, n)$ correspondence between C and an intermediate curve I and an $(m, 1)$ correspondence between I and D. When this is done, I is referred to as an *image curve of the correspondence*, since its places are in $(1, 1)$ correspondence with the pairs of corresponding places on C and D. We shall now give precision to these ideas by translating them into the language of function fields.

DEFINITION. If the function fields K_C and K_D of two irreducible curves C and D are isomorphic over K to subfields Σ_1 and Σ_2 of a one-dimensional algebraic function field Σ, and if some curve I of Σ is mapped unirationally on C and also on D, then the correspondence $\mathscr{P} \leftrightarrow \mathscr{P}'$, between places on C and places on D, which is such that $\mathscr{P}$ corresponds to $\mathscr{P}'$ if and only if there is a place $\mathscr{Q}$ on I which is mapped on both $\mathscr{P}$ and $\mathscr{P}'$, is said to be an *irreducible algebraic correspondence* between the curves. If $\Sigma : \Sigma_1 = n$ and $\Sigma : \Sigma_2 = m$, the correspondence is said to have *indices* m and n, or to be an (m, n) *correspondence* between C and D.

Suppose, in fact, that C, D, and I have generic points (ξ_1, η_1), (ξ_2, η_2), and (ξ, η). Then $\Sigma_1 = K(\xi_1, \eta_1)$, $\Sigma_2 = K(\xi_2, \eta_2)$, and $\Sigma = K(\xi, \eta)$. Since $\Sigma : \Sigma_1 = n$, I is mapped unirationally on C in such a way that there is a $(1, n)$ correspondence between $\mathscr{P}$ on C and $\mathscr{Q}$ on I. Similarly, there is a $(1, m)$ correspondence between $\mathscr{P}'$ on D and $\mathscr{Q}$ on I. Clearly, then, the correspondence $\mathscr{P} \leftrightarrow \mathscr{Q} \leftrightarrow \mathscr{P}'$ between $\mathscr{P}$ on C and $\mathscr{P}'$ on D is (m, n). As we have already remarked, the curve I—that is to say an arbitrary curve of Σ—is said to be an image curve of the correspondence.

EXAMPLE. If C and D are the axes OX and OY respectively, any irreducible K-equation $F(X,Y) = 0$, of degree m in X and degree n in Y, defines an irreducible (m,n) correspondence between C and D; and the curve $F(X,Y) = 0$ is an image curve I for this correspondence.

The (m,n) correspondence $\mathscr{P} \leftrightarrow \mathscr{P}'$ will have a set $(\mathscr{B}_1)$ of branch places on C, each of which is such that at least one of the n corresponding places on D is a coincidence place, counting multiply in its set of n places; and similarly there will be a set $(\mathscr{B}_2)$ of branch places on D, associated with coincidence places on C. By Theorem 6, the sets $(\mathscr{B}_1)$ and $(\mathscr{B}_2)$ are both finite.

For completeness, we define an irreducible $(0,1)$ correspondence between C and D as a degenerate correspondence $\mathscr{P} \leftrightarrow \mathscr{P}'_0$, such that every place $\mathscr{P}$ on C is associated with the same fixed place $\mathscr{P}'_0$ on D, and there are no further corresponding pairs of places; and we define a $(1,0)$ correspondence similarly.

Finally, we define the *sum of any finite set of irreducible correspondences* between C and D as follows. If $T_1,...,T_s$ are irreducible correspondences between C and D, of indices $(m_1,n_1),...,(m_s,n_s)$, their sum T is the (m,n) correspondence, with $m = \sum_{i=1}^{s} m_i$ and $n = \sum_{i=1}^{s} n_i$, such that to any place $\mathscr{P}$ on C there correspond all the $\sum n_i$ places on D which arise from $\mathscr{P}$ by any of the correspondences T_i, and to any place $\mathscr{P}'$ on D there correspond all the $\sum m_i$ places on C from which $\mathscr{P}'$ arises by any of the T_i. We write, symbolically,

$$T(\mathscr{P}) = \sum_{i=1}^{s} T_i(\mathscr{P}); \quad T^{-1}(\mathscr{P}') = \sum_{i=1}^{s} T_i^{-1}(\mathscr{P}').$$

According to this last definition, we are to envisage the most general algebraic correspondence between C and D as a finite sum of irreducible correspondences between the curves.

8. Correspondences on a curve

In the last two sections we have expressed our argument, for simplicity, in terms of correspondences between two different curves; but the theory is also applicable, of course, to correspondences of a curve with itself or, as we shall say, to *correspondences on a curve C.*

Every birational correspondence of C with itself (if any exists) arises, as we saw in § 4, from an automorphism of the associated field Σ, which carries one generic point (ξ, η) of C in Σ into another generic point (ξ', η') of C in Σ. In a similar way, we see that a unirational $(n, 1)$ correspondence of C with itself arises from an isomorphism τ of Σ with a subfield Σ' of Σ, the index n being the degree $\Sigma : \Sigma'$. Thus, for example, in the case of a rational curve, with $\Sigma = K(u)$, we might take Σ' to be $K(u^2)$ and τ to be the isomorphism arising from the correspondence $u \leftrightarrow u^2$. If we were to choose as C the conic $Y^2 = X$, with generic point (u^2, u), τ would yield the generic point (u^4, u^2) in Σ'; and we would have a $(2, 1)$ correspondence on the conic C, with equations $X' = X^2, Y' = Y^2$.

The general concept of an irreducible (m, n) correspondence on C involves reference to a second curve I, which functions as image curve of the correspondence.   Any two unirational mappings $\mathscr{Q} \to \mathscr{P}$ and $\mathscr{Q} \to \mathscr{P}'$ of I on C define a correspondence on C, consisting of a *forward correspondence* $T : \mathscr{P} \to \{\mathscr{P}'_1, ..., \mathscr{P}'_n\}$ and a *backward correspondence* $T^{-1} : \mathscr{P}' \to \{\mathscr{P}_1, ..., \mathscr{P}_m\}$. The indices n and m are the degrees of the field K_I over its two subfields Σ_1 and Σ_2, on which K_C is mapped by the isomorphisms which define the unirational mappings $\mathscr{Q} \to \mathscr{P}$ and $\mathscr{Q} \to \mathscr{P}'$. The only new feature which we encounter when we consider irreducible (m, n) correspondences on a single curve C instead of between two curves C and D is that there is now an isomorphism between the fields Σ_1 and Σ_2, such that the relevant generic points of C in these fields correspond by this isomorphism.

In addition to its sets $(\mathscr{B}_1)$ and $(\mathscr{B}_2)$ of branch places of T and T^{-1}, an (m, n) correspondence on C has a set $(\mathscr{U})$ of *united places*, each place $\mathscr{U}$ of this set having the property that $(\mathscr{U}, \mathscr{U})$ is a pair of the correspondence.

Having now given the basic definitions, we do not propose to proceed further here with the general theory of correspondences on a curve, especially as this development is largely dependent on the theory of linear series on a curve (to be discussed in Chapter X) and would in any case take us beyond the limits we have set ourselves in this book. Many excellent accounts of the subject exist, such as for example that given by Severi in his *Vorlesungen über algebraische Geometrie* (Leipzig, 1921).

9. Involutions on a curve

Theorem 6, on p. 164, tells us that any unirational $(n, 1)$ correspondence between a curve C and a curve C' puts the individual places on C' in $(1, 1)$ correspondence with certain sets of n places on C, a finite number only of these sets containing coincidences, i.e. places which count more than once in the set to which they belong. We shall now look more closely at the system of all these sets of places on C. Its most obvious characteristic is that it constitutes a separation of all the places on C into mutually exclusive sets, each place belonging to precisely one set, and each set comprising n members (except that a finite number of places count multiply in the sets to which they belong, so that these sets have less than n distinct members). We call such a system of sets of n places an 'involution of order n' on C.

DEFINITION. An *involution of order n* on an irreducible algebraic curve C is the system of sets of n places on C which are mapped on the individual places of a second irreducible curve C' by a uni-rational $(n, 1)$ mapping of C on C'.

If we denote the involution by I_n, and its sets generally by G, we may refer to C' as a *map of the sets G of the involution I_n on C*. Any birational transform of C' is equally a map of I_n. If $n = 1$, I_n reduces to the involution of single places on C, and we may take C itself as the map.

If a place $\mathscr{P}$ counts twice or more in the set G to which it belongs we call it a *double place* or a *multiple place* of I_n. The set of all multiple places of I_n, each counted to multiplicity one less than its multiplicity in I_n, is called the *Jacobian set J* of I_n. We may write symbolically $J = \sum_{\mathscr{P}} (s_{\mathscr{P}} - 1)\mathscr{P}$, where $s_{\mathscr{P}}$ denotes the multiplicity of $\mathscr{P}$ in the set G to which it belongs, and the summation $\sum_{\mathscr{P}}$ extends over all places on C. J may also be interpreted as the set of all double places of I_n, with the convention that an s-fold place is to be counted as the equivalent of $s - 1$ double places. We shall be much concerned with Jacobian sets in Chapter X.

9.1. Rational involutions

We now turn to a special type of involution that is of particular interest and importance, namely the rational involution.

DEFINITION. An involution I_n of sets of n places on a curve C is said to be *rational* if its maps C' are the rational curves of S_2, i.e. if we can take C' to be a line L.

Let I_n be any rational involution on a curve C, with equation $f(X, Y) = 0$, say. Then I_n can be mapped, in particular, on the axis OX, the equations of the unirational transformation of C into OX being of the form

$$X' = \phi(X, Y), \quad Y' = 0,$$

where $\phi(X, Y) \in K(X, Y)$ and $\phi(X, Y)$ defines a non-constant rational function on C. Let us consider any place $\mathscr{P}$ on C, with minimal representation $(X(u), Y(u))$. The corresponding place $\mathscr{P}'$ on OX is given by $X'(u) = \phi(X(u), Y(u))$; and the redundancy of this derived representation is equal to the multiplicity s of $\mathscr{P}$ in the set of n places on C which are transformed into $\mathscr{P}'$ (Theorem 6), i.e. the multiplicity of $\mathscr{P}$ in the set G of the involution to which it belongs. Thus, if we assume that $\mathscr{P}'$ has a finite centre $X = X'_0$, then $\phi(X(u), Y(u)) = X'_0 + a_s u^s + a_{s+1} u^{s+1} + \ldots$; and the order $O_{\mathscr{P}}(\phi - X'_0)$ of the rational function $\{\phi(X, Y) - X'_0\}$ on C at the place $\mathscr{P}$ is therefore s. In other words, the places on C which belong to the set G of I_n which is mapped on the (unique) place on OX at any assigned finite point $X = \lambda$ are those places $\mathscr{P}$ at which $O_{\mathscr{P}}(\phi - \lambda)$ is positive; and for each such place $\mathscr{P}$ the order $O_{\mathscr{P}}(\phi - \lambda)$ gives the multiplicity to which the place is to be counted as a member of the set G. In the same way, as the reader may verify, if $\bar{G}$ is the set of I_n that is mapped on the place at $X = \infty$ on OX, then the places of $\bar{G}$ are those for which $O_{\mathscr{P}}(\phi)$ is negative, and the multiplicity of each such place $\mathscr{P}$ in $\bar{G}$ is $-O_{\mathscr{P}}(\phi)$.

It is convenient to refer to a place on C at which a rational function ψ on C has positive order as a *zero-place of ψ on C* and a place where ψ has negative order as a *pole-place of ψ on C*. We may then say that the sets G of the rational involution I_n that we have been considering are the sets of zero-places of the rational functions $\phi - \lambda$ for all values of λ in K, together with the set of zero-places of $1/\phi$; or, as we may say, the *sets of constant level* of the rational function ϕ on C. Since we began the discussion by postulating an arbitrary unirational transformation of C into OX, it is clear that any non-constant rational function on C may be taken as ϕ. Conversely, therefore, the sets of constant level of any such rational function are the sets of a rational involution, and we can formulate the following theorem.

THEOREM 7. *Every rational involution on an irreducible curve C is the aggregate of sets of constant level of a rational function on C, and every non-constant rational function on C determines a rational involution on C as its aggregate of sets of constant level.*

We shall see later, in Chapter X, that two sets of n places on a curve C do not belong to a common rational involution I_n unless they are specially related, and that the relation of *equivalence* of sets of places on a curve which arises in this way is the basis of a general theory of linear series of sets of places on C. It follows from what we have said that two disjoint sets of n places G_1 and G_2 are equivalent ($G_1 \equiv G_2$) if and only if there is a rational function on C which has G_1 as its set of zero-places and G_2 as its set of pole-places.

So far we have considered involutions only in relation to places; but since every unirational transformation sets up a correspondence between ground points as well as between places we may interpret the involution in terms of sets of points, namely the sets of centres of the places already considered. From this point of view, a rational involution is a system of sets of n points of C; but now a point of C, if it is the centre of several places, may belong exceptionally to more than one set of I_n. If we write

$$\phi(X, Y) = \Phi_1(X, Y)/\Phi_2(X, Y),$$

where Φ_1 and Φ_2 are elements of $K[X, Y]$ with no common factor, then the point-sets of I_n are the sets cut on C—perhaps residually to a fixed set—by the curves of the pencil $\Phi_1(X, Y)-\lambda\Phi_2(X, Y) = 0$, each member of such a point-set being given its appropriate multiplicity as an intersection.

EXAMPLES. (i) If C is a proper conic and V is any point of S_2, the pencil of lines through V determines an I_2 on C if V does not lie on C and an I_1 if V lies on C.

(ii) If C is a curve C^n and V is any point not on C, then the sets of n places on C determined by the lines through V form a rational I_n on C, and the place of contact of any simple tangent to C that passes through V is a double place of I_n.

9.2. Involutions on a rational curve. Lüroth's Theorem

The rational involution, which we have just been examining, is a special type of involution, characterized by the fact that its maps are rational curves. We obtain a second special case of involution if we require the carrier of the involution, i.e. the curve C to which the places comprising the sets of I_n belong, to be a rational curve. This specialization is of interest because it leads us to the very important theorem of Lüroth, to which we devote this concluding section of the present chapter.

We consider, then, a general involution I_n on a rational curve. It is no restriction to take this curve to be a line L, and in particular the line OX. Suppose, therefore, that I_n is an involution on OX, defined by a unirational transformation, with equations

$$X' = \phi(X), \quad Y' = \psi(X) \qquad (\phi(X), \psi(X) \in K(X)), \qquad (1)$$

which carries OX into a curve C' in such a way that the sets of I_n are carried into the individual places on C'. Our first observation is that if we interpret X as a parameter, taking all values in $K \cup \{\infty\}$, equations (1) constitute a rational parametric representation in the sense of Chapter I, § 6, so that C' is a *rational parametric curve*. What we wish to prove is the stronger result that C' is a *rational curve*, that is to say a *birational* transform of a line—a result which has the interesting consequence that every involution on a line is necessarily a rational involution. We shall give two separate statements and proofs of the theorem, stated originally by Lüroth, which embodies the result just alluded to, the first being of a comparatively elementary character, and traditional in the literature, while the second is of a more formal kind.

THEOREM 8 (a) (*Lüroth's Theorem, first version*). *Every involution on a line (or on any rational curve) is rational.*

Proof. Let L be any given line, on which we take a projective parameter t (i.e. an affine coordinate in S_1), and let I_n be any involution of order n on L, defined by a unirational transformation

$$X = p(t)/q(t), \quad Y = r(t)/s(t) \qquad (2)$$

of L into a curve C of the X, Y plane, where $p(t)$, $q(t)$, $r(t)$, and $s(t)$ are elements of $K[t]$, and the fractions $p(t)/q(t)$ and $r(t)/s(t)$ are in their lowest terms. Equations (2) then define an $(n, 1)$ correspondence between L and C, in which the sets of I_n on L correspond to the individual places on C.

Now let us consider the correspondence T on L which is such that two points t and t' correspond if and only if they are both contained in some set† of I_n. The pairs (t, t') which correspond in T therefore satisfy simultaneously the equations

$$u(t, t') \equiv p(t)q(t') - p(t')q(t) = 0$$

and $\qquad v(t, t') \equiv r(t)s(t') - r(t')s(t) = 0;$

† Since I_n is an involution on a line, it makes no difference whether we consider its sets as sets of places or as sets of ground points.

and if the highest common factor in $K[t, t']$ of $u(t, t')$ and $v(t, t')$ is $j(t, t') \equiv (t - t')h(t, t')$, then the equation of T is

$$j(t, t') = 0. \tag{3}$$

Now $j(t, t')$ is of degree n in t and also in t'. For, since the correspondence defined by (2) is $(n, 1)$, the polynomials $p(t), q(t), r(t), s(t)$ are of order n, at most, in t, and therefore the orders of $j(t, t')$ in t and t' are each at most n; and they are not less than n, since T is plainly an (n, n) correspondence. Furthermore, $j(t, t')$ must have the property that, if t_0 is any member of any given set G_0 of I_n, then the roots of $j(t_0, t') = 0$, regarded as an equation in t', give the n points of G_0. In other words, equation (3) must reduce to the same equation for t', whichever of the values of t corresponding to some point of any particular set G of I_n is substituted for the indeterminate t in $j(t, t')$.

Now let us write (3) explicitly as an equation in t':

$$j(t, t') \equiv a_0(t)t'^n + a_1(t)t'^{n-1} + \ldots + a_n(t) = 0.$$

Since the roots vary with the value substituted for t, the coefficients cannot all be independent of t, and we may suppose that the ratio $a_i(t)/a_j(t)$ actually involves t. Then the expression

$$\theta = a_i(t)/a_j(t)$$

defines a rational function of t which takes the same value at all points of any set G of I_n. The sets of constant level of this function therefore have the sets G of I_n as subsets; and since $(j(t, t')$ being of degree n in t) these sets of constant level have at most n elements, they coincide with the sets G. This proves that the involution I_n is rational.

THEOREM 8 (b) (*Lüroth's Theorem, second version*). *If t is an indeterminate, and Σ is any subfield of $K(t)$ which has K as a proper subfield, then there exists an element θ of Σ (transcendental over K) such that $\Sigma = K(\theta)$.*

This purely algebraic form of Lüroth's Theorem asserts that any subfield of $K(t)$ which is a proper extension of K is isomorphic with $K(t)$ itself, that is to say that simple transcendental extension of K allows of no half-way stage. The equivalence between the two versions of Lüroth's Theorem, superficially so dissimilar, comes about in the following manner. Suppose we have an involution I_n on a line L, i.e. an $(n, 1)$ unirational transformation of L into an irreducible curve C. Then there is an isomorphism between a subfield Σ of K_L and K_C, the degree $K_L : \Sigma$ being equal to n. But we know that $K_L \cong K(t)$, where t is an indeterminate; and hence, by Theorem 8 (b), $\Sigma \cong K(\theta) \cong K(t)$. Thus $K_C \cong K(t)$, and therefore C is a rational curve. The involution I_n is therefore rational, as is asserted by Theorem 8 (a).

In order to make the proof of Theorem 8 (b) easier to follow, we begin by stating and proving a lemma.

LEMMA. *If θ and t are both transcendental over K, Σ is a field such that $K(\theta) \subset \Sigma \subset K(t)$, and* (i) *$t$ is algebraic of degree n over Σ,* (ii) *t is algebraic of degree m over $K(\theta)$, and* (iii) *$m \leqslant n$, then $\Sigma = K(\theta)$.*

Proof. Suppose, if possible, that there exists an element ϕ of Σ which does not belong to $K(\theta)$. Then $\phi \in K(t)$, and hence, by (ii)

$$\phi = c_0 + c_1 t + \ldots + c_{m-1} t^{m-1},$$

where $c_i \in K(\theta) \subset \Sigma$ $(i = 0, \ldots, m-1)$. Thus t satisfies a Σ-equation of degree $m-1 < n$, in contradiction to (i); and the lemma is accordingly proved.

Proof of Theorem 8 (b). The proof falls into two parts. In the first we give a construction for the required element θ of Σ, and in the second we verify that this element satisfies the conditions of the lemma.

(a) Let Σ be a subfield of $K(t)$ which has K as a proper subfield. We note, first of all, that t is then algebraic over Σ. For suppose that $\phi = p(t)/q(t)$ is any element of Σ which does not belong to K. Then the equation

$$p(x) - \frac{p(t)}{q(t)} q(x) = 0$$

is a Σ-equation in x which is of non-zero degree; and since t satisfies this equation it is algebraic over Σ. Suppose that the minimum polynomial of t over Σ is

$$F(x) \equiv a_0 + a_1 x + \ldots + a_n x^n,$$

where $a_i \in \Sigma$ and $a_n \neq 0$. By multiplying this polynomial by the least common denominator of the fractions a_i we may change it into a polynomial

$$f(t, x) \equiv b_0 + b_1 x + \ldots + b_n x^n,$$

in which the b_i are elements of $K[t]$, with no common factor involving t, and the *ratios* of the b_i are elements of Σ. These ratios are not all in K, since t is transcendental over K, and we may accordingly assume that b_i/b_j is not in K. Then this element of Σ, which we write in its lowest terms as

$$\theta \equiv b_i(t)/b_j(t) = r(t)/s(t),$$

being a rational function of t, is transcendental over K. We shall now show that it satisfies the conditions of the lemma.

(b) In the first place, the element

$$r(x) - \frac{r(t)}{s(t)} s(x)$$

is an element of $\Sigma[x]$ which becomes zero when t is substituted for x, and it is therefore divisible by the minimum polynomial $F(x)$ of t over Σ; i.e.

$$r(x) - \frac{r(t)}{s(t)} s(x) = G(x)F(x), \quad G(x) \in \Sigma[x].$$

Multiplying this equation by $s(t)$, we have

$$s(t)r(x) - r(t)s(x) = g(t, x)f(t, x), \tag{4}$$

where $g(t, x) \in K(t)[x]$. But $f(t, x)$ has no factor involving t only, and the left-hand side is a polynomial in t, and therefore

$$g(t, x) \in K[t][x] = K[t, x].$$

Now the degrees of $r(t)$ and $s(t)$ can neither of them exceed the degree in t of $f(t, x)$, since $r(t)$ and $s(t)$ are factors in $K[t]$ of the coefficients $b_i(t)$ and $b_j(t)$ of $f(x, t)$. Hence $g(t, x)$ cannot involve t. But the left-hand side of (4) has no factor in t alone and therefore, since it involves t and x symmetrically, no factor in x alone; and this means that $g(t, x)$ is an element of K. Thus equation (4) reduces to the form

$$s(t)r(x) - r(t)s(x) = cf(t, x), \quad c \in K;$$

and this shows that neither the degree of $r(x)$ nor the degree of $s(x)$ can exceed the degree of $F(x)$, that is to say, n. We have now proved that t satisfies an equation

$$r(x) - \theta s(x) = 0$$

over $K(\theta)$ which is of degree $m \leqslant n$ in x. Thus θ satisfies all the conditions of the lemma, and therefore $\Sigma = K(\theta)$. This is the conclusion asserted by Theorem 8 (b), and the theorem is accordingly proved.

NOTES AND EXERCISES ON CHAPTER VII

1. The elements ζ of a simple algebraic extension of $K(X)$ in which the equation $Y^2 = X$ has a root can be exhibited in the form

$$\left. \begin{array}{l} \zeta = \phi_1 + \eta\phi_2 \\ \eta^2 = X \end{array} \right\},$$

where $\phi_1, \phi_2 \in K(X)$. This is, in the first place, a representation of $K(X, \eta)$, but, by virtue of the relation $X = \eta^2$, we may write $K(X, \eta) = K(\eta)$. The required root of $Y^2 = X$ is η.

In $K(\eta)$ we have $\qquad Y^2 - X = (Y - \eta)(Y + \eta),$

the elements η and $-\eta$ being *conjugate elements* of $K(\eta)$; that is to say they correspond in the automorphism $\phi_1 + \eta\phi_2 \leftrightarrow \phi_1 - \eta\phi_2$ of $K(\eta)$.

To verify that $\phi_1 + \eta\phi_2$ is algebraic over $K(X)$, we observe that it is a root of the equation

$$\{Z - (\phi_1 + \eta\phi_2)\}\{Z - (\phi_1 - \eta\phi_2)\} \equiv (Z - \phi_1)^2 - X\phi_2^2 = 0.$$

[*Note.* The fact that the above extension can be expressed as $K(\eta)$, being therefore isomorphic over K with $K(X)$, reflects the *rationality* of the curve with equation $Y^2 = X$.]

2. Proceeding as in Exercise 1, we observe that the extension $K(X, \eta)$ of $K(X)$ in which the equation $Y^3 + X^3 - 1 = 0$ has a root η can be exhibited in the form

$$\left. \begin{array}{l} \zeta = \phi_1 + \eta\phi_2 + \eta^2\phi_3 \\ \eta^3 + X^3 - 1 = 0 \end{array} \right\},$$

where $\phi_1, \phi_2, \phi_3 \in K(X)$; and we have the decomposition

$$Y^3 + X^3 - 1 = (Y - \eta)(Y - \omega\eta)(Y - \omega^2\eta),$$

where ω is a primitive cube root of unity.

The conjugates of ζ are

$$\zeta' = \phi_1 + \omega\eta\phi_2 + \omega^2\eta^2\phi_3 \quad \text{and} \quad \zeta'' = \phi_1 + \omega^2\eta\phi_2 + \omega\eta^2\phi_3;$$

and ζ satisfies the equation over $K(X)$ given by

$$(Z - \zeta)(Z - \zeta')(Z - \zeta'')$$
$$\equiv (Z - \phi_1)^3 - 3(1 - X^3)\phi_2\phi_3(Z - \phi_1) - (1 - X^3)\phi_2^3 - (1 - X^3)^2\phi_3^3 = 0.$$

3. For the equation $Y^3 + X^2Y - 1 = 0$, the above procedure yields at first only the partial decomposition

$$Y^3 + X^2Y - 1 = (Y - \eta)(Y^2 + \eta Y + X^2 + \eta^2)$$

in $K(X, \eta)$, where $\eta^3 + X^2\eta - 1 = 0$; and we have to proceed to a further extension $K(X, \eta, \zeta)$, where $\zeta^2 + \eta\zeta + X^2 + \eta^2 = 0$, to obtain the complete decomposition

$$Y^3 - X^2Y - 1 = (Y - \eta)(Y - \zeta)(Y + \eta + \zeta).$$

Find the irreducible sextic equation over $K(X)$ that is satisfied by ζ; and show further that $K(X, \eta, \zeta) = K(X, \eta + 2\zeta)$.

4. If $p, q \in K(X)$, and the equation $Y^3 - 3pY + q = 0$ is irreducible over $K(X)$, show that

$$Y^3 - 3pY + q = (Y - \eta)(Y + \tfrac{1}{2}\eta - \tfrac{1}{2}\zeta)(Y + \tfrac{1}{2}\eta + \tfrac{1}{2}\zeta),$$

where η and ζ are such that

$$\eta^3 - 3p\eta + q = 0 \quad \text{and} \quad \zeta^2 + 3\eta^2 - 12p = 0.$$

Show that $\eta = 3q/(\zeta^2 - 3p)$ and hence that $K(X, \eta, \zeta) = K(X, \zeta)$; and verify that the minimum equation of ζ over $K(X)$ is

$$Z^6 - 18pZ^4 + 81p^2Z^2 + 27(q^2 - 4p^3) = 0.$$

5. If (ξ, η) is a generic point of the circle C with equation $X^2 + Y^2 = 1$, show that $\Sigma \equiv K(\xi, \eta)$ can be generated over K by the single element $\zeta = (1 - \xi)/\eta$. Interpret this result in terms of a birational projection of C from the point $(1, 0)$ on to the Y-axis.

Show that each of the pairs $(1 + \xi, \eta)$, $(\xi/(\xi^2 + \eta^2))$, $\eta/(\xi^2 + \eta^2))$, $(\xi\eta^2, \xi^2\eta)$ generates Σ, and that each of the pairs (ξ^2, η^2) $(\xi^2, \xi\eta)$ generates a proper subfield of Σ. Denoting each of the above pairs in turn by (ξ', η'), find in each case the curve C' with (ξ', η') as a generic point, and discuss in each case the resulting birational or unirational correspondence between C and C'.

6. Show that the equations $X' = X^2$, $Y' = Y^2$

(i) transform each of the four lines $\pm X \pm Y = 1$ birationally into the parabola $(X' - Y' - 1)^2 = 4Y'$;

(ii) give a unirational $(2, 1)$ transformation of each of the parabolas $Y^2 = \pm X$ into the parabola $Y'^2 = X'$;

(iii) give a $(4, 1)$ transformation of the circle $X^2 + Y^2 = 1$ into a line.

7. *Projection as a unirational transformation.* The simplest example of the methods of § 6 is given by the projection of a curve on to a line. Thus if C, being irreducible, has equation

$$f(X, Y) = a_0(X)Y^n + \ldots + a_n(X) = 0 \quad (n \geqslant 1, a_0(X) \neq 0),$$

then its projection from Y_∞ on to the X-axis has equations $X' = X$, $Y' = 0$; and the unirational correspondence between C and C' (the X-axis) is $(n, 1)$. Equations (1) of § 6 reduce to $\xi' = \xi$ (with $\eta' = 0$); the field $K(\xi, \eta)$ is the extension (of degree n) of $K(\xi', \eta') = K(\xi)$ that is generated by any root η of the equation

$$a_0(\xi)Y^n + \ldots + a_n(\xi) = 0;$$

and the whole theory of the correspondence between places C and C' reduces at once to that developed in detail in §§ 2, 3 of Chapter V.

8. *Rational involutions: Bertini's Theorem.* Discuss, in relation to the argument of § 9.1, the following simplest case of the classical *Theorem of Bertini.* The series of sets of points cut on an irreducible curve C by the curves of a pencil $F + \lambda G = 0$ is such that the general set of the series has no multiple member which is not common to all the sets of the series (i.e. no variable multiple point).

9. *Example of a rational involution.* As a further example of the general procedure followed in § 6, we consider the curve C with equation

$$Y^n = X^s \quad (s > 0, n - s = \mu > 0, (n, s) = 1),$$

and the unirational transformation of C into a line L (the axis OX) which is defined by the equation $X' = X/Y$ (together with $Y' = 0$). In the notation of § 6, the extension of $K(\xi') = K(\xi/\eta)$ that is generated by a root ζ of the equation

$$z^\mu = \xi' \ (= \xi/\eta)$$

is isomorphic over K with $K(\xi, \eta)$, the isomorphism being such that

$$\xi, \eta \to \zeta^n, \zeta^s, \qquad \zeta \to \xi^p \eta^q,$$

where p, q are integers such that $pn+qs = 1$.

If $a \in K$, the place on L with representation $X' = a+u$ corresponds, when $a \neq 0$, to each of μ simple places on C that have representations of the form $X = (a+u)^{n/\mu}$, $Y = (a+u)^{s/\mu}$, that is to say, to the μ places on C that have their centres at the intersections of C, other than O, with the line $X = aY$; but the place $X' = u$ on L corresponds to the single place on C with centre O and fractional parametric representation $X = u^{n/\mu}$, $Y = u^{s/\mu}$. In fact, the place on C at O counts μ-fold in the inverse transformation.

10. *Non-singular cubic*. If (ξ, η) is a generic point of the non-singular cubic C with equation $Y^2 = X^3 + pX^2 + qX$, show that each of the points $(q/\xi, \pm q\eta/\xi^2)$ is also a generic point of C, the associated birational self-transformations of C being of the first and second kinds respectively (see Exercise 20, p. 29).

11. *Elliptic curves*. An irreducible curve C is said to be *elliptic* if it is birationally equivalent to a plane non-singular cubic, the coordinates of a point of C (over the complex field K) being then expressible as rational functions of the Weierstrassian elliptic functions $\wp(u)$ and $\wp'(u)$ of a parameter u.

Show that a quartic curve C with two double points (ordinary double points or simple cusps) is elliptic, and show how to construct geometrically the two families of birational self-transformations of such a curve (see Exercise 20, p. 29).

12. *Hyperelliptic curves*. An irreducible curve C is said to be *hyperelliptic* if, being neither rational nor elliptic, it admits nevertheless of a unirational $(2, 1)$ transformation into a line. Show, by the methods of § 6, that any such curve is birationally equivalent to a curve C with an equation of the form

$$Y^2 = P(X),$$

where P is a K-polynomial, the correspondence between this curve and a line being then generated by projection from Y_∞ on to OX.

Show, conversely, that any irreducible curve C of order n with an $(n-2)$-fold point is either rational or elliptic or hyperelliptic.

13. If ξ and η are the elements $u^2/(1+u^2+u^4)$ and $(u+u^3)/(1+u^2+u^4)$ of $K(u)$, show that $K(\xi, \eta)$ is a proper subfield of $K(u)$, and find an element ζ of this field such that $K(\xi, \eta) = K(\zeta)$.

14. *Correspondences on a curve*. Let τ be any (m, n) correspondence on an irreducible curve C, and let the expression

$$(\mathscr{P}, \mathscr{Q}) \in \tau$$

stand for the statement that $\mathscr{Q}$ is one of the n places $\tau\mathscr{P}$ (or $\mathscr{P}$ one of the m places $\tau^{-1}\mathscr{Q}$). We say then that

 (i) τ is *symmetric* (this requiring $m = n$) if $(\mathscr{P}, \mathscr{Q}) \in \tau$ always implies that $(\mathscr{Q}, \mathscr{P}) \in \tau$, and

 (ii) τ is *cyclic-symmetric* if it is symmetric and if $(\mathscr{P}, \mathscr{Q}) \in \tau$, $(\mathscr{P}, \mathscr{R}) \in \tau$ $(\mathscr{Q} \neq \mathscr{R})$ always imply that $(\mathscr{Q}, \mathscr{R}) \in \tau$.

Any involution I_{n+1} clearly generates a cyclic-symmetric (n, n) correspondence τ on C, in which $\tau\mathscr{P}$ is the complement of $\mathscr{P}$ in the set of I_{n+1} to which $\mathscr{P}$ belongs. Conversely, it can be shown that any irreducible cyclic-symmetric (n, n) correspondence on C arises in this way from an involution I_{n+1} on the curve.

15. *Lüroth's Theorem.* If t is a projective parameter (or affine coordinate) for points on a line L, and if $U(t)$ and $V(t)$ are K-polynomials with no common factor and each of degree n (at least one of them being effectively of degree n), then the equation $U(t) + \lambda V(t) = 0$, where λ is a parameter, evidently defines the sets of an involution I_n on L. Also, this involution may be regarded as arising from the cyclic-symmetric $(n-1, n-1)$ correspondence between points t_1, t_2 of L such that $U + \lambda V = 0$ has t_1, t_2 as a pair of its roots for some value of λ.

Many elementary results can be derived from the following direct converse of the above: any irreducible cyclic-symmetric $(n-1, n-1)$ correspondence between points on L (or on any non-singular rational curve) determines an involution I_n on L, and the sets of I_n are then given, for different values of λ, by an equation of the form $U(t) + \lambda V(t) = 0$.

Thus, for example, the pairs of a symmetric $(1, 1)$ correspondence on a conic k (this being trivially cyclic-symmetric) are given by an equation $U + \lambda V = 0$, where U, V are quadratics in the projective parameter t of points on k; and this shows at once that these pairs are cut on k by the lines of a pencil. Again if k is triangularly circumscribed to a conic k', the triads of vertices of triangles inscribed in k and circumscribed to k' form an I_3 on k, and they can therefore be represented by an equation $U + \lambda V = 0$ in which U and V are cubics in t.

16. Deduce from Lüroth's Theorem that the sets of any I_3 on a twisted cubic curve in S_3 are cut on the curve by the planes of a pencil; and, generally, that the sets of any I_n on a rational normal curve $C^{(n)}$ in S_n are cut on the curve by the primes of a pencil.

17. *The integral domain of a curve.* If C is irreducible, with generic point (ξ, η), the ring $K[\xi, \eta]$ is called the *integral domain* of C. Its quotient field $K(\xi, \eta)$ is the function field of C (to within isomorphism over K) and therefore reflects only birationally invariant properties of C. The structural properties of $K[\xi, \eta]$, however, reflect affine invariant relations of C to all other curves C' of S_2. Thus, in particular, each element $P(\xi, \eta)$ of $K[\xi, \eta]$ characterizes the aggregate of curves C' that have equations of the form

$$P(X, Y) + f(X, Y) Q(X, Y) = 0,$$

where $f(X, Y) = 0$ is the equation of C and $Q(X, Y)$ is an arbitrary K-polynomial in X, Y. An ideal $\mathfrak{a}$ of $K[\xi, \eta]$ represents an aggregate of curves C' that have a certain relationship to C; and the decomposition of $\mathfrak{a}$ into its primary components corresponds to the analysis of this relationship into a set of local relationships of C' to C at separate points of the latter, e.g. into requirements that C' should pass through certain points of C or have assigned minimum multiplicities of intersection with C at those points.

In this connexion, each place $\mathscr{P} = (X(u), Y(u))$ on C determines a series of *valuation ideals* in $K[\xi, \eta]$, each of which consists of those elements $P(\xi, \eta)$ of the ring for which $O\{P(X(u), Y(u))\} \geqslant m$ for a given integer m (cf. Chapter XI, § 11).

CHAPTER VIII

ALGEBRAIC CURVES IN S_r

1. Topic of the chapter

IN the preceding chapters we have confined our attention wholly to the geometry of the projective plane S_2, and the most general topic that we have considered so far is the invariantive geometry of plane algebraic curves, which comprises those properties of curves which they possess in common with all their birational transforms. The properties which we study in this part of geometry are thus common to entire families of curves with the same function field. We are now ready to extend this idea further by defining curves in r-dimensional projective space S_r, for general r, and grouping these also under the function fields Σ to which they belong.

We shall not give any details here of the elementary linear geometry of S_r, which is a straightforward generalization of that of S_2 and S_3, and is in any case readily accessible in other books.† We merely remark that $S_r(K)$ has a class of allowable representations $\mathscr{R}$ by homogeneous coordinates $(x_0, ..., x_r)$, and with each of these is associated an affine representation $\mathscr{R}_A$ by non-homogeneous coordinates $(X_1, ..., X_r)$ of all those points which do not lie in the 'prime at infinity' $x_0 = 0$ (cf. Chapter I, § 2).

2. Transcendental points of S_r

Let K' be any extension field of the ground field K, and let $(\xi_1, ..., \xi_r)$ be a set of r elements of K'. We shall say that, in any allowable affine representation $\mathscr{R}_A$, the r-tuple $(\xi_1, ..., \xi_r)$ represents a point, this point being a *ground point* if $\xi_i \in K$ $(i = 1, ..., r)$ and a *transcendental point* if at least one of the ξ_i is transcendental over K.

There are r different kinds of transcendental point in S_r, which we distinguish according to the degree of transcendence of the minimum field of definition $K(\xi_1, ..., \xi_r)$ of the point $(\xi_1, ..., \xi_r)$ as an extension of K.

---

† For a brief summary of the essential ideas see van der Waerden, *Einführung in die algebraische Geometrie*; and for a full discussion see Hodge and Pedoe, *Methods of Algebraic Geometry*, vol. i.

DEFINITION. A transcendental point $(\xi_1,...,\xi_r)$ of S_r which is such that the degree of transcendence of $K(\xi_1,...,\xi_r)$ over K is s is said to be *of the s-th kind*.

We thus have $r+1$ kinds of point in S_r, ranging between the extremes of the ground point, with all its coordinates in K, and the *totally transcendental point* (for which $s = r$), with coordinates that are all algebraically independent over K.† The minimum field of definition of this last kind of point is, of course, isomorphic with the field $K(t_1,...,t_r)$ obtained when r indeterminates $t_1,...,t_r$ are adjoined to K. Our principal concern in the present chapter is with transcendental points of the first kind, i.e. points $(\xi_1,...,\xi_r)$ such that one, at least, of the coordinates ξ_i is transcendental over K, but any two of the coordinates are connected by a K-equation.

THEOREM 1. *If ξ is any transcendental point of the first kind, its minimum field of definition over K is a one-dimensional algebraic function field.*

Proof. We may suppose that ξ_1 is transcendental over K. Then, by hypothesis, each of $\xi_2,...,\xi_r$ is algebraic over $K(\xi_1)$; and since $K(\xi_1)$ is of characteristic zero, it follows, by Property 4 on p. 149, that $K(\xi_1,...,\xi_r) \equiv K(\xi_1)(\xi_2,...,\xi_r)$ is a simple algebraic extension of $K(\xi_1)$. This proves the theorem.

THEOREM 2. *Any transcendental point ξ of S_r of the first kind $(r \geqslant 3)$ can be projected into a transcendental point ξ' of S_2 in such a way that ξ and ξ' have the same minimum field of definition over K.*

Proof. We suppose, as before, that ξ_1 is transcendental over K. Then, again by Property 4, there exists a linear combination

$$\eta = a_2\xi_2+...+a_r\xi_r$$

of $\xi_2,...,\xi_r$, with coefficients a_i in K, such that

$$K(\xi_1)(\xi_2,...,\xi_r) = K(\xi_1)(\eta),$$

i.e. such that $K(\xi_1,...,\xi_r) = K(\xi_1, \eta).$

We may suppose that $a_2 \neq 0$. Then the equations

$$Y_1 = X_1, \quad Y_2 = a_2X_2+...+a_rX_r, \quad Y_3 = X_3, \quad ..., \quad Y_r = X_r$$

define an allowable transformation of affine coordinates in S_r, and

---

† It should be noted that we are only interested here in *algebraic* relations, and the present classification of points of S_r into kinds does not altogether correspond to the intuitive classification of variable points according to their number of degrees of freedom. A point of the sth kind cannot have more than s degrees of freedom, but it may have less. Thus, if $f(u)$ and $g(u)$ are the familiar power series for sin u and e^u, the point $(u, f(u), g(u))$ of S_3, defined in $K|u|$, has only one degree of freedom although it is totally transcendental.

the transformed coordinates of $\boldsymbol{\xi}$ are $(\xi_1, \eta, \xi_3, ..., \xi_r)$. The point $\boldsymbol{\xi}$ may therefore be projected into the point $(\xi_1, \eta, 0, ..., 0)$, i.e. the point (ξ_1, η) of the reference plane OY_1Y_2; and the minimum field of definition of the projected point is then the same as the minimum field of definition of the original point $\boldsymbol{\xi}$. This proves the theorem.

3. Formal transcendental points of S_r

As in S_2, any transcendental point $\mathbf{X}(u) \equiv (X_1(u), ..., X_r(u))$ with coordinates in $K|u|$ will be called a *formal transcendental point*. The fact that such a point may be of any of the $r+1$ possible kinds emphasizes particularly the limitation of our present interest to relations between the coordinates of a point that are expressible by means of K-equations; for a formal transcendental point always represents a curvilinear branch, whatever may be its kind. The basic properties of formal transcendental points—their representation by homogeneous coordinates, their reduction to normal or canonical form, their centres, etc.—are all obvious extensions of the corresponding properties of such points in S_2; and we shall take them for granted without setting them all down formally.

A *quasi-branch* of S_r may now be defined as a formal transcendental point $\mathbf{X}(u)$ that is only specified to within regular substitution for u. A quasi-branch is *minimal* if it cannot be derived from any other quasi-branch by a substitution of index $\nu > 1$; and every minimal quasi-branch has redundant transforms of all positive integral orders from 2 onwards. Here, as previously, we shall look upon a minimal quasi-branch together with all its transforms, redundant as well as non-redundant (and fractional as well as integral), as a class of representations of a single geometric *branch*.

Every branch $\mathbf{X}(u)$ has a *centre*. The centre is the ground point $\mathbf{X}(0)$ if none of the $X_i(u)$ is of negative order in u, and otherwise a point at infinity which can be identified in the system of homogeneous coordinates associated with the affine system adopted here. If the point $\mathbf{X}(u)$ is of the ith kind, we say that the branch which it defines is of the ith kind; and if the branch is of the first kind we also refer to it as an *algebraic branch*.

The *order* of a branch α is found by taking a minimal representation of α in any affine coordinate system for which the centre of α is a finite point. The order is then the least of the integers $O(X_i(u) - X_i(0))$ $(i = 1, ..., r)$. Also with such a choice of the representation, the *order on α of a primal* of S_r with equation

$F(X_1,...,X_r) = 0$ is $O(F(X_1(u),...,X_r(u)))$. This order is infinite only if $F(\mathbf{X}(u)) = 0$ in $K\{u\}$; and in such a case we say that α lies on (or is contained in) the primal. We leave it to the reader to formulate these definitions also for a representation $(x_0(u),...,x_r(u))$ of α in homogeneous coordinates.

4. The contact spaces of a branch

Consider a branch α with minimal representation

$$\mathbf{X}(u) \equiv (X_1(u),...,X_r(u)), \quad X_i(u) \in K\{u\};$$

and suppose that α has centre C with coordinates $(c_1,...,c_r)$, so that $X_i(0) = c_i$ $(i = 1,...,r)$. If F is any primal, with equation $F(X_1,...,X_r) = 0$, we denote the order of F on α, as defined in § 3, by $O_\alpha(F)$; and, in agreement with previous terminology, we shall regard this number as the *multiplicity of intersection of F with α*.

By writing the equation of an arbitrary prime through C in the form

$$V \equiv v_1(X_1-c_1)+v_2(X_2-c_2)+...+v_r(X_r-c_r) = 0,$$

we see at once that the order ν of α is the least possible multiplicity of intersection of such a prime with α. To see what successively higher multiplicities of intersection primes through C can have with α we arrange the expression $V(u) \equiv \sum\limits_{i=1}^{r} v_i(X_i(u)-c_i)$ in the form

$$V(u) \equiv L_1(v)u^\nu + L_2(v)u^{\nu_2}+...+L_n(v)u^{\nu_n}+...,$$

where the $L_i(v)$ are non-zero linear K-forms in $v_1,...,v_r$ and $0 < \nu < \nu_2 < ...$. If $O_u(V(u)) > \nu$, then the prime V must satisfy the condition $L_1(v) = 0$, and it must therefore contain a certain line through C. We call this line the *tangent* to the branch α, and we denote it by T.

If, now, $L_h(v)$ is the first of the $L_i(v)$ that is linearly independent of $L_1(v)$, then the minimum multiplicity of intersection of primes through T with α is ν_h; and this minimum is exceeded only by those primes which satisfy the condition $L_h(v) = 0$ in addition to the condition $L_1(v) = 0$. Such primes therefore contain a certain plane through T; and we call this plane the *osculating plane* of α.

Proceeding in the same way, we define a nest of contact spaces of α. An alternative procedure (supposing, for simplicity, that α does not lie in any prime of S_r) is to take C as origin O of coordinates and so to choose the axes $OX_1,...,OX_r$ that $X_i(u) = u^{\sigma_i}U_i(u)$ $(i = 1,...,r)$, where $0 < \sigma_1 < ... < \sigma_r$, and each $U_i(u)$ is a unit of

$K\{u\}$. Then the successive contact spaces of α are the axis OX_1, the plane $OX_1 X_2,...,$ the prime $OX_1 ... X_{r-1}$. This procedure is modified if α lies in one or more primes of S_r by arranging for a corresponding number of the $X_i(u)$ to be identically zero; and in this case some of the higher contact spaces will not be defined.

EXAMPLE. If α is a branch in S_3, with centre at the origin O and with minimal representation

$$X_i = a_{i1} u^{\nu_1} + a_{i2} u^{\nu_2} + ... \quad (i = 1, 2, 3),$$

where $a_{ij} \in K$ and $a_{11} a_{21} a_{31} \neq 0$, then the line

$$X_1/a_{11} = X_2/a_{21} = X_3/a_{31}$$

is the tangent to α; and, if the three quantities $\alpha_{kl} = a_{k1} a_{l2} - a_{l1} a_{k2}$ are not all zero, the plane $\alpha_{23} X_1 + \alpha_{31} X_2 + \alpha_{12} X_3 = 0$ is the osculating plane of α.

A branch α is said to be a *linear branch* if it is of order $\nu = 1$; and it then has the characteristic property of intersecting with multiplicity 1 every prime which passes through its centre but not through its tangent line. If the minimum multiplicity of intersection of α with primes through its tangent is $\mu > 2$, then α is said to be inflexional. In the very special case in which $\mu = \infty$, we say that α is a *line-branch*, since it is contained in every prime through its tangent line.

5. Projection of branches

One of the ways in which we can study the properties of curves in S_r is by projecting any such curve into a plane curve and then making use of the general theory that we have developed in the earlier chapters of this book. In order to take full advantage of this possibility we need to know how algebraic curves behave when projected, and as a first step towards gaining such knowledge we shall now ask how branches project.

Projection in S_r can be from any subspace S_{p-1} of S_r, as vertex, on to a subspace S_{r-p} that has no point in common with the S_{p-1}; but it will not always be necessary for us to deal directly with projections of this most general type, since any projection from S_{p-1} on to S_{r-p} can be replaced by a sequence of p projections from point vertices, or *point-projections* as we may call them. To do this we select p linearly independent points $A_0,..., A_{p-1}$ arbitrarily in

S_{p-1} and then proceed as follows. We first project any general point P of S_r from A_0 into a point P_0 of the S_{r-1} spanned by S_{r-p} together with $A_1,..., A_{p-1}$; we then project P_0 (in the S_{r-1} just defined) from A_1 into a point P_1 of the S_{r-2} spanned by S_{r-p} together with $A_2,..., A_{p-1}$; and so on until finally we project P_{p-2} from A_{p-1} into a point P' of S_{r-p}.

In view of this reduction of general projections to point projections, it will be sufficient if, in investigating the effect of the operation of projection on branches, we consider the result of projecting any branch α in S_r from a ground point V, as vertex, on to a prime Π which does not pass through V. We shall exclude straight away the trivial case in which α is a line-branch with its tangent line through V.

To handle the projection most conveniently, we treat separately the two cases in which the centre of α is distinct from V and in which it coincides with V. In both cases, however, we choose an affine coordinate system such that Π is the prime $X_r = 0$, V is the point at infinity on the axis OX_r, and α is not contained in the prime at infinity. Then the projection is represented by the scheme

$$(X_1,..., X_{r-1}, X_r) \to (X_1,..., X_{r-1}, 0).$$

When the centre of α is distinct from V we can choose the coordinate system in such a way that this centre is a finite point. We may then suppose that α has a minimal representation $\mathbf{X}(u)$, with $X_i(u) \in K\{u\}$ $(i = 1,..., r)$; and then, since α is not a line-branch on a line through V, at least one of $X_1(u),..., X_{r-1}(u)$ actually involves u. The projection on Π of the transcendental point $(X_1(u),..., X_r(u))$, namely the point $(X_1(u),..., X_{r-1}(u), 0)$, is also transcendental, and it represents a branch α' in Π. We shall accordingly say that α' is the projection of α. It is important to notice, however, that the representation of α' that is obtained in this way is not necessarily minimal—for a minimal quasi-branch $(X_1(u),..., X_r(u))$ need not remain minimal when $X_r(u)$ is replaced by 0. The integer $v' = \min O(X_i(u) - X_i(0))$ $(i = 1,..., r-1)$, which is equal to the order of α' if the quasi-branch $(X_1(u),..., X_{r-1}(u), 0)$ is minimal and to a multiple of this order if the quasi-branch is redundant, will be called the *virtual order* of α'. If, for example, we take as α the branch in S_3 given by (u^2, u^4, u^3), the representation obtained for α' is $(u^2, u^4, 0)$. In this case $v = 2$ and $v' = 2$, but the order of α' is 1.

The virtual order of α' cannot be less than the order of α, but it may possibly be greater. It will be greater if and only if

$$O(X_r(u)-X_r(0)) < O(X_i(u)-X_i(0)) \quad (i = 1,...,r-1),$$

i.e. if and only if V is a point of the tangent to α. Applying this result to the particular case of a linear branch α ($\nu = 1$) we obtain the following theorem.

THEOREM 3. *If a linear branch α is projected from any point which does not lie on its tangent line, the projected branch is also linear.*

COROLLARY. *If a linear branch α is projected from any vertex space S_{p-1} in S_r which does not meet the tangent to α, then the projection is another linear branch α'.*

If, in the case that we have been considering, α is linear and V does not lie on its tangent, α' is of virtual order 1, and the quasi-branch $(X_1(u),...,X_{r-1}(u), 0)$ is certainly minimal; but if α is not linear the projected quasi-branch may possibly be redundant. If V is any point (other than the centre of α) on the tangent to α, then the virtual order ν' of α' is greater than ν.

When V is the centre of α, we can arrange that the tangent line of α does not lie in the prime at infinity of the affine coordinate system. The representation $\mathbf{X}(u)$ of α is then such that

$$O(X_i(u)) \geqslant 0 \quad (i = 1,...,r-1) \quad \text{and} \quad X_r(u) = u^{-\nu}U(u),$$

where $U(u)$ is a unit of $K\{u\}$ and ν is the order of α. In this case we see that $(X_1(u),...,X_{r-1}(u), 0)$ represents (though not necessarily non-redundantly) a branch α' which we take as the projection of α; and it appears readily that the centre of α' is the projection of the tangent to α, which in this case is a line through V.

6. Irreducible curves in S_r

In the geometry of S_2 we were able to define an irreducible curve directly as the aggregate of ground points that satisfy a given irreducible K-equation in point-coordinates; and then, at a later stage, we showed how every such curve can be regarded as containing transcendental points as well as its ground points, any one of the transcendental points alone being sufficient to determine the curve completely. In defining irreducible curves in S_r we shall find it convenient to reverse this procedure. We shall thus begin with a given transcendental point (of the first kind) which will define the curve; and we shall look upon the aggregate of all K-equations that are satisfied by the coordinates of this point as the set of equations

of the curve. Any point, whether it is a ground point or a transcendental point, which satisfies all these equations, will be considered to be a point of the curve.

DEFINITION. An *irreducible algebraic curve* of S_r is the aggregate
of all the points of S_r (ground points in the first instance, but also
transcendental points) which satisfy every K-equation that is
satisfied by a given transcendental point of the first kind.

Suppose that C is such an irreducible curve, defined by a
transcendental point $(\xi_1, ..., \xi_r)$ of the first kind, and that (E) is the
set of all K-equations $f(X_1, ..., X_r) = 0$ that are satisfied by
$X_i = \xi_i$ $(i = 1, ..., r)$. The set of all the K-polynomials $f(X_1, ..., X_r)$
which form the left-hand sides of these equations is an ideal p in
the ring $K[X_1, ..., X_r]$, and the points of C may be called the *zeros*
of p. Plainly p is a prime ideal, i.e. it cannot contain any product of
two polynomials, neither of which belongs to p. The connexion
between the curve C and the ideal p, which we shall call the *ideal
of C*, is very close. Indeed, instead of choosing to characterize C
by means of a transcendental point of the first kind, we could
equally well characterize it as the set of zeros of a prime ideal of
suitably defined type—and this procedure in fact corresponds to
one of the standard approaches to the theory of algebraic curves
and algebraic varieties generally, an approach that is alternative
to the one that we have chosen to adopt in this book.

Having defined C by reference to one particular transcendental
point ξ, we next show that every transcendental point of C serves
equally well to define the curve.

THEOREM 4. *If a transcendental point ξ of S_r determines an irreducible curve C, then every transcendental point η of C determines
this same curve; and the fields*

$$K(\xi) \equiv K(\xi_1, ..., \xi_r) \quad and \quad K(\eta) \equiv K(\eta_1, ..., \eta_r)$$

are isomorphic over K.

Proof. Let (E) be the set of all K-equations $f(X_1, ..., X_r) = 0$ that
are satisfied by ξ. Then, since η is a point of C, η satisfies all the
equations in (E). In order to prove that ξ and η determine the
same curve, we have only to show that η does not satisfy any other
K-equation in addition to those belonging to (E).

Suppose, if possible, that η satisfies a K-equation $g(X_1, ..., X_r) = 0$
that is not satisfied by ξ. Since η is a transcendental point, we may
suppose that η_1 is transcendental over K; and this implies that ξ_1

also is transcendental over K. Now, since the degree of transcendence of $K(\xi)$ over K is 1, and ξ_1 and $g(\xi_1, ..., \xi_r)$ are both elements of $K(\xi)$, there exists a K-polynomial $F(X, Y)$, irreducible over K, such that $F(\xi_1, g(\xi_1, ..., \xi_r)) = 0$; and, since ξ_1 is transcendental, $F(X, 0) \neq 0$. But then $F(X_1, g(X_1, ..., X_r)) = 0$ is an equation in (E), and therefore $F(\eta_1, g(\eta_1, ..., \eta_r)) = 0$, i.e. $F(\eta_1, 0) = 0$. This means, however, that η_1 is algebraic over K, contrary to hypothesis.

The points ξ and η thus satisfy exactly the same K-equations, and therefore determine the same curve C. We may show further, using the same method as in Chapter III, § 3 to generate a suitable isomorphism, that $K(\xi) \cong K(\eta)$ over K.

In virtue of Theorem 4, we may refer to ξ, or any other transcendental point of C, as a *generic point* of C. We shall denote the field $K(\xi) \equiv K(\xi_1, ..., \xi_r)$ by Σ, and we shall refer to Σ (defined to within isomorphism over K) as the *field of C* (or the *function field of C*).

Any parametrization of the field Σ—that is to say any isomorphic mapping of Σ on to a subfield H_u of $K|u|$ (cf. p. 155)—transforms the generic point $(\xi_1, ..., \xi_r)$ of C into a formal transcendental point $(X_1(u), ..., X_r(u))$ of the curve. Any formal transcendental point of C, given to within substitution for the parameter, defines an *algebraic branch of C*; and we shall refer to the branches of C as the *places on C*. We shall think of places, wherever possible, as given by *minimal integral* representations; and thus *the places on an irreducible algebraic curve C of S_r (i.e. the algebraic branches of S_r that belong to C) are defined by all the minimal parametrizations of the field Σ of C*. It is now easy to verify, as for curves in S_2, that the centres of the places on C are ground points of C.

7. Birational equivalence

If Σ is any given one-dimensional function field $\mathscr{A}_1(K)$, we shall say that an irreducible curve C of S_r belongs to Σ (or is a curve of Σ) if it possesses a generic point ξ, in some affine representation $\mathscr{R}_A$ of S_r, such that $K(\xi_1, ..., \xi_r) = \Sigma$. In this way we look upon every field $\mathscr{A}_1(K)$ as defining a totality of curves of the field, in spaces of all possible dimensionalities. Any set of elements $(\xi_1, ..., \xi_r)$ of Σ, where $r \geqslant 2$, such that $K(\xi_1, ..., \xi_r)$ is the full field Σ, defines such a curve of Σ; and we thus arrive at the completed form of the concept of the *totality of curves of Σ*, which we formerly envisaged as applying only to plane curves.

Now let $(\xi_1,...,\xi_r)$ and $(\eta_1,...,\eta_s)$ be any two generating sets of elements of Σ as an extension of K, and let C and D be the curves of Σ, in S_r and S_s respectively, with $\boldsymbol{\xi}$ and $\boldsymbol{\eta}$ as generic points. There then exist relations

$$\eta_i = \phi_i(\xi_1,...,\xi_r) \quad (i = 1,...,s),$$

and $$\xi_j = \psi_j(\eta_1,...,\eta_s) \quad (j = 1,...,r),$$

in which the ϕ_i and ψ_j are rational functions over K; and we say accordingly that C and D are *birational transforms* of each other by the correspondence with equations

$$Y_i = \phi_i(X_1,...,X_r) \quad (i = 1,...,s),$$
$$X_j = \psi_j(Y_1,...,Y_s) \quad (j = 1,...,r).$$

The relation of birational equivalence between two curves in spaces of arbitrary dimensionality, together with all its basic properties, is an immediate generalization of the relation between plane curves discussed in Chapter VII, § 4. In particular, every birational correspondence defines an unexceptional $(1, 1)$ correspondence between places on the two curves concerned.

Since a field $\mathscr{A}_1(K)$ such as Σ necessarily contains a generating pair of elements (ξ, η), and each such pair defines a plane curve C_0, it follows that *any irreducible curve C of S_r ($r \geqslant 3$) can be obtained (in infinitely many ways) as a birational transform of an irreducible plane curve C_0.*

Although what we have been saying in this section amounts, in a way, only to our original conception of curves in S_r with a different emphasis, it should serve to draw attention to the fact that most of what we want to know about curves in S_r ($r \geqslant 3$) will have to be deduced at present from the information that we already possess about plane curves. In dealing with that special case we could make use of the fortunate circumstance that every plane curve can be represented conveniently by a single equation; and this enabled us to make substantial progress without undue difficulty.

8. Correspondences between curves

As well as the theory of birational correspondences, we can now transfer to curves in S_r, with only minor modifications, the whole theory of unirational correspondences and general (m, n) correspondences that we developed in some detail in Chapter VII, §§ 6–8. The reason why we are able to do this, of course, is that the theory in question is based on the function field Σ and on the places of the curves concerned; and it makes no important difference whether our curves are associated with generating sets of only two elements of Σ or with generating sets of a larger number of elements.

Thus, in particular, if curves C and C' have generic points $(\xi_1,\ldots,\xi_r)$ and $(\eta_1,\ldots,\eta_s)$, with coordinates in a field Σ, and if $K(\xi) = \Sigma$ while $K(\eta)$ is a proper subfield Σ' of Σ, then we have

$$\eta_i = \phi_i(\xi_1,\ldots,\xi_r) \quad (i = 1,\ldots,s),$$

where the ϕ_i are rational functions over K; and we say that C' is the *unirational transform* of C by the transformation with equations

$$Y_i = \phi_i(X_1,\ldots,X_r) \quad (i = 1,\ldots,s).$$

Looking back now over the discussion leading up to Theorem 6 on p. 164, we see that the proof of that theorem carries over, with only linguistic modifications, to curves in spaces of any number of dimensions. We can therefore make the following general assertion.

THEOREM 5. *With the appropriate linguistic adjustments, all the results contained in Theorem 6 of Chapter VII are valid for any unirational transformation of one irreducible curve C into another such curve C', the two curves being defined in spaces of any dimensionalities whatever.*

The special kind of unirational transformation that is of most interest to us at the moment is the one defined by the operation of projection, and we shall now consider this in more detail.

9. Projection of a curve

We begin with a formal definition of the type of transformation to be discussed.

DEFINITION. Let S_{p-1} and S_{r-p} $(1 \leqslant p \leqslant r-1)$ be non-intersecting subspaces of S_r, and let ξ be a generic point, not in S_{p-1}, of a curve C of S_r. If ξ projects from S_{p-1} into a point ξ' of S_{r-p}, and if ξ' is not a ground point, then the curve C' with generic point ξ' is the *projection of C from S_{p-1} on to S_{r-p}*.

To justify this definition we need to show, of course, that C' is independent both of the choice of coordinate system in S_r and of the choice of the particular generic point ξ of C; but this verification may be left to the reader. We note that C' exists except only when ξ is in S_{p-1} or when ξ' is a ground point of S_{r-p}—that is to say, except when C is entirely contained either in S_{p-1} itself or in a space S_p through S_{p-1}. When the projection is from a point $V (= S_0)$ on to a prime $\Pi (= S_{r-1})$, the only curves that do not project into curves are the lines through V.

Taking account of the above definition, we can now restate Theorem 2 in the following form.

THEOREM 6. *Every irreducible curve C of S_r $(r \geqslant 3)$ can be projected birationally into an irreducible curve C' of S_2.*

In this case, namely, we have $p = r-2$ and $K(\xi') = K(\xi)$, so that C' is a plane curve, birationally equivalent to C. The theorem that we arrive at in this way, however, is a pure existence theorem, and it tells us nothing about how the vertex and plane of projection must be chosen in order to ensure that the projection will be birational. This greatly detracts from its usefulness, and we shall see shortly how a different approach to the problem leads to a more informative result.

Returning now to our definition of the projection C' of C from a vertex S_{p-1} on to a space S_{r-p}, we study the relation of C' to C by choosing a convenient affine representation $\mathscr{R}_A$ of S_r. To this end, we choose as prime at infinity a prime passing through S_{p-1} but not containing C; we take as origin O some point of S_{r-p}; and we choose the axes $OX_1,..., OX_r$ in such a way that $OX_1,..., OX_{r-p}$ lie in S_{r-p}, while $OX_{r-p+1},..., OX_r$ lie in the space joining O to S_{p-1}. By this means (supposing that C does not lie in any S_p through S_{p-1}) we secure that:

(i) the projection is given by the scheme

$$(X_1,..., X_{r-p}, X_{r-p+1},..., X_r) \rightarrow (X_1,..., X_{r-p}, 0,..., 0);$$

(ii) C has a finite generic point $\xi = (\xi_1,..., \xi_r)$ such that one, at least, of $\xi_1,..., \xi_{r-p}$ is transcendental over K, and C' has $(\xi_1,..., \xi_{r-p}, 0,..., 0)$ as a generic point.

With this representation, the equations (E') of C' are precisely those of the equations (E) of C which do not involve any of the coordinates $X_{r-p+1},..., X_r$. We deduce, in particular, that *every ground point P of C that does not lie in S_{p-1} projects into a ground point P' of C'.* For we can always choose our special coordinate system in such a way that P is a finite point; and it is then obvious that, if P satisfies (E), then P' satisfies (E').

A place $\mathscr{P}$ on C cannot be contained in a space S_p which contains

S_{p-1}, and it therefore always projects† into a place $\mathscr{P}'$ on C'. We can easily verify that the centre of $\mathscr{P}$, if it is not a point of S_{p-1}, projects into the centre of $\mathscr{P}'$. But if the centre of $\mathscr{P}$ is a point of S_{p-1}, then we can see, by an extension of the argument at the end of § 5, that the centre of $\mathscr{P}'$ is the projection of the tangent line to $\mathscr{P}$, or, if this tangent also is contained in S_{p-1}, it is the projection of the least of the contact spaces of $\mathscr{P}$ that is not in S_{p-1}. Thus *every place $\mathscr{P}$ on C projects into a unique place $\mathscr{P}'$ on C', the centre of $\mathscr{P}$, if it is not in S_{p-1}, projecting into the centre of $\mathscr{P}'$. If $\mathscr{P}$ has its centre in S_{p-1}, then the least contact space of $\mathscr{P}$ that does not lie in S_{p-1} projects into the centre of $\mathscr{P}'$.*

We now consider the consequences which follow from the observation that our projection of C into C' is a unirational (possibly a birational) transformation of C into C', the field $\Sigma' \equiv K(\xi_1,...,\xi_{r-p})$ of C' being a subfield of the field $\Sigma \equiv K(\xi_1,,,.\,\xi_r)$ of C. By Theorem 5, if $\Sigma:\Sigma' = \mu$ there is a $(\mu, 1)$ correspondence between places $\mathscr{P}$ on C and their projections $\mathscr{P}'$ on C', in the sense that (i) each place $\mathscr{P}'$ is the projection of a set of μ places $\mathscr{P}$ if these are properly counted (to their correct multiplicities), and (ii) except for a finite set of places $\mathscr{P}'$, the μ places $\mathscr{P}$ that project into any given place $\mathscr{P}'$ are all distinct. If $\mu = 1$, the projection of C into C' is, of course, birational.

Thus, for example, if C is a proper conic in S_2, the projection of C from a point V on to a line C' is birational ($\mu = 1$) if V lies on C, but only unirational ($\mu = 2$) if V does not lie on C. Or again, if C is the section of a quadric cone in S_3 with vertex A by a quadric surface which does not pass through A, the projection of C from A on to a plane is a (repeated) conic ($\mu = 2$), whereas the projection of C from almost any other point of S_3 is a quartic curve, birationally equivalent to C.

In the general argument given above, we have referred to a place $\mathscr{P}$ as projecting into a place $\mathscr{P}'$. It may well happen, of course, as the proof of Theorem 5 indicates, that if $\mathscr{P}$ is given as a minimal quasi-branch $(X_1(u),...,X_r(u))$, the projected quasi-branch $(X_1(u),...,X_{r-p}(u), 0,...,0)$ is of redundancy $j > 1$, so that it only properly represents a place $\mathscr{P}'$ on C' after reduction by a substitution of index j. If we assign the value 1 to j when the projected

---

† The direct application of the equations of projection to a minimal representation of $\mathscr{P}$ may, however, give a redundant representation of $\mathscr{P}'$, as we note later on in this section.

quasi-branch is minimal, then one of the results contained in Theorem 5 states that *j is the multiplicity of $\mathscr{P}$ in the set of μ places on C that project into the same place $\mathscr{P}'$ on C'*.

We now use this result to prove the following theorem.

THEOREM 7. *If C' is the projection of C from a space S_{p-1}, and if there exists a place $\mathscr{P}'$ on C' which is the projection of a unique place $\mathscr{P}$, of order unity, on C, the tangent to C at $\mathscr{P}$ not meeting S_{p-1}, then the projection of C into C' is birational.*

Proof. Since $\mathscr{P}$ is the only place which projects into $\mathscr{P}'$, the multiplicity μ of the projection is equal to the multiplicity *j* of $\mathscr{P}$ in the set of μ places projecting into $\mathscr{P}'$, i.e. the redundancy of the transformed representation. But, by the remark following the corollary to Theorem 3, p. 185, this redundancy is 1. Thus $\mu = 1$, and the projection is accordingly birational.

10. The ground points of a curve C

We have been mainly concerned in the foregoing sections with the places on a curve C of S_r, but we shall now look more particularly at the ground points of the curve, which are after all our primary concern. So far we have noted only that these points must satisfy all the equations (E) of C, and that the centre of any place on C is necessarily a ground point of C. As a preliminary to establishing the converse of this last result, which is our next objective, we need to make certain general remarks.

(i) *If $r > 1$, the ground points of C cannot exhaust all the points of S_r*. For the set (E) of equations satisfied by all the points of C must contain at least one member.

(ii) More precisely, *if $r > 1$, there exist always spaces S_{r-2} (i.e. secunda of S_r) which contain no point of C*. For let us suppose, on the contrary, that every secundum contains a point of C. Then, projecting C from a point V not on itself, we obtain a curve C' in S_{r-1} such that every secundum of S_{r-1} contains a point of C'. The original situation is thus reproduced in a space of one dimension less; and, by repeating the reduction a sufficient number of times, we obtain eventually a curve $C^{(r-2)}$ in S_2 which passes through every point of S_2. This is impossible, by (i), and therefore the original curve C cannot meet every secundum of S_r.

(iii) *No ground point of C can be the centre of an infinite number of places on C*. Let C in S_r be projected from an S_{r-3} into a curve C' in a plane S_2. Then every place $\mathscr{P}$ on C projects into a unique place $\mathscr{P}'$

on C' and (the projection being arranged suitably) the centre of $\mathscr{P}$ projects into the centre of $\mathscr{P}'$. If, now, a point P were the centre of infinitely many places on C, its projection P' would be the centre of infinitely many places on C'; and we already know this to be impossible for a plane curve (Theorem 4, p. 86).

We come now to our main theorem.

THEOREM 8 (*Fundamental Theorem for Curves in S_r*). *Every ground point of an irreducible curve C of S_r is the centre of at least one place on the curve.*

Proof. We have already proved the theorem for curves in S_2 (p. 86) and we now propose to use this special case to prove it generally.

Let P be any ground point of a curve C (not a line) in S_r, $r > 2$. We can then project C from P into a curve C^* lying in a prime S_{r-1} of S_r. By (ii) above, there exists a secundum S_{r-3} of S_{r-1} which contains no point of C^*; and the subspace S_{r-2} of S_r that is spanned by S_{r-3} and P contains no point of C other than P itself, for any other point of C in S_{r-2} would project from P into a point of C^* in S_{r-3}.

Now let C' be the projection of C, from the space S_{r-3} as vertex, on to a plane S_2. The point P of C projects into a point P' of C'; and, since C' is a plane curve, P' is the centre of at least one place $\mathscr{P}'$ on C'. Now $\mathscr{P}'$ is the projection of some place $\mathscr{P}$ on C (Theorem 5), and the centre of $\mathscr{P}$ projects into the centre P' of $\mathscr{P}'$ unless it lies in S_{r-3}. But there is no point of C in S_{r-3}, and P is the only point of C that projects into P'. It follows that P is the centre of $\mathscr{P}$, and therefore that there exists a place on C with P as its centre. This proves the theorem.

The upshot of Theorem 8 is simply that the ground points of any irreducible algebraic curve are the centres of the places on the curve, and we have already seen that each ground point is the centre of at most a finite number of such places. In this connexion, we now adopt the following definitions.

DEFINITIONS. (i) A *simple point* of an irreducible algebraic curve C is a point P such that there is one and only one place on C with centre P, and this place is of order unity. The tangent to the place (as a linear branch) is called the *tangent to C at P*.

(ii) The *multiplicity* of any point on C is the sum of the orders of the places on C with the point as centre (being unity for a simple point).

(iii) A *singular point* of C is a point P of multiplicity $\mu > 1$. The tangents to the places at P on C are called the *nodal tangents* to C at the singular point.

(iv) A *unisecant space* of C is a space S_s, of any dimensionality s $(1 \leqslant s \leqslant r-2)$, which contains a unique point P of C, this point being simple for C, and which does not contain the tangent to C at P.

We now have the following useful consequence of Theorem 7.

THEOREM 9. *If a space S_p is unisecant to C at a (simple) point P, then C projects birationally from any space S_{p-1} which lies in S_p and does not contain P.*

Proof. Let C project from S_{p-1} into a curve C' in a space S_{r-p}, and let P project into P'. Then S_{p-1} and P span the given space S_p, and the simple place on C at P projects into the unique place at P' on C'. Also S_{p-1} does not meet the tangent to C at P since, if it did, the space S_p spanned by S_{p-1} and P would not be unisecant. The theorem now follows.

We can now infer, for example, that a curve C in S_3 projects birationally into a plane curve from any point through which it is possible to draw a unisecant line to C.

11. The order of a curve in S_r. Bézout's Theorem

Our next task is to prove that every irreducible curve C of S_r has an *order*—that is to say that it is met by every prime which does not contain it in the same fixed number of points (properly counted). More generally, we wish to prove an analogous result for the intersections of C with primals of any given order N, thereby extending the theorem of Bézout, already proved for curves in S_2, to curves in any space S_r. Here, once again, we derive the general results for curves in S_r from the known results for the special case $r = 2$. Since the properties with which we are now concerned are 'global' instead of local—that is to say, they involve consideration of all the places on a curve simultaneously—we shall naturally want to use homogeneous coordinates in preference to non-homogeneous affine coordinates in this investigation.

We suppose, then, that in a convenient coordinate representation $\mathscr{R}$ of S_r the curve C has a generic point $(1, \xi_1, ..., \xi_r)$. The field of C is then $\Sigma \equiv K(\xi_1, ..., \xi_r)$. We define the *order* $O_{\mathscr{P}}(F)$ *of any K-form*

$F(x_0,...,x_r)$ *at a place* $\mathscr{P}$ *on* C, in the usual way, as the order in u of the power series $F(x_0(u),...,x_r(u))$, where $\mathbf{x}(u)$ is any regular representation of $\mathscr{P}$ (i.e. such that $x_0(u),...,x_r(u)$ all belong to $K\{u\}$, at least one of them is of order 0, and the representation is minimal). This done, we can define the geometrical concepts that we require in the following manner.

DEFINITIONS. (i) The *multiplicity of intersection of a primal* $F(\mathbf{x}) = 0$ *with a curve* C *at a place* $\mathscr{P}$ is the order $O_{\mathscr{P}}(F)$ of the form $F(\mathbf{x})$ at $\mathscr{P}$.

(ii) The *multiplicity of intersection of a primal* F *with a curve* C *at a point* P is the sum of its multiplicities of intersection with C at all the places $\mathscr{P}$ at P.

(iii) The *total number of intersections of* F *with* C (*properly counted*) is $\sum O_{\mathscr{P}}(F)$, where the summation extends over all places $\mathscr{P}$ on C, this number being equal to the sum of the multiplicities of intersection of F with C at all points common to both.

We note at once that $O_{\mathscr{P}}(F) = \infty$ if and only if $F = 0$ is one of the equations (E) of C, i.e. if and only if the primal F contains C. If, therefore, the relation $O_{\mathscr{P}}(F) = \infty$ holds for one place $\mathscr{P}$ on C, then it holds for every place $\mathscr{P}$ on C. We shall prove, almost immediately, that even the weaker hypothesis $\sum O_{\mathscr{P}}(F) = \infty$ implies that F contains C.

An elementary calculation is sufficient to show that *an intersection* P *of* F *with* C *is simple* (*i.e. of multiplicity unity as an intersection*) *if and only if* (i) P *is a simple point of* C, (ii) P *is a simple point of* F,† *and* (iii) *the tangent prime to* F *at* P *does not contain the tangent line to* C *at* P, *i.e.* F *does not touch* C *at this point.*

In order to extend Bézout's Theorem from S_2 to S_r, let us now take any plane curve D with the same function field Σ as the curve that we are interested in. Let the curve be of order d, and let it be given by the irreducible equation $f(y_0, y_1, y_2) = 0$. Then C is a birational transform of D by a set of equations

$$x_i = m_i(y_0, y_1, y_2) \quad (i = 0,...,r), \tag{1}$$

in which the $m_i(\mathbf{y})$ are $r+1$ forms, all of the same degree μ, in y_0, y_1, y_2. If $\mathbf{y}(u)$ is a representation in standard form of any place

---

† A point of F is simple if at least one of the partial derivatives $\partial F/\partial x_i$ is different from zero at the point. The tangent prime to F at a simple point $\mathbf{a}$ is the prime
$$\sum_{i=0}^{r} x_i(\partial F(\mathbf{a})/\partial a_i) = 0.$$

$\mathcal{Q}$ on D, then equations (1) give a representation

$$x_i = m_i(\mathbf{y}(u)) \quad (i = 0,...,r)$$

of the corresponding place $\mathcal{P}$ on C, but this representation of $\mathcal{P}$ is not necessarily in standard form, since the exponent q of the highest power of u that is a common factor of the $m_i(\mathbf{y}(u))$ may be greater than zero. In standard form, $\mathcal{P}$ has the representation

$$x_i = u^{-q}m_i(\mathbf{y}(u)) \quad (i = 0, ..., r;\ q \geqslant 0).$$

Now, taking any K-form $F(x_0,...,x_r)$ of degree N in $x_0,...,x_r$, let us consider the K-form

$$G(y_0, y_1, y_2) \equiv F(m_0(\mathbf{y}),..., m_r(\mathbf{y})),$$

of degree $N\mu$ in y_0, y_1, y_2. The order of $F(\mathbf{x})$ at $\mathcal{P}$ is

$$O(F(\mathbf{x}(u))) = O(u^{-Nq}F(m_0(\mathbf{y}(u)),..., m_r(\mathbf{y}(u))))$$
$$= O(G(\mathbf{y}(u)))-Nq;$$

and we may write, more briefly,

$$O_{\mathcal{P}}(F) = O_{\mathcal{Q}}(G)-Nq, \tag{2}$$

where $\mathcal{P}$ and $\mathcal{Q}$ are corresponding places on C and D.

To proceed further we now investigate the non-negative integer q, which is defined, for any place $\mathcal{Q}$ on D, by the equation

$$q = \min\{O(m_0(\mathbf{y}(u))),..., O(m_r(\mathbf{y}(u)))\}.$$

This equation implies that q is the minimum order at $\mathcal{Q}$ of any of the $r+1$ curves with equations $m_i(\mathbf{y}) = 0$ $(i = 0,...,r)$; or, as we may say, q is the order at $\mathcal{Q}$ of the generic curve of the linear system Λ with equation

$$\lambda_0 m_0(\mathbf{y})+\lambda_1 m_1(\mathbf{y})+...+\lambda_r m_r(\mathbf{y}) = 0$$

(cf. p. 114). Thus $q > 0$ if and only if the centre of $\mathcal{Q}$ is one of the base points $B_1,..., B_s$ of Λ on D; and *the sum $\sum\limits_{\mathcal{Q}} q$ of the values of q for all $\mathcal{Q}$ on D is the total multiplicity of intersection of the generic curve of Λ with D at the points $B_1,..., B_s$.* We may therefore write

$$\sum_{\mathcal{Q}} q = \beta, \tag{3}$$

where β is a finite non-negative integer, defined by the transformation (1).

From (2) and (3) we deduce that

$$\sum_{\mathcal{P}} O_{\mathcal{P}}(F) = \sum_{\mathcal{Q}} O_{\mathcal{Q}}(G)-N\beta. \tag{4}$$

This proves, in the first place, that the primal F contains C if and only if the curve G has D as a component. Further, it shows that if F does not contain C then

$$\sum_{\mathscr{P}} O_{\mathscr{P}}(F) = N(\mu d - \beta) = Nn, \text{ say,}$$

where $n = \mu d - \beta$; for $\sum_{\mathscr{Q}} O_{\mathscr{Q}}(G) = N\mu . d$ by Bézout's Theorem for curves in S_2. The number n, being the total number of intersections of C with any prime not containing C, is called the *order* of C.

The simple but comprehensive result that we have just proved may now be stated in the following terms.

THEOREM 10 (*Bézout's Theorem*). *An irreducible algebraic curve C of S_r is met by all primes which do not contain it in the same total number of points (properly counted), this number being called the order of C. All the primals of any given order N which do not contain C meet C in the same number of points, namely Nn, where n is the order of C.*

It follows at once from Bézout's Theorem that no point of C can be the centre of an infinite number of places on the curve—a result which we obtained earlier in a different way (p. 192). The theorem also has the following important corollaries.

COROLLARY 1. *A prime which contains more than n distinct ground points of an irreducible curve of order n contains the curve.*

COROLLARY 2. *An irreducible curve C of S_r has at most a finite number of singular points.*

Proof. By Theorem 6, we can project C birationally from a vertex space S_{r-3} into a plane curve C'; and then any place $\mathscr{P}$ on C, with centre P, projects into a unique place $\mathscr{P}'$ of C', with centre at the projection of P, provided only that P does not lie in S_{r-3} (see p. 191). In particular, every singular point of C which does not lie in S_{r-3} projects into a singular point of C'. S_{r-3} can only meet C, however, in a finite number of points. For if it met it in an infinite number, every prime through it would do the same and, by Corollary 1, would contain C. Thus S_{r-3} would contain C, and there would be no projection. It now follows that if C were to have an infinite number of singular points the same would be true of C'; and this is impossible, by the corollary to Theorem 6, p. 10.

COROLLARY 3. *Any irreducible curve C of S_r has infinitely many unisecant secunda S_{r-2}.*

Proof. By Corollary 2, all but a finite number of the points of
C are simple. We may therefore select a simple point P of C in
infinitely many ways, and having selected P we may project C
from this point into a curve C' in a prime S_{r-1}. But then (cf. p. 192,
(ii)), there is a secundum S_{r-3} of S_{r-1} which has no point in common
with C'. The secundum of S_r that is spanned by P and S_{r-3} is
accordingly unisecant to C at P.

This last corollary, taken in conjunction with Theorem 9, gives
us positive information about the freedom of choice of a vertex
S_{r-3} from which C projects birationally into a plane curve.

12. The order of a projected curve

In this section we shall establish a relation between the order n
of a curve C of S_r and the order n' of its projection C' from a space
S_{p-1} on to a space S_{r-p}.

If Σ and Σ' are the function fields of C and C', and if $\Sigma:\Sigma' = \mu$,
then the projection is a $(\mu, 1)$ transformation of C into C'. Let us
consider, first of all, a place $\mathscr{P}$ on C with its centre not in S_{p-1}. We
may choose an affine coordinate system, as in § 9, in such a way that
the projection is given by the scheme

$$(X_1,...,X_{r-p}, X_{r-p+1},...,X_r) \to (X_1,...,X_{r-p}, 0,...,0),$$

and the centre of $\mathscr{P}$ is a finite point. Let $\mathbf{X}(u)$ be a minimal representation of $\mathscr{P}$, with $X_i(u) \in K\{u\}$ $(i = 1,...,r)$. Then

$$\mathbf{X}'(u) \equiv (X_1(u),..., X_{r-p}(u), 0,...,0)$$

is a representation, of redundancy $j \geqslant 1$, of the projection $\mathscr{P}'$ of $\mathscr{P}$;
and the number j, as we saw in § 9, gives the multiplicity of $\mathscr{P}$ in the
set of μ places on C that project into $\mathscr{P}'$ on C'.

If $\overline{U}$ is any (finite) prime through S_{p-1}, with equation

$$\overline{U}(X) \equiv a_0 + a_1 X_1 + ... + a_{r-p} X_{r-p} = 0 \quad (a_i \in K),$$

then plainly, since $\mathscr{P}$ has a finite centre,

$$O_{\mathscr{P}}(\overline{U}) = O(\overline{U}(X(u))) = O(\overline{U}(X'(u))) = jO_{\mathscr{P}'}(\overline{U}),$$

the redundancy having been taken into account. But any prime
U' of S_{r-p} is the section of S_{r-p} by a unique prime $\overline{U}$ of S_r through
S_{p-1}; and hence *if $\mathscr{P}$, with centre not in S_{p-1}, counts j-fold in the set
of places on C which project into $\mathscr{P}'$ on C', if U' is any prime of S_{r-p},
and if $\overline{U}$ is the prime of S_r spanned by U' and S_{p-1}, then*

$$O_{\mathscr{P}}(\overline{U}) = jO_{\mathscr{P}'}(U').$$

If it happens that S_{p-1} contains no point at all of C, so that the above relation holds for all places $\mathscr{P}$ on C and their projections $\mathscr{P}'$ on C', we deduce at once that

$$n = \sum_{\mathscr{P}} O_{\mathscr{P}}(\overline{U}) = \mu \sum_{\mathscr{P}'} O_{\mathscr{P}'}(U') = \mu n'.$$

Now suppose, on the other hand, that S_{p-1} contains the centres of s places $\overline{\mathscr{P}}_1, ..., \overline{\mathscr{P}}_s$ on C, these places being of orders $\nu_1, ..., \nu_s$. Let us suppose, for simplicity, that none of the associated tangent lines $L_1, ..., L_s$ lies in S_{p-1}. Also, let $\overline{U}$ be a prime of S_r which passes through S_{p-1} but not through any of $L_1, ..., L_s$, so that its projection U' does not pass through the centres of any of the projections $\overline{\mathscr{P}}'_1, ..., \overline{\mathscr{P}}'_s$ of $\overline{\mathscr{P}}_1, ..., \overline{\mathscr{P}}_s$. Then

$$n = \sum_{\mathscr{P}} O_{\mathscr{P}}(\overline{U}) = \nu_1 + ... + \nu_s + {}^*\!\!\sum_{\mathscr{P}} O_{\mathscr{P}}(\overline{U}),$$

where the summation ${}^*\!\!\sum_{\mathscr{P}}$ extends over all places $\mathscr{P}$ on C except the $\overline{\mathscr{P}}_i$; and, since $O_{\overline{\mathscr{P}}'_i}(U') = 0$ $(i = 1, ..., s)$, we have

$${}^*\!\!\sum_{\mathscr{P}} O_{\mathscr{P}}(\overline{U}) = \mu {}^*\!\!\sum_{\mathscr{P}'} O_{\mathscr{P}'}(U') = \mu \sum_{\mathscr{P}'} O_{\mathscr{P}'}(U') = \mu n',$$

the summation ${}^*\!\!\sum_{\mathscr{P}'}$ extending over all places $\mathscr{P}'$ on C' except the $\overline{\mathscr{P}}'_i$. This gives us the following theorem.

THEOREM 11. *If C' is a μ-fold projection $(1 \leqslant \mu < \infty)$ of an irreducible curve C of S_r from a vertex S_{p-1} $(1 \leqslant p \leqslant r-1)$ on to a space S_{r-p}, and if there are s places on C, with orders $\nu_1, ..., \nu_s$, that have their centres in S_{p-1}, and if none of the tangent lines at these places lies in S_{p-1}, then the orders of C and C' are connected by the equation*

$$\mu n' = n - \sum_{i=1}^{s} \nu_i.$$

More generally, it can be seen that $\mu n' = n - I$, where I is the minimum total number of intersections (properly counted) of any prime of S_r through S_{p-1} with C at points in S_{p-1}.

As a very special case of the above theorem, we note that when C is projected from a secundum S_{r-2}, which does not meet it, on to a line L, we have $\mu = n$. This result may be put in the following form.

COROLLARY. *If S_{r-2} is any secundum of S_r which does not meet a given irreducible curve C of order n, then all but a finite number of primes through S_{r-2} meet C in n distinct points.*

For the $(n, 1)$ correspondence between C and the previously mentioned line L has the known property that each place on L, with at most a finite number of exceptions, is the projection of n distinct places on C; and, since C has at most a finite number of singular points, it must be the case, again with at most a finite number of exceptions, that the centres of the n places are distinct.

13. Curves of intersection

In this concluding section of the present chapter we shall discuss briefly the connexion between the somewhat abstract theory of curves in S_r that we have now developed and the more traditional concepts of an algebraic curve in S_3 as a complete or partial intersection of two surfaces and of an algebraic curve in S_r as the intersection, or a part of the intersection, of $r-1$ primals. For the brief discussion we propose we shall find it convenient to confine our attention to the three-dimensional case.

We consider, then, a pair of surfaces F and G in S_3, represented by K-equations $F(X, Y, Z) = 0$ and $G(X, Y, Z) = 0$ in affine coordinates. We suppose, as we may without loss of generality, that the equations $F = 0$ and $G = 0$ are irreducible and distinct. We shall assume further, though for convenience only, that no curve common to the surfaces lies in a plane $X = X_0$. Any such curve can, in fact, easily be discovered; and the procedure that we shall describe can then be used to find the remaining curve or curves of intersection of the surfaces.

Under the conditions stated, then, every irreducible (finite) curve common to F and G must have a generic point of the form (ξ, η, ζ), where ξ is transcendental over K(i.e. ξ is an indeterminate) and η and ζ are each algebraic over $K(\xi)$. We now consider the equations

$$F(\xi, Y, Z) = 0, \quad G(\xi, Y, Z) = 0, \tag{1}$$

which we may treat as the equations of two irreducible algebraic curves, $\mathscr{F}$ and $\mathscr{G}$, defined over the algebraically closed field $K' = K^*|\xi|$ as ground field. The curves $\mathscr{F}$ and $\mathscr{G}$ will then have a finite set of points of intersection (η_i, ζ_i) $(i = 1, ..., s)$, with $\eta_i, \zeta_i \in K'$; and these points will determine s transcendental points Π_i of the original space $S_3(K)$, Π_i having coordinates (ξ, η_i, ζ_i), $(i = 1, ..., s)$. Each of the points Π_i satisfies equations (1), and therefore generates a subfield Σ_i of $K^*|\xi|$ which is algebraic over $K(\xi)$. It may happen that the Σ_i are all conjugate extensions of $K(\xi)$, so that the Π_i are a complete set of conjugate points with respect to $K(\xi)$; and in this case the Π_i are all generic points of the same irreducible curve C common to F and G. In general, however, the points Π_i will fall into a number of subsets $(\Pi^{(1)}),...,(\Pi^{(p)})$, $1 \leqslant p \leqslant s$, each of which is a complete set of conjugate points with respect to $K(\xi)$. In this case F and G will have p irreducible curves $C_1,...,C_p$ in common, the points of the set $(\Pi^{(j)})$ all being generic points of the curve C_j $(j = 1,...,p)$.

We now illustrate this analysis of the intersection of a pair of surfaces by two simple examples.

(i) Let F and G be the quadrics with equations

$$X^2+Y^2+Z^2 = 1 \quad \text{and} \quad 2X^2-2Y^2-Z^2 = 1,$$

so that their common points are the points which satisfy the equations

$$Y^2 = 3X^2-2 \quad \text{and} \quad Z^2 = 3-4X^2.$$

In the projective plane $S_2(K')$, where $K' = K^*|\xi|$, the curves with equations

$$Y^2 = 3\xi^2-2 \quad \text{and} \quad Z^2 = 3-4\xi^2$$

are the two pairs of parallel lines $Y = \pm\sqrt{(3\xi^2-2)}$ and $Z = \pm\sqrt{(3-4\xi^2)}$, the radicals being interpreted appropriately as particular elements of $K^*|\xi|$; and these line-pairs intersect in the four points (η_i, ζ_i) $(i = 1,...,4)$ with coordinates $(\pm\sqrt{(3\xi^2-2)}, \pm\sqrt{(3-4\xi^2)})$. These four points, as may easily be verified,† are a complete set of conjugates over $K(\xi)$ with coordinates in the extension $K(\xi, \rho)$ of K, where $\rho = \sqrt{(3\xi^2-2)}+\sqrt{(3-4\xi^2)}$ is a root of the irreducible quartic equation

$$x^4-2(1-\xi^2)x^2+(5-7\xi^2)^2 = 0.$$

Thus each of the four points $(\xi, \pm\sqrt{(3\xi^2-2)}, \pm\sqrt{(3-4\xi^2)})$ is a generic point of the unique irreducible (quartic) curve common to F and G.

(ii) Next let F and G be the quadrics with equations

$$X^2+Y^2+Z^2 = 1 \quad \text{and} \quad X^2-2Y^2-Z^2 = 1,$$

so that their common points are given also by

$$Y^2 = -2(1-X^2) \quad \text{and} \quad Z^2 = 3(1-X^2).$$

As in the previous case, the curves $Y^2 = -2(1-\xi^2)$ and $Z^2 = 3(1-\xi^2)$ in $S_2(K')$ have four common points, the coordinates of these points being $(\pm i\sqrt{2}\sigma, \pm\sqrt{3}\sigma)$, where $\sigma = \sqrt{(1-\xi^2)}$. The four points therefore all have coordinates in the extension $K(\xi, \sigma)$

---

† If $\sqrt{(3\xi^2-2)} = P$ and $\sqrt{(3-4\xi^2)} = Q$, then $P+Q = \rho$ and $P^2-Q^2 = 7\xi^2-5$. Hence $P-Q = (7\xi^2-5)/\rho$ and $P = \frac{1}{2}(\rho+(7\xi^2-5)/\rho)$, $Q = \frac{1}{2}(\rho-(7\xi^2-5)/\rho)$, so that $P, Q \in K(\xi, \rho)$.

of $K(\xi)$; and since this extension is of degree 2, i.e. $K(\xi, \sigma):K(\xi) = 2$, the points must fall into two conjugate pairs. These are $\pm(i\sqrt{2}\sigma,\ \sqrt{3}\sigma)$ and $\pm(i\sqrt{2}\sigma,\ -\sqrt{3}\sigma)$. It follows that in this case F and G have two irreducible curves (conics) in common, with generic points $(\xi,\ i\sqrt{2}\sigma,\ \sqrt{3}\sigma)$ and $(\xi,\ i\sqrt{2}\sigma,\ -\sqrt{3}\sigma)$ respectively, where $\sigma = \sqrt{(1-\xi^2)}$.

NOTES AND EXERCISES ON CHAPTER VIII

1. State for each of the following transcendental (affine) points of S_3 whether it is of the first, second, or third kind (u and v being indeterminates):

$$(1, u, u^2),\quad (1, u, e^u),\quad (u, u^2, u^3),\quad (u, v, u^2+v^2),$$

$$(u, \sin u, \cos u),\quad (u, \sin u, \sinh u).$$

2. Show that the branch (u, u^2, u^3) in S_3 has OX as branch tangent and OXY as osculating plane. Discuss its projections from $X_\infty, Y_\infty, Z_\infty$ on to the three reference planes and (by use of homogeneous coordinates) its projection from O on to the plane at infinity.

3. A branch α in S_3 has equations

$$X = t^3,\quad Y = t^3+t^5+t^7+...,\quad Z = t^3-t^5+t^7-....$$

Show that its tangent has equations $X = Y = Z$ and that its osculating plane has equation $Y+Z = 2X$.

Discuss the orders of the projections of α from all points, finite or infinite, of S_3.

Show that α is algebraic, being contained in the curve of intersection of the cylinders $(Y-X)^3 = X^2Y^3$ and $(X-Z)^3 = X^2Z^3$.

4. A branch α in S_4 is given by the equations

$$x_0 = 1,\quad x_1 = t^3,\quad x_2 = t^4,\quad x_3 = t^4+t^5,\quad x_4 = t^4+t^5+t^6.$$

Discuss its projections (a) from the reference point X_0 on to the solid $x_0 = 0$, (b) from the unit point $(1, 1, 1, 1, 1)$ on to the solid $x_4 = 0$, (c) from each of the reference lines X_3X_4, X_0X_4, X_0X_1 on to the opposite reference plane.

Discuss in each of the last two cases the plane of S_4 that projects into the centre of the projected branch.

5. *Conic and twisted cubic.* The equations

$$\mathbf{x} = (y_0^2, y_0y_1, y_0y_2, y_1y_2),\quad \mathbf{y} = (x_0, x_1, x_2) \tag{1}$$

transform the conic D with parametric representation $\mathbf{y} = (1, \theta, \theta^2)$ into the cubic C with parametric representation $\mathbf{x} = (1, \theta, \theta^2, \theta^3)$, and conversely. The places on D comprise in all a place $\mathscr{Q}(\theta) = (1, (\theta+u), (\theta+u)^2)$ for every finite value of θ (in K), and a place $\mathscr{Q}(\infty) = (u^2, u, 1)$; and these are carried by (1) into the standard and non-standard representations

$$(1, (\theta+u),\ (\theta+u)^2,\ (\theta+u)^3)\quad \text{and}\quad (u^4, u^3, u^2, u)$$

of the corresponding places $\mathscr{P}(\theta)$ and $\mathscr{P}(\infty)$ on C. That is to say, in the notation of p. 196, $\mathscr{Q}(\infty)$ is the only place on D with a positive q ($q = 1$); and the constant β for the transformation of D into C is 1, giving $3 = 2.2 - 1$ for the order of C.

The conics of the linear system Λ with equation

$$\lambda_0 y_0^2 + \lambda_1 y_0 y_1 + \lambda_2 y_0 y_2 + \lambda_3 y_1 y_2 = 0$$

have a single base point on D, namely the point $Y_2 = (0, 0, 1)$, their other base point $Y_1 = (0, 1, 0)$ being irrelevant since it does not lie on D; and the general conic of the system has a simple intersection with D at Y_2. The conics of Λ therefore meet D residually in triads of (variable) points which are carried by the transformation into the triads of points in which C is met by the planes of S_3. This situation is conveniently described by saying that C is the transform of D by a web (linear ∞^3-system) of conics with a simple base point on D.

6. *Transform of a curve D by a linear system Λ.* The general procedure for constructing birational transforms C of a plane curve D may be given the following geometrical form.

Let D have equation $f(\mathbf{y}) = 0$, and let Λ be any linear system of curves in S_2 with equation

$$\lambda_0 g_0(\mathbf{y}) + \lambda_1 g_1(\mathbf{y}) + \ldots + \lambda_r g_r(\mathbf{y}) = 0 \quad (g_0 \not\equiv 0 \;(\mathrm{mod} f))$$

such that the set of rational functions on D defined by the quotients

$$\frac{g_1}{g_0}, \frac{g_2}{g_0}, \ldots, \frac{g_r}{g_0}$$

generate the whole function field of D. Further, let the base points, if any, of Λ on D be $B_1, \ldots, B_s$, and let the total multiplicity of intersection of the general curve of Λ with D at $B_1, \ldots, B_s$ be β. Then the equations $x_i = g_i(\mathbf{y})$ $(i = 0, \ldots, r)$ define a birational transform C of D in S_r, and the order of C is $n = ld - \beta$, where d is the order of D and l is the order of the curves of Λ.

The sets of n points (properly counted) in which C is met by primes that do not contain it correspond to the sets of $n = ld - \beta$ points (properly counted) in which D is met, residually to the β fixed intersections at the base points B_i, by curves of Λ which do not have D as component.

We say then that C *is the (birational) transform of D by the linear system of curves Λ; or, alternatively, that C is the projective model of the linear series of sets of points, of order $n = ld - \beta$, cut on D, residually to the β fixed intersections, by curves of Λ.*

A necessary and sufficient condition that C should span the space S_r (not lie in any prime of S_r) is that the forms $g_i(\mathbf{y})$ $(i = 0, \ldots, r)$ should be linearly independent over K and that no member of Λ should have D as component.

7. *Rational curves $^0C^n[r]$.* Every rational curve of order $n \geqslant 1$ that properly belongs to S_r (and not to any space of lower dimensionality) will be said to be a $^0C^n[r]$, the superscript 0 indicating its genus. We have already referred (Exercise 27, p. 31) to the fact that any such curve, if $r < n$, is a projection of the projectively unique rational normal curve $^0C^n[n]$ from a suitable vertex S_{n-r-1} of S_n.

From our present point of view, a $^0C^n[r]$ may be regarded primarily as the projective model of an r-dimensional linear series of sets of n points on a line.

Any $^0C^n[r]$, however, can equally well be defined as the birational transform of a conic D of S_2 by a linear system of curves of some suitable order l such that (a) a number $\beta = 2l-n$ of the $2l$ intersections of D with the general curve of Λ are fixed, and (b) Λ is r-dimensional and such that none of its members has D as component. Thus, in particular:

(i) any $^0C^3[3]$ (twisted cubic curve) is the transform of D by a web (linear ∞^3-system) of conics (not containing D) which has one simple base point on D;

(ii) any $^0C^4[3]$ (rational space quartic) is the transform of D by a similar web of conics with no base point on D;

(iii) any $^0C^4[4]$ (rational normal quartic) is the transform of D by a linear ∞^4-system of conics (not containing D) with no base point on D;

(iv) any $^0C^5[3]$ (rational space quintic) is the transform of D by a web of cubic curves, none having D as component, with one simple base point on D;

and so on.

As exercises on the above definitions, the reader should deduce from them some of the simpler projective properties of the curves concerned: (a) the $^0C^3[3]$ lies on three linearly independent quadrics, and precisely one of its chords passes through a general point of S_3; (b) a $^0C^4[3]$ of the most general kind lies on only one quadric surface and possesses an infinity of trisecant lines; (c) the $^0C^4[4]$ is such that three of its chords meet a general line of S_4; (d) a $^0C^5[3]$ of the most general kind does not lie on any quadric surface but on each of four linearly independent cubic surfaces (and it possesses a unique quadrisecant line); while there exists a special kind of $^0C^5[3]$ that is a $(4, 1)$ curve on a quadric surface (possessing therefore an infinity of quadrisecants).

[Thus, for example, to identify the trisecant lines of a $^0C^4[3]$ we may proceed as follows. The ∞^3-system Λ consists in this case of all the conics apolar to two fixed conic envelopes Σ_1 and Σ_2. D is apolar to one and only one envelope Σ of the range $\Sigma_1+\lambda\Sigma_2$, all the conics of Λ being also apolar to this envelope Σ. D contains an infinity of triads of points P, Q, R which are self-polar for Σ, and conics of Λ through two points of any such triad must then contain the third also. The triads P, Q, R represent triads P', Q', R' on $^0C^4[3]$ such that planes through P', Q' necessarily contain R' also; that is to say, P', Q', R' are the intersections of $^0C^4[3]$ with a trisecant line.]

8. *The elliptic quartic* $^1C^4[3]$. Any birational transform of a plane non-singular cubic D is called an *elliptic curve*; and we also call it a $^1C^n[r]$ if its order is n and the dimensionality of its ambient space is r.

For $r \geqslant 3$, the simplest example of such a curve is the *elliptic quartic* $^1C^4[3]$ which is the transform of D by a web Λ of conics with two base points on D.

We may take the two base points to be $Y_1 = (0, 1, 0)$ and $Y_2 = (0, 0, 1)$, and the equation of D to be

$$F(\mathbf{y}) \equiv ay_0^3 + (by_1 + cy_2)y_0^2 + (dy_1^2 + ey_1y_2 + fy_2^2)y_0 + (gy_1 + hy_2)y_1y_2 = 0.$$

Then the equation of Λ is

$$\lambda_0 y_0^2 + \lambda_1 y_0 y_1 + \lambda_2 y_0 y_2 + \lambda_3 y_1 y_2 = 0;$$

and the equations of the birational transformation may be taken to be

$$x_0 = y_0^2, \quad x_1 = y_0 y_1, \quad x_2 = y_0 y_2, \quad x_3 = y_1 y_2,$$

since any other choice of a basis for Λ leads only to a projective transform of the resulting curve C.

If $S(\mathbf{x})$ is a quadratic form in the x_i, then the quadric $S(\mathbf{x}) = 0$ passes through C if and only if the form $T(\mathbf{y}) = S(y_0^2, y_0 y_1, y_0 y_2, y_1 y_2)$ is zero at all points of D. Since the equation $T(\mathbf{y}) = 0$, if $T(\mathbf{y})$ is not identically zero, necessarily represents a quartic curve with double points at Y_1, Y_2, and can only have D as component if the residual component is the line $y_0 = 0$, it follows that $T(\mathbf{y})$ is zero at all points of D if and only if it is of the form

$$T(\mathbf{y}) = ky_0 F(\mathbf{y}) \quad (k \in K);$$

and we see then that $S(\mathbf{x})$ must be of the form

$$S(\mathbf{x}) = \alpha(x_0 x_3 - x_1 x_2) +$$
$$+ \beta\{ax_0^2 + (bx_1 + cx_2)x_0 + dx_1^2 + ex_1 x_2 + fx_2^2 + (gx_1 + hx_2)x_3\},$$

where α, β are constants. Thus $C = {}^1C^4[3]$ lies on two independent quadrics S_1 and S_2, and it is therefore the complete curve of intersection of S_1 and S_2.

If S is any proper quadric through C, then C is a $(2, 2)$-curve on S.

9. *The curves ${}^1C^5[3]$ and ${}^1C^5[4]$.* The transforms of a non-singular cubic D of S_2 by linear ∞^3- and ∞^4-systems of conics with one base point on D are curves ${}^1C^5[3]$ and ${}^1C^5[4]$ respectively. Show that ${}^1C^5[3]$ does not lie on any quadric surface, but that it is a partial intersection of two cubic surfaces in S_3. Show also that ${}^1C^5[4]$ lies on five linearly independent quadrics of S_4, and that any ${}^1C^5[3]$ is a projection of a curve ${}^1C^5[4]$ from a point not on the latter.

10. *Curves ${}^2C^n[r]$.* If D is an irreducible quartic of S_2 with one ordinary node, being therefore of genus (deficiency) 2, then we shall call any birational transform of D a ${}^2C^n[r]$, where n is its order and r the dimensionality of its ambient space.

If O is the node of D, then the transform of D by the ∞^3-system Λ of conics that pass through O and one other fixed point A of D is a curve ${}^2C^5[3]$.

Verify, by the methods of Exercise 8, that this curve lies on only one quadric S, being a $(3, 2)$ curve on S; and show that it is the residual intersection of the quadric S with a cubic surface K that contains a generator of S.

11. *A curve ${}^4C^6[3]$.* If D is a plane quintic with two ordinary nodes A, B, and therefore of genus (deficiency) 4, show that its transform by the web of conics with A, B as base points is a curve ${}^4C^6[3]$ which is the complete intersection of a quadric and a cubic surface.

12. *The hyperelliptic ${}^3C^6[3]$ and the non-hyperelliptic ${}^3C^6[3]$.* If D is a non-singular plane quartic ($p = 3$), then its transform by the web of cubics through six of its points $A_1, ..., A_6$ is a curve ${}^3C^6[3]$ which does not (in general) lie on any quadric surface. But if D' is a (hyperelliptic) quintic curve with a triple point O (this curve also having $p = 3$), then its transform by conics that pass through O and one other point A of D' is a hyperelliptic ${}^3C^6[3]$ which is a $(4, 2)$ curve on the unique quadric containing it.

13. *Curves on a quadric.* Show that any irreducible (α, β)-curve on a non-singular quadric surface in S_3 can be obtained either as the birational

transform of a plane curve $C^{\alpha+\beta}(A^\alpha, B^\beta)$ by conics through A, B, or as the birational transform of a plane curve $C^{\alpha+\beta-1}(A^{\alpha-1}, B^{\beta-1})$ by conics through A, B.

14. *Birational projection.* If $(\xi, \eta, 0)$ is a generic point of a curve D in the plane $Z = 0$, and if ζ is any element of $K(\xi, \eta)$, show that D is always a birational projection from the point Z_∞ of the curve C with generic point (ξ, η, ζ). Discuss the circumstances under which C has one or more places at Y_∞, and discuss the projections of these places.

If D is the circle $X^2 + Y^2 - 1 = 0 = Z$ and $\zeta = \xi/\eta$, show that C is a quartic curve with two places at Z_∞ and that these project into the places on D with centres on OX.

15. We apply the method of § 13 to discuss the intersection of the surfaces F and G with equations $Y^2 = XZ$ and $YZ = X$ respectively.

In the plane of Y, Z over the field $K^*|X|$, the equations represent conics which intersect in the triad of conjugate points $(X^{\frac{2}{3}}, X^{\frac{1}{3}})$, $(\omega X^{\frac{2}{3}}, \omega^2 X^{\frac{1}{3}})$, $(\omega^2 X^{\frac{2}{3}}, \omega X^{\frac{1}{3}})$; and these give rise to three (conjugate) generic points

$$(X, X^{\frac{2}{3}}, X^{\frac{1}{3}}), \quad (X, \omega X^{\frac{2}{3}}, \omega^2 X^{\frac{1}{3}}), \quad (X, \omega^2 X^{\frac{2}{3}}, \omega X^{\frac{1}{3}})$$

of one and the same twisted cubic C common to F and G.

In the plane of Z, X over $K^*|Y|$, we obtain similarly two (conjugate) generic points

$$(Y^{\frac{3}{2}}, Y, Y^{\frac{1}{2}}), \quad (-Y^{\frac{3}{2}}, Y, -Y^{\frac{1}{2}})$$

of the same curve C.

In the plane of X, Y over $K^*|Z|$, the equations represent a conic and a line which meet in the points $(0, 0)$ and (Z^3, Z^2); and these give rise to generic points

$$(0, 0, Z) \quad \text{and} \quad (Z^3, Z^2, Z)$$

of the line OZ and the twisted cubic C respectively.

F and G meet therefore in the line OZ and in the curve C (which touches OZ at O).

16. Analyse in the same manner the intersection of the surfaces with equations $Z^2 = X$ and $Z^2 = XY$.

[In this case, in the plane of X, Z over $K^*|Y|$, the equations represent conics which touch at $X = Z = 0$; and the associated transcendental point $(0, Y, 0)$ is a generic point of the line OY, which therefore counts *twice* as a component of the curve of intersection of the two surfaces. The residual component, arising in each of the other two operations, is a conic.]

17. Discuss the total curve of intersection (a conic and four lines) of the quadric $X - X^2 + YZ = 0$ with the four-nodal cubic surface

$$(X - X^2)(Y + Z) + YZ = 0;$$

and show in a diagram the intersections of the components.

18. Show that the quadric $(X + 1)X = YZ$ meets the ruled cubic surface $(X + 1)Z^2 = XY^2$ in a quartic curve C and in a pair of lines meeting C.

19. Show that the quadric $X = YZ$ meets the quartic surface

$$Y^2Z^2 + Z^2X^2 - X^2Y^2 = XYZ$$

(a surface with three concurrent double lines) in two conics and two lines, each of the lines counting doubly as a component of the complete intersection.

CHAPTER IX

THE COORDINATES OF A CURVE

1. Introduction

IT sometimes happens, when we are considering how best to represent algebraically a geometric object of some particular kind, that we are faced with the alternatives of either using many equations of a relatively simple kind or else using a single equation of a much more complicated kind. In such circumstances, the second mode of representation has the very great advantage that the coefficients in the single equation, no matter how complicated this may be, can be taken as a set of *coordinates* of the object in question, and we are thus able to map all the objects of the kind envisaged on the points of an image manifold in a projective space. We saw in Chapter II, § 1.2, for example, how any finite point-set in S_2 may be represented by either of two single equations: (a) a two-way equation $G(x_0, x_1, x_2; y_0, y_1, y_2) = 0$, which expresses (apart from the multiplicities of the factors) the condition for the line joining the points **x** and **y** to pass through some point of the given set, and (b) a line-equation $G(u_0, u_1, u_2) = 0$ which expresses similarly the condition for the line **u** to contain some point of the set. In this way every finite point-set G gives rise to two different *associated forms* $G(\mathbf{x}; \mathbf{y})$ and $G(\mathbf{u})$, and so to two representations of G by sets of coordinates.

The problem with which we shall be concerned in the present chapter is directly related to the one solved in Chapter II, although of much greater complexity; for what we now wish to do is to find some way of representing all the algebraic curves of S_r, without ambiguity, by single equations of some fixed type, and so to secure a comprehensive coordinate representation, free from exception, of the whole aggregate of curves of any given order in S_r. For the curves C^n of S_2 the problem is trivial, since any such curve is ordinarily defined by a single equation $f(x_0, x_1, x_2) = 0$. If we take the $\frac{1}{2}(n+1)(n+2)$ coefficients in the equation as coordinates of the curve, we get a mapping of the curves of order n in S_2 on the points of a projective space of dimensionality $\frac{1}{2}n(n+3)$—cf. p. 19. When we turn to the C^n of S_3, however, the situation is already radically

different; and the difficulties that have to be overcome in this case
are exactly the same in principle as those which confront us when
we consider the C^n of any projective space S_r—or indeed when we
deal, even more generally, with the algebraic manifolds V_d^n, of given
order n and given dimensionality d, in S_r. For simplicity, therefore,
we shall limit our discussion of coordinates of algebraic manifolds
in the main to the one case of curves C^n in S_3. The reader who
subsequently studies the general theory, as set out, for example, in
van der Waerden's *Einführung*, chapter v, or in Hodge and Pedoe's
Methods, volume ii, chapter x, will find that no radically new ideas
are involved.

The credit for first drawing attention to the fundamental
character of the problem of assigning coordinates to curves in S_3
is due to Cayley, and it was he also who made the first fruitful
suggestion as to how the problem might be solved, in a paper
entitled 'A New Analytical Representation of Curves in Space'
(*Quart. J. Math.* 3 (1860), 225). Cayley's idea, in brief, was that a
C^n in S_3 can always be characterized uniquely by the equation of
the cone $Y(C^n)$—possibly a cone with multiple components—
which projects it from a 'general' point $\mathbf{y}$. He took for granted that
such a cone can always be represented by an equation of the form
$F(\mathbf{x}; \mathbf{y}) = 0$, in which the left-hand side is a two-way form F of
degree n in each of the sets of coordinates (x_0, x_1, x_2, x_3) and
(y_0, y_1, y_2, y_3); and he noted the alternative interpretation of the
equation as a necessary and sufficient condition for the line joining
the points $\mathbf{x}$ and $\mathbf{y}$ to meet C^n. He assumed, furthermore, that the
same equation must be equivalent to the equation $\Phi(\mathbf{p}) = 0$ of the
complex of lines which meet C^n, i.e. that the highly special two-way
form $F(\mathbf{x}; \mathbf{y})$ must be expressible as a one-way form of degree n
in the six expressions $p_{23} = x_2 y_3 - x_3 y_2, ..., p_{03} = x_0 y_3 - x_3 y_0$. And
finally, taking the coefficients in $F(\mathbf{x}; \mathbf{y})$ as coordinates of C^n, he
attempted to find a basis for the invariant relations between them,
that is to say, a set of necessary and sufficient conditions for a two-
way form $F(\mathbf{x}; \mathbf{y})$ to represent a C^n, or a set of necessary and
sufficient conditions for a complex $\Phi(\mathbf{p}) = 0$ to be the complex of
lines meeting a C^n. In this he was not successful, obtaining only
certain necessary conditions, which he himself recognized to be not
sufficient. Nevertheless, for the special case $n = 2$, and more
particularly for the (irreducible) eight-fold family of conics in S_3,
Cayley's programme was in fact ultimately carried through in full

detail; that is to say, the coordinates of a conic in S_3 were defined, and a complete basis for the invariant relations connecting them was explicitly given (cf. p. 224).

Some 77 years after the publication of Cayley's original paper, the general problem of defining coordinates for the V_d^n of S_r was formulated and completely solved by Chow and van der Waerden in their paper 'Zur algebraischen Geometrie, IX' (*Math. Ann.* **113** (1937), 692); and the results established in that paper have ever since been a basic part of the structure of modern algebraic geometry. Expositions and amplifications of the results in question are given in the books of van der Waerden and Hodge and Pedoe already referred to.

2. Algebraic varieties

As our aim throughout this book has been to introduce the reader to some of the fundamental concepts and methods of modern algebraic geometry by means of a discussion of algebraic curves, so we wish in this chapter to present the theory of co-ordinates of algebraic manifolds as exemplified by the Cayley representation of curves in S_3. But in order that the full generality of the ideas may become clear (as well as for the more immediate purpose of handling the basic classification of algebraic curves into families) we shall first of all indicate how algebraic manifolds in general are defined.

We have already seen in Chapter VIII that the elementary way of defining a plane curve by means of its equation does not extend easily to spaces of higher dimensionality, and that in order to arrive at a satisfactory theory of curves in S_r we do best to regard an irreducible algebraic curve as defined by a generic point. Similar considerations apply to algebraic manifolds in general. Plane curves are the primals of S_2, and just as a plane curve has a single equation $f(x_0, x_1, x_2) = 0$, so a primal (or $(r-1)$-dimensional algebraic manifold) of S_r has a single equation $f(x_0,..., x_r) = 0$; but when we turn to manifolds in S_r of dimensionality less than $r-1$, the most convenient way of characterizing such manifolds is by means of suitably defined generic points. In the present section we shall state briefly, without going into the details of the theory, how this can be done. We shall normally refer to an algebraic manifold as a *variety*, this being the term in current use.

In the first place, then, we define an *irreducible variety* V_{r-1}, of dimensionality $r-1$, in $S_r(K)$ as an irreducible primal of S_r, i.e. the set of all points which satisfy a given irreducible K-equation $f(x_0,...,x_r) = 0$. Any formal sum of primals, with assigned multiplicities, is regarded as a reducible $(r-1)$-dimensional variety of S_r, and it has an equation $f_1^{q_1}...f_s^{q_s} = 0$, which is unique to within a factor in K.

Every irreducible primal V_d of S_{d+1} has a function field Σ_d, which is analogous to the function field of an irreducible plane curve. It can be shown that every such function field is a d-*dimensional algebraic function field* or field of the type $\mathscr{A}_d(K)$ (cf. p. 154), i.e. a field $K(\eta_1,...,\eta_d, \zeta)$, where $\eta_1,...,\eta_d$ are transcendental and algebraically independent over K and ζ is algebraic over $K(\eta_1,...,\eta_d)$.

Now suppose that we begin by taking some field Σ_d of the type $\mathscr{A}_d(K)$, and that $\{\xi_1,...,\xi_r\}$ is a set of r generators of Σ_d over K $(r > d)$. Thus $\Sigma_d = K(\xi_1,...,\xi_r)$. Then the point $(1, \xi_1,...,\xi_r)$ is a transcendental point of S_r, of the dth kind since Σ_d has degree of transcendence d over K, and we shall say that $(1, \xi_1,...,\xi_r)$ is a *generic point* of an irreducible d-dimensional variety V_d in S_r. The points of V_d are all those points of S_r (transcendental points as well as ground points) which satisfy all the K-equations that are satisfied by $(1, \xi_1,...,\xi_r)$, i.e. all the *equations of V_d*. It follows from Hilbert's Basis Theorem (see Appendix A, § 14) that a finite subset of this set of equations is sufficient to determine the variety.

Any formal combination $V_d = m_1 V_d^{(1)}+...+m_p V_d^{(p)}$ of irreducible d-dimensional varieties $V_d^{(i)}$ in S_r $(d < r)$, with positive integral multiplicities m_i, will be called a *multiplicative d-dimensional algebraic variety* of S_r. In addition to this concept we also require that of a *point-set algebraic variety* of S_r, such a variety being defined as the aggregate of points of S_r that satisfy a given finite set of K-equations $f_i(x_0, x_1,...,x_r) = 0$ $(i = 1,...,s)$.

It follows from what we have already said that every irreducible variety V_d is a point-set variety; but the converse statement is by no means true. We have, in fact, the following basic theorem.

THEOREM 1. *Every algebraic point-set variety W of S_r is the union of a finite number of irreducible algebraic varieties, possibly of different dimensionalities.*

The maximal irreducible varieties that make up W are called the *components* of W; and the greatest of their separate dimensionalities is taken as the *dimensionality* of the point-set variety.

We have said above that a point of S_r is a point of the irreducible variety defined by a given generic point $(1, \xi_1, ..., \xi_r)$ if and only if it satisfies every K-equation that is satisfied by the generic point; and this fact is expressed by saying that the points of the variety defined by $(1, \xi_1, ..., \xi_r)$ are all the *specializations* of this generic point (cf. the note on specialization on p. 134).

DEFINITION. Let $\xi = (\xi_0, ..., \xi_r)$ be any point of S_r, with minimum field of definition Σ_d of the type $\mathscr{A}_d(K)$. By a *specialization* of ξ is meant any point ξ' which satisfies every K-equation that is satisfied by ξ.

The concept of specialization, as so defined, is evidently capable of generalization to the case of points in p-way projective spaces. Thus, for example, if $(\xi; \eta)$ is a two-way point of a space S_{r_1, r_2}, then another point $(\xi'; \eta')$ of the same space is said to be a specialization of $(\xi; \eta)$ if it satisfies every two-way K-equation satisfied by $(\xi; \eta)$. It is evident that, when this is so, the one-way points ξ' and η' are specializations of ξ and η respectively. A theorem on specializations that we shall need to make use of below runs as follows.

THEOREM 2 (*Extension of specialization*). If $\left(\overset{1}{\xi}; \overset{2}{\xi}; ...; \overset{p}{\xi} \right)$ is a point of a p-way projective space $S_{r_1, r_2, ..., r_p}$, and if $\left(\overset{1}{\xi}'; ...; \overset{q}{\xi}' \right)$ is a specialization of $\left(\overset{1}{\xi}; ...; \overset{q}{\xi} \right)$, where $q < p$, then there exists at least one specialization $\left(\overset{q+1}{\xi}'; ...; \overset{p}{\xi}' \right)$ of $\left(\overset{q+1}{\xi}; ...; \overset{p}{\xi} \right)$ such that $\left(\overset{1}{\xi}'; ...; \overset{p}{\xi}' \right)$ is a specialization of $\left(\overset{1}{\xi}; ...; \overset{p}{\xi} \right)$.

A proof of this theorem by the standard theory of elimination is to be found in Hodge and Pedoe's *Methods*, ii, p. 92. For an interesting alternative proof, based on a device of Chevalley 'which, it may be hoped, finally eliminates from algebraic geometry the last traces of elimination-theory', see Weil's *Foundations of Algebraic Geometry*, chapter ii, § 2.

3. Associated forms of an irreducible curve C^n of S_3

Considering now an irreducible curve C, of order n, in S_3, we shall show that C can be uniquely defined by a single equation in each of the three following ways:

(i) by its *primary Cayley equation* $F(\mathbf{x}; \mathbf{y}) = 0$, which gives the condition for two points **x** and **y**, when they are distinct, to lie on a line which meets C;

(ii) by its *secondary Cayley equation* $H(\mathbf{u}\,;\mathbf{v}) = 0$, which gives the condition for two planes **u** and **v**, when they are distinct, to intersect in a line which meets C;

(iii) by its *complex equation* $\Phi(\mathbf{p}) = 0$, which gives the condition for a line **p** to meet C.

We shall show that there exist irreducible two-way K-forms $F(\mathbf{x}\,;\mathbf{y})$ and $H(\mathbf{u}\,;\mathbf{v})$, each of degrees (n,n), with the required properties, and that each of them is unique to within a factor in K. $\Phi(\mathbf{p})$ also exists as an irreducible form of degree n, but if $n \geqslant 2$ it is indeterminate to the extent of a factor in K and also an additive term $\Omega_{pp}\Phi'$, where $\Omega_{pp} = 0$ is the invariant quadratic relation $p_{01}p_{23}+p_{02}p_{31}+p_{03}p_{12} = 0$ between the line-coordinates p_{ik}, and Φ' is an arbitrary form of degree $n-2$ in these coordinates. The three forms $F(\mathbf{x}\,;\mathbf{y})$, $H(\mathbf{u}\,;\mathbf{v})$, and $\Phi(\mathbf{p})$, which are known as *associated forms* of C, may be called respectively the *first* and *second Cayley forms* and the *complex form* of the curve.

For simple types of curve, such as a line or conic or twisted cubic, the reader will have little difficulty in constructing each of the associated forms. To establish the existence of the forms for an arbitrary irreducible curve, we begin by proving the following theorem.

THEOREM 3. *Every irreducible curve C^n of S_3 has a unique irreducible primary Cayley equation $F(\mathbf{x}\,;\mathbf{y}) = 0$.*

Proof. Let C^n be an irreducible curve of S_3, defined by means of a generic point $(1,\xi_1,\xi_2,\xi_3)$. Then $K(\xi_1,\xi_2,\xi_3)$ is a function field of the type $\mathscr{A}_1(K)$, i.e. a field $K(\eta,\zeta)$, where η is transcendental over K and ζ is algebraic over $K(\eta)$.

Now let $(1,a_1,a_2,a_3)$ be an indeterminate point of S_3, the a_i being distinct indeterminates, and let the point $(1+\mu,\ \xi_1+\mu a_1,\ \xi_2+\mu a_2,\ \xi_3+\mu a_3)$, where μ is a further indeterminate, have a normalized representation $(1,b_1,b_2,b_3)$, so that

$$b_i = (\xi_i+\mu a_i)/(1+\mu) \quad (i = 1, 2, 3).$$

Then (b_1,b_2,b_3) can be envisaged as a representation in affine coordinates of a generic point of the cone which projects the curve C from the point (a_1,a_2,a_3).

If, now, K' denotes the pure transcendental extension $K(a_1,a_2,a_3)$

of K, we see that b_1, b_2, b_3 all belong to the field

$$K'(\mu, \xi_1, \xi_2, \xi_3) = K'(\mu, \eta, \zeta),$$

which has degree of transcendence 2 over K'. Since

$$\xi_i = (1+\mu)b_i - \mu a_i \quad (i = 1, 2, 3), \tag{1}$$

it is evident that $K'(\mu, b_1, b_2, b_3) = K'(\mu, \xi_1, \xi_2, \xi_3)$, so that $K'(\mu, b_1, b_2, b_3)$ also has degree of transcendence 2 over K'. We are able, further, to show that μ is algebraic over $K'(b_1, b_2, b_3)$, and this means that the degree of transcendence of $K'(b_1, b_2, b_3)$ over K' is again 2.

In order to establish the fact that μ is algebraic over $K'(b_1, b_2, b_3)$, we argue as follows. Let $F(x_1, x_2, x_3) = 0$ be any K-equation that is satisfied by the generic point (ξ_1, ξ_2, ξ_3) of C (that is to say, an equation of some surface through C). Then, by (1),

$$F((1+\mu)b_1 - \mu a_1, \ (1+\mu)b_2 - \mu a_2, \ (1+\mu)b_3 - \mu a_3) = 0. \tag{2}$$

We have here an equation for μ with coefficients in

$$K(a_1, a_2, a_3, b_1, b_2, b_3),$$

and therefore in $K'(b_1, b_2, b_3)$. Let the degree of this equation be h. If $h = 0$, so that the terms involving μ all cancel out, equation (2) remains valid when 0 is substituted for μ. In this case, therefore, $F(b_1, b_2, b_3) = 0$. But, since (b_1, b_2, b_3) is not a point of C, we can certainly choose the polynomial $F(x_1, x_2, x_3)$ in such a way that $F(b_1, b_2, b_3) \neq 0$; and with this choice of F the degree h of equation (2) will be positive. This proves that μ is algebraic over $K'(b_1, b_2, b_3)$.

Now, since $K'(b_1, b_2, b_3)$ has degree of transcendence 2 over K', there exists one and (apart from a factor in K') only one irreducible equation

$$\Phi(z_1, z_2, z_3) = 0 \quad (\Phi(z_1, z_2, z_3) \in K'[z_1, z_2, z_3]),$$

which is satisfied by $z_i = b_i$ $(i = 1, 2, 3)$. By multiplying Φ by a suitable element of the ring $K[a_1, a_2, a_3]$ we can convert it into a polynomial in z_1, z_2, z_3, the coefficients of which are K-polynomials in a_1, a_2, a_3 with highest common factor unity. We thus obtain a relation

$$\Psi(a_1, a_2, a_3, b_1, b_2, b_3) = 0,$$

such that $\Psi(y_1, y_2, y_3, z_1, z_2, z_3)$ is an irreducible K-polynomial in $y_1, ..., z_3$. By making the substitutions $a_i \to a_i/a_0$, $b_j \to b_j/b_0$, and multiplying through by a suitable factor $a_0^p b_0^q$, we can put this relation into the homogeneous form

$$F(a_0, a_1, a_2, a_3 ; b_0, b_1, b_2, b_3) = 0;$$

and in this way we obtain a (uniquely defined) irreducible two-way K-equation
$$F(\mathbf{x}; \mathbf{y}) = 0 \tag{3}$$
which is satisfied by the point-pair $(\mathbf{a}; \mathbf{b})$. All that now remains is for us to identify this equation with the primary Cayley equation of C.

Suppose that $\mathbf{a}'$, $\mathbf{b}'$, $\boldsymbol{\xi}'$ are homogeneous coordinate-tetrads of any three ground points of S_3 which are such that $\boldsymbol{\xi}'$ is on C and $\mathbf{a}'$, $\mathbf{b}'$ are distinct points collinear with $\boldsymbol{\xi}'$. Then we may suppose, without loss of generality, that $\mathbf{b}' = \boldsymbol{\xi}' + \mu' \mathbf{a}'$, where $\mu' \in K$; and the four-way point $(\mathbf{a}'; \mathbf{b}'; \boldsymbol{\xi}'; \mu')$ is therefore a proper specialization of the four-way point $(\mathbf{a}; \mathbf{b}; \boldsymbol{\xi}; \mu)$, satisfying all the K-equations that are satisfied by $(\mathbf{a}; \mathbf{b}; \boldsymbol{\xi}; \mu)$. In particular, $F(\mathbf{a}'; \mathbf{b}') = 0$. Conversely, if $\mathbf{a}'$ and $\mathbf{b}'$ are any two points of S_3 such that $F(\mathbf{a}'; \mathbf{b}') = 0$, then, by extension of specialization (Theorem 2, p. 211), there exist a point $\boldsymbol{\xi}'$ of C and an element μ' of K such that $\mathbf{b}' = \boldsymbol{\xi}' + \mu' \mathbf{a}'$. Hence $F(\mathbf{a}'; \mathbf{b}') = 0$ is a necessary and sufficient condition for two distinct points $\mathbf{a}'$ and $\mathbf{b}'$ of S_3 to be collinear with some point of C.

Finally, since the equation (3) is essentially unique, the degrees of $F(\mathbf{x}; \mathbf{y})$ must be the same; and their common value is n, since the pairs of points in a given general plane π which satisfy the condition $F(\mathbf{a}'; \mathbf{b}') = 0$ are those which are collinear with at least one of the n points in which π is met by C. Thus the existence and properties of the primary Cayley equation $F(\mathbf{x}; \mathbf{y}) = 0$ of C have now been established.

3.1. The complex form $\Phi(\mathbf{p})$

Our next step is to show that the primary Cayley equation $F(\mathbf{x}; \mathbf{y}) = 0$ of any irreducible curve C can be rewritten as a complex equation $\Phi(\mathbf{p}) = 0$ of the curve.

THEOREM 4. *If $p_{ik} = x_i y_k - x_k y_i$ $(i, k = 0, 1, 2, 3)$, then the first Cayley form $F(\mathbf{x}; \mathbf{y})$ of any irreducible curve C^n of S_3 can be expressed as a K-form $\Phi(\mathbf{p})$, of degree n, in the six expressions $p_{23}, p_{31}, p_{12}, p_{01}, p_{02}, p_{03}$.*

Proof. The following proof, essentially due to van der Waerden, is based on the simple observation that, if two points $\mathbf{x}$ and $\mathbf{y}$ satisfy the Cayley equation $F(\mathbf{x}; \mathbf{y})$ of a curve C, then so also must every pair of distinct points of the line joining them. Thus $F(\mathbf{x}; \mathbf{y})$ is an *invariant* of the four linear forms $x_i \lambda + y_i \mu$ $(i = 0, 1, 2, 3)$ in λ and μ; for a non-singular linear substitution for λ and μ leaves it unchanged to within a factor dependent only on the substitution. It follows, by a standard theorem of the theory of invariants (see Appendix A, § 22), that $F(\mathbf{x}; \mathbf{y})$ is expressible as a rational function $\Phi(\mathbf{p})$ of the skew forms $p_{ik} = x_i y_k - x_k y_i$; and, since we already know that $F(\mathbf{x}; \mathbf{y})$ is a K-form of degree n in the x_i and also in the y_j, it follows that $\Phi(\mathbf{p})$ is a K-form of degree n in the p_{ik}.

If we are given the complex form $\Phi(\mathbf{p})$ of C^n $(n > 1)$, we can at once derive from it the first Cayley form $F(\mathbf{x}; \mathbf{y})$ by the operation of *dispersion*, i.e. the substitution $p_{ik} \rightarrow x_i y_k - x_k y_i$. The complex form is not unique, being defined only modulo Ω_{pp}, as well as only to within a factor in K; but since dispersion annihilates any multiple of Ω_{pp}, this ambiguity in $\Phi(\mathbf{p})$ is not incompatible with the uniqueness of $F(\mathbf{x}; \mathbf{y})$ apart from a factor in K.

3.2. The second Cayley form $H(\mathbf{u}; \mathbf{v})$

From the complex form $\Phi(\mathbf{p})$ of an irreducible curve C^n we can construct at once a *dual complex form* $\Psi(\boldsymbol{\pi})$ of the same curve, simply by making the substitution

$$(p_{23}, p_{31}, p_{12}, p_{01}, p_{02}, p_{03}) \rightarrow (\pi_{01}, \pi_{02}, \pi_{03}, \pi_{23}, \pi_{31}, \pi_{12});$$

and the equations $\Phi(\mathbf{p}) = 0$ and $\Psi(\boldsymbol{\pi}) = 0$ express exactly the same geometrical condition on a line of S_3. If $\mathbf{u}$ and $\mathbf{v}$ are any two planes through the line in question, the π_{ik} are proportional to the expressions $u_i v_k - u_k v_i$; and it follows that the dispersion $\pi_{ik} \rightarrow u_i v_k - u_k v_i$ converts $\Psi(\boldsymbol{\pi})$ into the secondary Cayley equation $H(\mathbf{u}; \mathbf{v}) = 0$ of C^n. The second Cayley form $H(\mathbf{u}; \mathbf{v})$ obtained in this way is clearly unique to within a factor in K, and we can accordingly state the following further theorem on the associated forms of an irreducible curve.

THEOREM 5. *Every irreducible curve C^n of S_3 has a secondary Cayley equation $H(\mathbf{u}; \mathbf{v}) = 0$, and the form $H(\mathbf{u}; \mathbf{v})$ is unique apart from a factor in K.*

The interdependence of the two Cayley forms with the two complex forms can be represented schematically as follows, the arrows indicating dispersions:

$$F(\mathbf{x}; \mathbf{y}) \longleftarrow \Phi(\mathbf{p}) \longrightarrow \Psi(\boldsymbol{\pi}) \longrightarrow H(\mathbf{u}; \mathbf{v}).$$

Since the complex forms $\Phi(\mathbf{p})$ and $\Psi(\boldsymbol{\pi})$ are connected by a substitution which amounts effectively to a permutation, it might be imagined at first sight that their dispersed forms $F(\mathbf{x}; \mathbf{y})$ and $H(\mathbf{u}; \mathbf{v})$ ought to be related to the curve in ways which are not significantly different. This is not the case, however; for, whereas the representation $\boldsymbol{\pi}$ of a line is dual to the representation $\mathbf{p}$, both the Cayley forms $F(\mathbf{x}; \mathbf{y})$ and $H(\mathbf{u}; \mathbf{v})$ belong to the curve as a locus of points. Consider, for example, the conic C^2 given by

$$x_0 = 0 = x_1 x_3 - x_2^2.$$

Its associated Cayley forms are

$$F(\mathbf{x}; \mathbf{y}) \equiv (x_0 y_1 - x_1 y_0)(x_0 y_3 - x_3 y_0) - (x_0 y_2 - x_2 y_0)^2$$

and

$$H(\mathbf{u}; \mathbf{v}) \equiv (u_2 v_3 - u_3 v_2)(u_1 v_2 - u_2 v_1) - (u_3 v_1 - u_1 v_3)^2,$$

and they are easily seen to have special properties of quite different kinds. Thus $F(\mathbf{x}; \mathbf{y})$ involves all four subscripts, but $H(\mathbf{u}; \mathbf{v})$ does not. Furthermore, $H(\mathbf{u}; \mathbf{v})$ must plainly have the property that, when $\mathbf{v}$ is regarded as fixed, it decomposes into two linear factors

$$(\xi_1 u_1 + \xi_2 u_2 + \xi_3 u_3)(\xi_1' u_1 + \xi_2' u_2 + \xi_3' u_3),$$

corresponding to the two points $(0, \xi_1, \xi_2, \xi_3)$ and $(0, \xi_1', \xi_2', \xi_3')$ in which C^2 is met by the plane $\mathbf{v}$; but $F(\mathbf{x}; \mathbf{y})$ has no similar factorization property.

In the above treatment of the associated forms of an irreducible curve C^n, we have deduced the existence of $H(\mathbf{u}; \mathbf{v})$ indirectly from the existence of $F(\mathbf{x}; \mathbf{y})$. It should be remarked, however, that we might equally well have first given a direct proof of the existence of $H(\mathbf{u}; \mathbf{v})$, and then deduced the existence of $F(\mathbf{x}; \mathbf{y})$. This was, in fact, the procedure originally adopted by Chow and van der Waerden, and developed later by Hodge and Pedoe. The general lines of argument used by these authors can be summarized in the following terms.

(i) For the case of a C^n of S_3, the starting-point of Chow and van der Waerden is the theorem that a generic plane $\mathbf{v}$ of S_3 meets C^n in n points $\overset{1}{\boldsymbol{\eta}},\ldots,\overset{n}{\boldsymbol{\eta}}$ which are conjugate over the field

$$K(\mathbf{v}) = K(v_0, v_1, v_2, v_3);$$

and hence the product

$$\prod_{\lambda=1}^{n} (u_0 \overset{\lambda}{\eta_0} + u_1 \overset{\lambda}{\eta_1} + u_2 \overset{\lambda}{\eta_2} + u_3 \overset{\lambda}{\eta_3})$$

is integral rational in the u_i and rational in the v_j. By multiplying this product by a suitable polynomial in the v_j we can make it integral rational and primitive (see Appendix A, § 16), and we thus obtain a two-way form

$$H(\mathbf{u};\mathbf{v}) \equiv \rho \prod_{\lambda=1}^{n} (u_0\overset{\lambda}{\eta_0} + u_1\overset{\lambda}{\eta_1} + u_2\overset{\lambda}{\eta_2} + u_3\overset{\lambda}{\eta_3})$$

which is irreducible over K. This is the required second Cayley form of C^n. Its degree in the u_i is plainly n; and its further properties—uniqueness apart from a factor in K, symmetry, etc.—can be established.

(ii) For the same case of a C^n of S_3 the method of Hodge and Pedoe is of necessity somewhat different, since it is the intention of these authors ultimately to *define* the order of C as the common degree n of its Cayley form $H(\mathbf{u};\mathbf{v})$ in each of the sets of coordinates $\{u_i\}$ and $\{v_j\}$. The procedure which they adopt is to start from a generic point $\boldsymbol{\xi} = (1,\xi_1,\xi_2,\xi_3)$ of C, then to introduce u_1, u_2, u_3 and v_1, v_2, v_3 as distinct indeterminates, and to define u_0 and v_0 as the elements $-(u_1\xi_1+u_2\xi_2+u_3\xi_3)$ and $-(v_1\xi_1+v_2\xi_2+v_3\xi_3)$ of the field $K(\boldsymbol{\xi},\mathbf{u},\mathbf{v}) = K(\xi_1,\xi_2,\xi_3,u_1,u_2,u_3,v_1,v_2,v_3)$. If $K(\mathbf{u},\mathbf{v}) = K'$, then $K(\boldsymbol{\xi},\mathbf{u},\mathbf{v}) = K'(\boldsymbol{\xi})$ is an algebraic function field of degree of transcendence unity over K'; and the two elements u_0 and v_0 of this field are connected by a (unique) irreducible K'-equation $G(u_0,v_0) = 0$. This equation, when multiplied by a suitable K-polynomial in $u_1, u_2, u_3, v_1, v_2, v_3$, gives an equation

$$H(\mathbf{u},\mathbf{v}) \equiv H(u_0,u_1,u_2,u_3,v_0,v_1,v_2,v_3) = 0$$

which is such that, if u_0 and v_0 are interpreted as indeterminates, $H(\mathbf{u},\mathbf{v})$ is an irreducible K-polynomial in eight indeterminates. It can be shown further that $H(\mathbf{u},\mathbf{v})$ is homogeneous and of the same degree n in the u_i and in the v_j, so that it is a two-way form $H(\mathbf{u};\mathbf{v})$, and that the equation $H(\mathbf{u};\mathbf{v}) = 0$ has all the properties required for its interpretation as the secondary Cayley equation of the curve C.

4. Associated forms of composite curves C^n of S_3

Having dealt so far only with irreducible curves, we now proceed, exactly as we did previously for curves in S_2, to represent every reducible C^n of S_3, by a single equation, which may be of any of the three types already considered in this chapter.

Suppose, in fact, that we take any formal combination

$$m_1 C_1^{n_1} + m_2 C_2^{n_2} + \ldots + m_s C_s^{n_s}$$

of irreducible curves $C_1,\ldots,C_s$, of orders $n_1,\ldots,n_s$ respectively, and counted to multiplicities $m_1, ..., m_s$. Such a combination will be referred to as a *composite* or *reducible* curve of S_3, of *order* $n = \sum_{i=1}^{s} m_i n_i$. Then if $C_i^{n_i}$ has a first Cayley form $F_i(\mathbf{x}; \mathbf{y})$, we define the first Cayley form of the composite curve C^n to be the product

$$F(\mathbf{x}; \mathbf{y}) \equiv \prod_{i=1}^{s} (F_i(\mathbf{x}; \mathbf{y}))^{m_i},$$

and we note that $F(\mathbf{x}; \mathbf{y})$ is a two-way form of degrees (n, n). The second Cayley form and the complex form of C^n are similarly defined in terms of the corresponding forms of the components of C^n. Thus we have the following theorem.

THEOREM 6. *Every curve C^n, of order n, in S_3, whether reducible or not, can be represented by a unique Cayley equation $F(\mathbf{x}; \mathbf{y}) = 0$, of degree n in x_0, x_1, x_2, x_3 and also in y_0, y_1, y_2, y_3; or by a unique Cayley equation $H(\mathbf{u}; \mathbf{v}) = 0$, of degree n in u_0, u_1, u_2, u_3 and also in v_0, v_1, v_2, v_3; or by a complex equation $\Phi(\mathbf{p}) = 0$, of degree n in the line-coordinates p_{ik}, which is uniquely defined modulo Ω_{pp}.*

Each of the forms $F(\mathbf{x}; \mathbf{y})$, $H(\mathbf{u}; \mathbf{v})$, and $\Phi(\mathbf{p})$ is, of course, a very special form of its kind; that is to say, a form in the appropriate indeterminates must satisfy a complicated set of conditions (invariant, as a set, over allowable transformation of coordinates in S_3) for the form to represent a C^n in the relevant way. Nevertheless, Theorem 6 permits us to define the following two representations of all the C^n of S_3 by homogeneous coordinates:

(i) the *Cayley coordinates of the first kind* of a C^n in S_3 are the coefficients $a_0, ..., a_M$ in the first Cayley form $F(\mathbf{x}; \mathbf{y})$ of C^n, arranged in some fixed order, the number $M+1$ of the coordinates being equal to $\binom{n+3}{3}^2$ (see Appendix A, § 15);

(ii) the *Cayley coordinates of the second kind* of C^n are the coefficients $b_0, ..., b_M$ in the second Cayley form $H(\mathbf{u}; \mathbf{v})$ of C^n, again taken in some fixed order.

Yet a third coordinate representation of the C^n of S_3 can be derived from their complex forms $\Phi(\mathbf{p})$; but since, when $n > 1$, $\Phi(\mathbf{p})$ is indeterminate to within an additive multiple of Ω_{pp}, we have to begin by 'normalizing' this expression, i.e. devising some procedure whereby a form $\overline{\Phi}(\mathbf{p})$ that is unique to within a factor in K is singled out from among all the forms $\Phi(\mathbf{p})$ which correspond to any particular curve C^n. Normalization can always be effected by imposing on the coefficients of $\Phi(\mathbf{p})$ a suitable set of fixed linear constraints. Thus, for example, if $n = 2$, a single constraint does what is required and this one has usually been taken to be the vanishing of the sum of the coefficients of $p_{23}p_{01}$, $p_{31}p_{02}$, and $p_{12}p_{03}$ in $\Phi(\mathbf{p})$. If $n = 3$, six normalizing constraints are required, and these may be taken to be the vanishing of the six coefficients of products such as $p_{ij}^2 p_{kl}$ (i, j, k, l all different) in $\Phi(\mathbf{p})$. Generally, then, using a normalized complex form $\overline{\Phi}(\mathbf{p})$, which is a form of the nth degree in the six indeterminates p_{23}, p_{31}, p_{12}, p_{01}, p_{02}, p_{03}, and which therefore involves $N+1 = \dbinom{n+5}{5}$ coefficients, we obtain our third coordinate representation of C^n;

(iii) the *complex coordinates* of C^n are the coefficients $c_0, ..., c_N$, in a fixed order, in an appropriately normalized complex form $\overline{\Phi}(\mathbf{p})$ of the curve.

As regards the mutual relations of the three coordinate representations (a_λ), (b_μ), and (c_ν) of C^n we make only one observation. *The a_λ and the b_μ are all linear forms in the c_ν with coefficients that are rational integers.* The statement about the a_λ follows from the fact that $F(\mathbf{x}; \mathbf{y})$ is the dispersed form of $\overline{\Phi}(\mathbf{p})$; and the statement about the b_μ follows similarly when we note that every normalized form $\overline{\Phi}(\mathbf{p})$ gives rise to a correspondingly normalized form $\overline{\Psi}(\boldsymbol{\pi})$, with the same coefficients differently arranged, and this then yields $H(\mathbf{u}; \mathbf{v})$ on dispersion.

We note finally that the complex coordinates c_ν, being far less numerous than the a_λ or the b_μ, are easier to handle in applications which involve detailed computations.

4.1. Bézout's Theorem for two surfaces in S_3

As a first application of the representation of curves by their primary Cayley equations, we now discuss the curve of intersection of a pair of surfaces in S_3.

We consider two surfaces f and g, with no common component, which are represented by equations $f(x_0, x_1, x_2, x_3) = 0$ and $g(x_0, x_1, x_2, x_3) = 0$, of degrees N_1 and N_2 respectively; and we suppose that the aggregate of common points of the surfaces constitutes a set of s irreducible curves $C_1, ..., C_s$, of orders $n_1, ..., n_s$, with first Cayley forms $F_1, ..., F_s$. Proceeding as we did in Chapter II, § 2, we construct the resultant $F(\mathbf{y}; \mathbf{z})$ of the equations

$$f(\lambda\mathbf{y}+\mu\mathbf{z}) = 0, \quad g(\lambda\mathbf{y}+\mu\mathbf{z}) = 0,$$

and we observe that $F(\mathbf{y}; \mathbf{z}) = 0$ is a necessary and sufficient condition for the line joining the points $\mathbf{y}$ and $\mathbf{z}$ to contain a point common to f and g. It follows that the decomposition of F into factors irreducible over K is of the form

$$F = k F_1^{\sigma_1} F_2^{\sigma_2} \dots F_s^{\sigma_s}, \tag{1}$$

where $k \in K$ and $\sigma_1, \sigma_2, \dots, \sigma_s$ are positive integers; and we propose then to regard σ_i as defining, at least provisionally,[†] the multiplicity of C_i as a component of the (multiplicative) curve of intersection of f and g. As in Chapter II, the multiplicities which we define in this way are invariant for all allowable transformations of coordinates in S_3.

The curve of intersection of the surfaces f and g, regarded as a multiplicative one-dimensional algebraic variety of S_3 (cf. p. 210), may now be represented by the symbol $C = \sum\limits_{i=1}^{s} \sigma_i C_i$, and its order is $n = \sum\limits_{i=1}^{s} \sigma_i n_i$. On the other hand, the order of the resultant $F(\mathbf{y}; \mathbf{z})$ in the coordinates of each of the points $\mathbf{y}$ and $\mathbf{z}$ has the value $N_1 N_2$, and therefore, by (1), $N_1 N_2 = \sum\limits_{i=1}^{s} \sigma_i n_i$. This proves Bézout's Theorem on the order of the curve of intersection of two surfaces.

THEOREM 7 (*Theorem of Bézout for two surfaces in S_3*). *If the intersection of two surfaces f and g of S_3 consists of one or more irreducible curves $C_1, \dots, C_s$, then multiplicities can be assigned invariantively to $C_1, \dots, C_s$, as curves of intersection of f and g, in such a way that the order of the total multiplicative curve of intersection of f and g is equal to the product of the orders of these surfaces.*

COROLLARY. *If two surfaces, of orders N_1 and N_2, intersect only in an irreducible curve C, and this curve does not count multiply as an intersection, then the order of C is $N_1 N_2$.*

5. The Cayley model of the totality of the C^n of S_3

Each of the coordinate representations of the curves C^n of S_3 that we have obtained in § 4 establishes a (1, 1) correspondence between the curves C^n and the points of a certain image manifold W in a projective space Σ. Our main object in devising such a model is,

---

† The definition—to be other than provisional—must be shown to fit in with a general theory of multiplicity of intersection such as that set out in chapter xii of Hodge and Pedoe's *Methods*.

of course, to give precise meaning to the very valuable notion of an *algebraic system* (and, more particularly, an *irreducible algebraic system*) of curves C^n in S_3. The model, indeed, does even more than this, for it provides a basis for a *classification* of all the C^n into certain distinct 'maximal families' in a sense that we shall soon explain. The first and most fundamental question that we must ask about the model W is one concerning the nature of the manifold W itself. Is W an algebraic variety (in the point-set sense of § 2); or is it only a part of such a variety, certain subvarieties being excluded; or is it perhaps outside this range of concepts altogether ?

In considering this problem we shall follow precedent by selecting for examination that particular coordinate representation

$$(b_0, b_1, ..., b_M) \quad \left(M + 1 = \binom{n+3}{3}^2 \right)$$

of curves C^n that is derived from the second Cayley form $H(\mathbf{u}; \mathbf{v})$. The space Σ is in this case of dimensionality M, and the manifold W in Σ_M will be called briefly the *Cayley model of the C^n of S_3*.

It can be proved that this Cayley model W is in fact an algebraic variety in Σ, a result that we now state as our basic theorem in the following terms.

THEOREM 8. *The Cayley model W of all the C^n of S_3 is an algebraic variety in Σ_M, where $M = \binom{n+3}{3}^2 - 1$.*

Proof. For a full proof of this theorem (as a particular case of a general result concerning the Cayley model of all multiplicative V_d^n of S_r) we refer the reader to van der Waerden's *Einführung* and Hodge and Pedoe's *Methods*. All that we propose to do here is to give a description and analysis of the basic conditions involved —i.e. the conditions which a two-way form $G(\mathbf{u}; \mathbf{v})$ of degrees (n, n) must satisfy in order to be the second Cayley form of some C^n—together with a verification of their algebraic character.

We begin, then, by considering an arbitrary two-way form $G(\mathbf{u}; \mathbf{v})$ of degrees (n, n), with coefficients $(B_0, ..., B_M)$, and formulating a set of necessary and sufficient conditions for these coefficients to be the coefficients in some Cayley form $H(\mathbf{u}; \mathbf{v})$.

We observe, in the first place, that the equation $G(\mathbf{u}; \mathbf{v}) = 0$ determines a correspondence $\mathscr{K}$ between planes $\mathbf{u}$ and $\mathbf{v}$. In the particular case in which $n = 1$, $\mathscr{K}$ is a correlation, such that the planes $\mathbf{u}$ (or $\mathbf{v}$) which correspond to a given plane $\mathbf{v}$ (or $\mathbf{u}$) all pass through a point. In general, all the **u** which correspond to a given **v** generate an envelope $U_{\mathbf{v}}$ of class n, and all the **v** which correspond to a given **u** generate an envelope $V_{\mathbf{u}}$, also of class n. It may happen, however, that to some particular **v** (or **u**) there correspond *all* planes **u** (or **v**) of S_3, in which case **v** (or **u**) is said to be a *total plane* **v** (or a *total plane* **u**) of $\mathscr{K}$.

The conditions which are obviously necessary, and which can be proved sufficient, for a form $G(\mathbf{u}; \mathbf{v})$ to be a Cayley form $H(\mathbf{u}; \mathbf{v})$ can now be formulated as follows.

(i) $G(\mathbf{u}; \mathbf{v})$, *as a form in the* u_i, *must factorize completely, in an extension field of* $K(\mathbf{v})$, *into linear factors*:

$$G(\mathbf{u}; \mathbf{v}) = \rho \prod_{i=1}^{n} \left(\overset{i}{\xi_0} u_0 + \overset{i}{\xi_1} u_1 + \overset{i}{\xi_2} u_2 + \overset{i}{\xi_3} u_3 \right). \tag{1}$$

This condition, by itself, only requires the correspondence $\mathscr{K}$ to be such that every envelope $U_{\mathbf{v}}$ breaks up into n points $\overset{i}{\boldsymbol{\xi}}$; or, as we may say, it requires that every plane **v** which is not total for $\mathscr{K}$ shall have n *poles* $\overset{i}{\boldsymbol{\xi}}$ $(i = 1,...,n)$, forming its associated envelope $U_{\mathbf{v}}$. A correlation $(n = 1)$ certainly has this property, and so also, for arbitrary n, has any correspondence $\mathscr{K}$ that is composed of n correlations.

(ii) *Each of the poles* $\overset{i}{\boldsymbol{\xi}}$ *of* **v** $(i = 1,...,n)$, *determined in accordance with* (i), *must lie in* **v**; *i.e. we must have*

$$\overset{i}{\xi_0} v_0 + \overset{i}{\xi_1} v_1 + \overset{i}{\xi_2} v_2 + \overset{i}{\xi_3} v_3 = 0 \quad (i = 1,...,n). \tag{2}$$

For $n = 1$, this is the further condition for the correlation to be a null polarity.

(iii) *Each of the poles* $\overset{i}{\boldsymbol{\xi}}$ $(i = 1,...,n)$ *of any plane* **v** *must be a total point of* $\mathscr{K}$, *such that every pair of planes* **u**′, **v**′ *through* $\overset{i}{\boldsymbol{\xi}}$ *correspond in* $\mathscr{K}$.

We express this last condition algebraically by writing

$$G\left(\mathbf{S}_1 \overset{i}{\boldsymbol{\xi}}, \, \mathbf{S}_2 \overset{i}{\boldsymbol{\xi}} \right) = 0 \quad (i = 1,...,n), \tag{3}$$

where $\mathbf{S}_1$ and $\mathbf{S}_2$ are skew-symmetric matrices with indeterminate elements $\left(\text{so that the vectors } \mathbf{S}_1 \overset{i}{\boldsymbol{\xi}} \text{ and } \mathbf{S}_2 \overset{i}{\boldsymbol{\xi}} \text{ represent independent generic planes through } \overset{i}{\boldsymbol{\xi}}\right)$, and interpreting the equations (3) as identities in all the indeterminates which enter into S_1 and S_2. For $n = 1$, condition (iii) requires the null polarity which arises from condition (ii) to degenerate in such a way that it has a line of total points.

We now proceed to convert the combined conditions (i), (ii), and (iii) into a set of conditions imposed directly on the coefficients B_μ of $G(\mathbf{u}; \mathbf{v})$.

In the first place, by equating coefficients on both sides of (1) we obtain a set of relations

$$\phi_\nu(\mathbf{v}) = \rho \psi_\nu \left(\overset{1}{\xi}, \ldots, \overset{n}{\xi} \right) \quad \left(\nu = 1, \ldots, \binom{n+3}{3} \right);$$

and then, eliminating ρ, we have

$$\phi_\mu \psi_\nu - \phi_\nu \psi_\mu = 0 \quad \left(\mu, \nu = 1, \ldots, \binom{n+3}{3} \right). \tag{4}$$

Equations (2) are already in a convenient form

$$\sum_{\alpha=0}^{3} v_\alpha \overset{i}{\xi}_\alpha = 0 \quad (i = 1, \ldots, n); \tag{5}$$

and since, for each $\overset{i}{\xi}$, equations (3) yield a certain number q of conditions, we have a further set of nq conditions

$$\chi_j \left(B_0, \ldots, B_M; \overset{i}{\xi}_0, \ldots, \overset{i}{\xi}_3 \right) = 0 \quad (i = 1, \ldots, n; j = 1, \ldots, q). \tag{6}$$

On elimination of the n sets of quantities $\overset{i}{\xi}$ $(i = 1, \ldots, n)$, from equations (4), (5), and (6), we obtain a resultant system of equations

$$R_\sigma(B_0, \ldots, B_M; v_0, \ldots, v_3) = 0,$$

which must hold identically in v_0, v_1, v_2, v_3. Finally, therefore, we have a set of relations

$$T_\omega(B_0, \ldots, B_M) = 0,$$

which are a formal expression of the set of conditions (i), (ii), and (iii) on $G(\mathbf{u}; \mathbf{v})$. Taking for granted the sufficiency of these conditions for $G(\mathbf{u}; \mathbf{v})$ to be a Cayley form, we are now able to assert that the Cayley forms $H(\mathbf{u}, \mathbf{v})$ of the curves C^n of S_3 constitute an algebraic system, in the sense made precise in the statement of Theorem 8; and this completes our outline of the proof of that theorem.

Note. From conditions (i), (ii), and (iii), as formulated above, we can derive the slightly simpler conditions for a line complex $\mathcal{K}$ of order n to be the complex of secants of a C^n. These are as follows:

(i') *every complex envelope of $\mathcal{K}$ must degenerate into n points;*

(ii') *each of these n points must be total for $\mathcal{K}$.*

From Theorem 8, taken in conjunction with Theorem 1, we can now deduce the following corollary.

COROLLARY. *The Cayley model W of the C^n of S_3 is composed of a finite number of irreducible varieties $W_1,...,W_s$, possibly of different dimensionalities.*

This corollary establishes, in theory at least, a basic classification of all the C^n of S_3 into a finite number of *maximal families*, represented by the maximal irreducible components $W_1,...,W_s$ of W.

6. The problem of classification of the C^n of S_3

Having established on theoretical grounds the existence, for each value of n, of a finite set of maximal families of C^n in S_3, we ought next to turn to the quite different problem of identifying and enumerating all these families, at least for small values of n. Since the theoretical procedure is, in general, impossible to follow in practice, we would have to adopt other and very different methods from this point on. A full account of these methods is out of place here, but for the purpose of illustrating the general character of the problem and its relation to the formal theory of this chapter, we shall conclude our discussion of the Cayley representation by outlining very briefly the kinds of classification that are obtained for the first few values of n.

The lines C^1 of S_3. For a line with dual coordinate vector $\boldsymbol{\pi}$, the relevant Cayley equation is

$$H(\mathbf{u};\mathbf{v}) \equiv \sum (\pi_{01}(u_2 v_3 - u_3 v_2) + \pi_{23}(u_0 v_1 - u_1 v_0)) = 0,$$

the summation being over three terms. It is easy to see that the forms $H(\mathbf{u};\mathbf{v})$ which arise in this manner are mapped, in the space S_{15} of bilinear forms $G(\mathbf{u};\mathbf{v})$, by the points of a quadric fourfold $W_4^2[5]$, contained in an S_5 in S_{15}. We have thus a reversion to the familiar mapping of the lines of S_3 on the points of a quadric primal of S_5. The lines form a single maximal family.

The C^2 of S_3. The curves of order 2 in S_3 form two distinct 8-parameter maximal families, namely conics and line-pairs; and the Cayleyan W in this case decomposes into two irreducible varieties W_1 and W_2, each of dimensionality 8. W_1 and W_2 intersect in a 7-dimensional subvariety $W_{1,2}$, also algebraic and irreducible, which represents the 7-parameter family of intersecting line-pairs of S_3.

The model W_1 of all conics in S_3 was investigated in full detail by Todd ('Conics and their Representation in 19-space', *Proc. Lond.*

Math.Soc. (2) **36** (1933), 172–206), who showed that it is a $V_8^{92}[19]$, that is to say an 8-dimensional algebraic variety, of order 92, the ambient space of which (i.e. the projective space of lowest dimensionality that contains it) is an S_{19}.

The C^3 of S_3. The cubic curves of S_3 form, in all, four distinct families, each of which is such that specification of its 'general' member requires twelve independent parameters. These families are (i) the twisted cubics, (ii) the plane cubics, (iii) the cubics composed of a conic and a line, and (iv) the triads of lines. W correspondingly decomposes in this case into four irreducible (algebraic) varieties W_1, W_2, W_3, W_4, each of dimensionality 12. The reader should examine for himself the subfamilies of C^3 common to two or more of the maximal families in question, noting in particular that all four of the families have in common the fourfold family of triple lines of S_3.

The C^4 of S_3. The quartic curves of S_3 form eight distinct maximal families, of which seven are 16-parameter systems and one is a 17-parameter system. The 17-parameter system consists of all the plane quartic curves in S_3, while the seven 16-parameter systems have as their 'general' members curves of the following types: (i) a rational C^4, (ii) an elliptic C^4 (the curve of intersection of two quadrics), (iii) a twisted cubic and a line, (iv) a plane cubic and a line, (v) two conics, (vi) a conic and two lines, and (vii) four lines. W decomposes in this case into seven irreducible components of dimensionality 16 and one of dimensionality 17.

The above examples indicate how, as n increases, the total number of maximal families of C^n of S_3 increases very rapidly, although most of the families consist entirely of reducible curves. The number of maximal families of irreducible curves C^n (i.e. families not all of whose members are reducible) increases more slowly with n. It is, of course, with these latter families alone that the problem of classification of curves in S_3 is essentially concerned.

7. The theory for curves in S_r

We conclude this chapter by mentioning briefly how the theory of Cayley forms may be extended to curves C^n, of given order n, in a space of arbitrary given dimensionality r.

We start, as previously, by taking an irreducible curve C, of the given order n, in S_r $(r \geqslant 3)$. Then C has a primary Cayley equation

$$F\left(\overset{1}{\mathbf{x}};\ldots;\overset{r-1}{\mathbf{x}}\right) = 0,$$

the left-hand side of which is an irreducible $(r-1)$-way K-form of degrees $(n,...,n)$ in the coordinates of $r-1$ points $\overset{1}{\mathbf{x}},...,\overset{r-1}{\mathbf{x}}$. The equation $F = 0$ expresses the condition for the secundum Π which joins the $r-1$ points in question (supposing them to be linearly independent) to intersect C.

Similarly, C has a secondary Cayley equation

$$H\left(\overset{1}{\mathbf{u}}; \overset{2}{\mathbf{u}}\right) = 0,$$

the left-hand side of this equation being an irreducible two-way form of degrees (n, n) in the coordinates of two primes $\overset{1}{\mathbf{u}}$ and $\overset{2}{\mathbf{u}}$. The equation expresses the condition for the secundum Π which is common to $\overset{1}{\mathbf{u}}$ and $\overset{2}{\mathbf{u}}$ to meet C.

Finally, C has a complex equation, which may be written in either of the two forms

$$\Phi(\mathbf{p}) = 0, \quad \Psi(\boldsymbol{\pi}) = 0,$$

and which expresses the condition for the secundum Π with Grassmann coordinate vector $\mathbf{p}$ or $\boldsymbol{\pi}$ to meet C. The vector $\mathbf{p}$ is that of the ordinary Grassmann coordinates $p_{i_1,...,i_{r-1}}$ of Π, these being defined as the $(r-1)$-rowed determinants of the coordinate matrix of any $r-1$ linearly independent points of Π; and the vector $\boldsymbol{\pi}$ is that of the dual Grassmann coordinates $\pi_{j_1 j_2}$, obtained from the coordinate matrix of any two linearly independent primes through Π. Since the $\pi_{j_1 j_2}$, arranged in a suitable order, are proportional to the $p_{i_1,...,i_{r-1}}$, the equations $\Phi(\mathbf{p}) = 0$ and $\Psi(\boldsymbol{\pi}) = 0$ are readily convertible into each other. And once again, in this more general theory, $F\left(\overset{1}{\mathbf{x}};...;\overset{r-1}{\mathbf{x}}\right)$ can be regarded as a dispersed form of $\Phi(\mathbf{p})$, and $H\left(\overset{1}{\mathbf{u}}; \overset{2}{\mathbf{u}}\right)$ as a dispersed form of $\Psi(\boldsymbol{\pi})$.

From this point on, the theory of Cayley forms for curves of S_r proceeds on exactly the same lines as the theory for curves of S_3.

NOTES AND EXERCISES ON CHAPTER IX

1. Verify that the second Cayley form of the line with equations $x_1 = 0 = x_2$ is $H(\mathbf{u}; \mathbf{v}) = u_0 v_3 - u_3 v_0$.

By writing $\mathbf{u} = \mathbf{Sx}$, $\mathbf{v} = \mathbf{S'x}$, where $\mathbf{S}$ and $\mathbf{S'}$ are skew-symmetric 4×4 matrices of indeterminates, substituting in $H(\mathbf{u}; \mathbf{v})$, and equating the resulting expression to zero (identically in all the indeterminates occurring in $\mathbf{S}, \mathbf{S'}$), recover the original equations $x_1 = 0 = x_2$ of the line.

2. For the conic $x_0 x_2 = x_1^2$ in S_2, show that the second Cayley form is

$$H(\mathbf{u}; \mathbf{v}) = (u_1 v_2 - u_2 v_1)(u_0 v_1 - u_1 v_0) - (u_2 v_0 - u_0 v_2)^2.$$

Verify that if $v_0:v_1:v_2 = 1:-(\alpha+\beta):\alpha\beta$, then $H(\mathbf{u};\mathbf{v})$ factorizes as a quadratic form in u_0, u_1, u_2, and find the factors.

If $\mathbf{S}, \mathbf{S}'$ are skew-symmetric 3×3 matrices of indeterminates and we put $\mathbf{u} = \mathbf{Sx}$, $\mathbf{v} = \mathbf{S'x}$, verify that

$$H(\mathbf{u};\mathbf{v}) = (x_0 x_2 - x_1^2)(Ax_0 + Bx_1 + Cx_2)^2,$$

where $A = S_{01}S'_{02} - S_{02}S'_{01}$, etc.; and deduce from this that if $H(\mathbf{u};\mathbf{v})$ is to be zero identically in the indeterminates S_{ij}, S'_{kl}, we must have $x_0 x_2 - x_1^2 = 0$.

3. Show that the line $\mathbf{p}$ meets the curve of intersection of the quadrics $x_0 x_2 = x_1^2$ and $x_1 x_3 = x_2^2$ if and only if

$$R(\mathbf{p}) \equiv \begin{vmatrix} p_{01} & p_{02} & p_{12} & 0 \\ p_{12} & p_{13} & p_{23} & 0 \\ 0 & p_{01} & p_{02} & p_{12} \\ 0 & p_{12} & p_{13} & p_{23} \end{vmatrix} = 0,$$

and hence deduce that the complex equation of the twisted cubic $(1, \theta, \theta^2, \theta^3)$ is $\Phi(\mathbf{p}) = 0$, where $\Phi(\mathbf{p}) = R/p_{12}$.

Hence or otherwise compute the first Cayley form $F(\mathbf{x};\mathbf{y})$ of the same twisted cubic.

4. Show that the second Cayley form of the twisted cubic $(1, \theta, \theta^2, \theta^3)$ may be written in the form

$$H(\mathbf{u};\mathbf{v}) = \begin{vmatrix} u_0 & u_1 & u_2 & u_3 & 0 & 0 \\ 0 & u_0 & u_1 & u_2 & u_3 & 0 \\ 0 & 0 & u_0 & u_1 & u_2 & u_3 \\ 0 & 0 & v_0 & v_1 & v_2 & v_3 \\ 0 & v_0 & v_1 & v_2 & v_3 & 0 \\ v_0 & v_1 & v_2 & v_3 & 0 & 0 \end{vmatrix},$$

and exhibit its decomposability, as a form in the u_i, for given values of the v_j.

5. If $\overset{1}{S} = 0$, $\overset{2}{S} = 0$, $\overset{3}{S} = 0$ are the equations of any three linearly independent quadrics through a twisted cubic C, show that the first Cayley form of C is given by

$$F(\mathbf{x};\mathbf{y}) = \begin{vmatrix} \overset{1}{S}_{xx} & \overset{1}{S}_{xy} & \overset{1}{S}_{yy} \\ \overset{2}{S}_{xx} & \overset{2}{S}_{xy} & \overset{2}{S}_{yy} \\ \overset{3}{S}_{xx} & \overset{3}{S}_{xy} & \overset{3}{S}_{yy} \end{vmatrix},$$

where $\overset{i}{S}_{xx}$ is the quadratic form $\overset{i}{S}(\mathbf{x})$, $\overset{i}{S}_{yy}$ is $\overset{i}{S}(\mathbf{y})$, and $\overset{i}{S}_{xy}$ is the polarized form of $\overset{i}{S}(\mathbf{x})$.

When C is the curve $(1, \theta, \theta^2, \theta^3)$, deduce from the above the Cayley form $F(\mathbf{x};\mathbf{y})$ of C, using the work of Exercise 3 as a check.

6. Show that the complex form of the complete curve of intersection of the surfaces with equations $2x_0 x_1 + x_3^2 = 0$ and $2x_1 x_2 + x_3^2 = 0$ is

$$\Phi(\mathbf{p}) = p_{13}^2 G(\mathbf{p}),$$

where $G(\mathbf{p}) = (p_{23} - p_{03})^2 - 2p_{02}(p_{12} + p_{01})$. Interpret this result.

7. *Quadratic complexes.* The general quadratic form in $p_{23}, ..., p_{03}$ has twenty-one coefficients $a_{ij,kl}$, so that it defines a point of a projective space

S_{20} and is defined, to within a constant factor, by any such point. The points of the prime S_{19} defined by the normalizing relation

$$a_{01,23} + a_{02,31} + a_{03,12} = 0$$

are then in $(1, 1)$ correspondence with the quadratic line-complexes of S_3, and we may say that there are ∞^{19} such complexes.

The so-called *quadric complexes*—each the complex of tangent lines to a quadric surface—form an ∞^9-system and are mapped, as may be shown, on the points of an irreducible algebraic variety M_9 of S_{19}.

The *conic complexes*—each the complex of secants to a conic—are specializations of quadric complexes, and they are mapped, as has been shown by Todd, by the points of an irreducible sub-variety V_8^{92} of M_9 (see reference on p. 224). Among other developments, Todd considered properties of *linear complexes of conics in* S_3, represented by prime sections of V_8^{92}.

8. *Cubic complexes.* A cubic form $\Phi_3(\mathbf{p})$ in the p_{ij} has fifty-six coefficients; but, as already stated, any cubic complex can be represented without ambiguity by a unique equation $\Phi_3(\mathbf{p}) = 0$ in which the coefficients of the six power products $p_{01}^2 p_{23}, \dots, p_{01} p_{23}^2, \dots$ are all zero. Thus the cubic complexes in S_3 form an ∞^{49}-system, being in $(1, 1)$ correspondence with the points of a projective space S_{49}. Those of them that are secant-complexes of cubic curves are represented, as was also noted, by the points of four irreducible 12-dimensional varieties in S_{49}, of which one in particular, W_1 say, contains the image points of all secant-complexes of twisted cubics of S_3. Surprisingly little is known about the properties of W_1, though some attempts to investigate it in detail have been made. Thus, in particular, there is no knowledge of the multiplicity on W_1 of its subordinate fourfold variety representing the triple lines of S_3.

9. *The complex equation of a Cremona transformation of S_3.* Let τ be any Cremona (birational) transformation of a space S_3 into a space T_3, and let $\mathbf{p}$ and $\mathbf{q}$ be the coordinate vectors of lines p and q of S_3 and T_3. Show, then, that τ is uniquely defined by the single two-way equation

$$\Phi(\mathbf{p}, \mathbf{q}) = 0,$$

which expresses the condition that either of the lines p, q should meet the curve into which the other is transformed by τ (it being assumed that this transform is a determinate curve).

Interpret the degrees of Φ in the two sets of variables p_{ij}, $q_{i'j'}$, as characters of τ, and show that $\Phi(\mathbf{p}, \mathbf{q})$ is the complex (Cayley) form of the curve in S_3 corresponding to a *given* line $\mathbf{q}$ of T_3.

10. *Twisted cubics of S_3 through four fixed points.* Show that the reciprocal transformation $y_0 : y_1 : y_2 : y_3 = 1/x_0 : 1/x_1 : 1/x_2 : 1/x_3$ carries a general line of the space T_3 of $\mathbf{y}$ into a twisted cubic through the vertices of the tetrahedron of reference in the space S_3 of $\mathbf{x}$. Discuss also the exceptional cases—lines of T_3 that meet one or more of the edges of the reference tetrahedron in this space.

If the *dual* coordinate vectors $(\pi_{01}, \dots, \pi_{12})$ and $(\rho_{01}, \dots, \rho_{12})$ of lines p and q of S_3 and T_3 are written as

$$(l, m, n, l', m', n') \quad \text{and} \quad (L, M, N, L', M', N')$$

respectively, show that the normalized complex form of the twisted cubic in S_3 corresponding to the line q of T_3 is

$$\Phi(l,...;\ L,...) = LMNlmn + LM'N'lm'n' + L'MN'l'mn' + L'M'Nl'm'n$$
$$+ LL'mn(Nm' + Mn') + ... + ...$$
$$+ LL'm'n'(N'm + M'n) + ... + ...$$

Deduce from this a parametric representation of the irreducible V_4 in S_{49} (cf. Exercise 8) such that the corresponding fourfold algebraic system of cubic curves in S_3 contains all the twisted cubics through the vertices of the tetrahedron of reference in S_3.

Show, in particular, that the V_4 in question can be mapped birationally on a quadric fourfold Ω of S_5 in such a way that its prime sections correspond to sections of Ω by cubic primals through four planes α_0, α_1, α_2, α_3 of the same system on Ω.

[For a full consideration of this and other analogous representations, the reader is referred to a paper 'Cayley Models of some Homaloidal Curve-Systems of S_3' by R. O. Gibson and J. G. Semple, *Proc. Lond. Math. Soc.*, Ser. 3, **7** (1957), 75–86.]

CHAPTER X

LINEAR SERIES ON A CURVE

1. Sets of places on a curve C

THROUGHOUT this chapter the symbol C will always denote some selected model of a given one-dimensional algebraic function field Σ, and we shall for the most part regard this irreducible curve C as an aggregate of places $\mathscr{P}$.

Geometry *on* C, as we conceive it, is concerned with the classification and general properties of finite sets of places on the curve, mainly in connexion with a certain relation of equivalence which can hold between such sets. The sets which primarily concern us are ordinary multiplicative sets, in which a place $\mathscr{P}$ can count any number of times. A set of this kind will be called an *effective set* (of places) on C, and we shall represent it as a formal sum

$$m_1\mathscr{P}_1 + m_2\mathscr{P}_2 + \dots + m_s\mathscr{P}_s,$$

where m_i, a non-negative integer, is the multiplicity of $\mathscr{P}_i$ in the set. In addition, we define the *null set* (of places) on C, which we represent by the symbol 0, as the unique effective set with no members.

This natural concept of effective set can usefully be generalized by allowing the multiplicities to take negative as well as positive values, and in this way we obtain the formal concept of *virtual set* (of places). A set which may be effective or virtual will be referred to simply as a set.

Suppose A is any set $\sum_{i=1}^{s} m_i\mathscr{P}_i$ on C. If we denote by $\mu_{\mathscr{P}}$ the integer 0 if $\mathscr{P}$ is a place on C distinct from all the $\mathscr{P}_i$ and the integer m_i (which may be positive, negative, or zero) if $\mathscr{P} = \mathscr{P}_i$ ($i = 1,\dots,s$), we may write formally

$$A = \sum_{\mathscr{P}} \mu_{\mathscr{P}}\,\mathscr{P},$$

the summation being over all the places $\mathscr{P}$ on C. In this way we associate with the set A a uniquely defined place-function $\mu_{\mathscr{P}}$ on C. If, conversely, we begin with an integral valued place function $\mu_{\mathscr{P}}$ which is zero at all but a finite number of places on C, this function determines a unique set A. Any such function $\mu_{\mathscr{P}}$ will be referred to as the *index function* of the set which it determines. Plainly two index functions $\mu_{\mathscr{P}}$ and $\mu'_{\mathscr{P}}$ belong to the same set if and only if $\mu_{\mathscr{P}} = \mu'_{\mathscr{P}}$ for all $\mathscr{P}$ on C. The set A determined by $\mu_{\mathscr{P}}$ is effective if and only if $\mu_{\mathscr{P}} \geqslant 0$ for all $\mathscr{P}$, and it is the null set if and only if $\mu_{\mathscr{P}} = 0$ for all $\mathscr{P}$. The sum $\sum_{\mathscr{P}} \mu_{\mathscr{P}}$ is called the *order* of A; and if A is effective its order is the number of its members in the usual (multiplicative) sense.

If $A = \sum_{\mathscr{P}} \mu_{\mathscr{P}} \mathscr{P}$ is a set of places on C, then A determines in an obvious way an associated multiplicative point-set $\delta(A)$, namely the set of centres of the places in A, each counted to the multiplicity of the place. Thus
$$\delta(A) = \sum_{P} \nu_P P,$$
summed over all the ground points of C, ν_P being defined as $\sum_{\mathscr{P}} \mu_{\mathscr{P}}$, summed over all the places $\mathscr{P}$ with P as centre.

If A and A' are two sets of places, with index functions $\mu_{\mathscr{P}}$ and $\mu'_{\mathscr{P}}$, we define the *sum* set $A + A'$ and the *difference* set $A - A'$ as the sets with index functions $\mu_{\mathscr{P}} + \mu'_{\mathscr{P}}$ and $\mu_{\mathscr{P}} - \mu'_{\mathscr{P}}$ respectively. This is legitimate since the sum or difference of two index functions is clearly again an index function. We observe, in particular, that *every set A can be represented, in one and only one way, as a difference $A_1 - A_2$ of two disjoint effective sets*.

From what we have already said, we can at once deduce the following theorem.

THEOREM 1. *The aggregate of all sets on C is an abelian group W with respect to addition, and the aggregate of all effective sets on C is a semigroup W' contained in W. Every set in W is uniquely representable as a difference of two disjoint sets in W'.*

We shall now turn our attention to sets on C that are defined by various special procedures.

1.1. The trace of a primal on C

Suppose that C is a curve of order q in S_d $(d \geqslant 2)$, and let $\boldsymbol{\xi}$ be a generic point of C. Then $\Sigma = K(\boldsymbol{\xi})$. Let $F(\mathbf{x}) = 0$ be the equation of a primal F of order N of S_d which does not contain C. Thus $F(\boldsymbol{\xi}) \neq 0$, and, at each place $\mathscr{P}$ on C, F has a finite order $O_{\mathscr{P}}(F)$.

DEFINITIONS. The *trace $F.[C]$ on C of a primal F* which does not contain C (or of a K-form $F(x_0,...,x_d)$) is the effective set of places with index function $\mu_{\mathscr{P}} = O_{\mathscr{P}}(F)$.

The *set of zeros F . C of F on C* is the set of centres of the places belonging to $F . [C]$, each counted to the appropriate multiplicity, i.e. the point-set $\delta(F . [C])$.

If, for example, C is a plane cubic with a double point D at which there are two places $\mathscr{D}_1$, $\mathscr{D}_2$ with tangents T_1, T_2, then the trace on C of the nodal tangent T_1 is the set $2\mathscr{D}_1 + \mathscr{D}_2$, while the set of zeros of T_1 on C is the point D counted three times.

In the general case, the order of the set $F . [C]$—which is identical with the order of the multiplicative point-set $F . C$—is equal to the product qN of the orders of C and F (Bézout's Theorem, p. 197).

THEOREM 2. *For two primals F and F', neither of which contains C, to have the same trace on C, it is necessary and sufficient that they are of the same order and that some primal of the pencil $F + \lambda F'$ contains C.*

Proof. Suppose, in the first place, that $F . [C] = F' . [C]$. Then, since the orders of the sets are the same, $qN = qN'$, where N, N' are the orders of F, F'; and thus $N = N'$. Further, for every $\lambda \in K$ and every $\mathscr{P}$ on C,

$$\mu_{\mathscr{P}} = O_{\mathscr{P}}(F) = O_{\mathscr{P}}(F') \leqslant O_{\mathscr{P}}(F + \lambda F').$$

By Bézout's Theorem, there is either equality on the right for all $\mathscr{P}$ or else $F + \lambda F'$ contains C (in which case $O_{\mathscr{P}}(F + \lambda F') = \infty$ for all $\mathscr{P}$). By choosing λ, therefore, so that $F + \lambda F'$ passes through some chosen point of C that is not common to F and F', we obtain a unique primal of the pencil $F + \lambda F'$ which contains C.

Now suppose, conversely, that C is contained in some primal $F + \lambda_0 F'$, but not in F or F'. Then, since $\lambda_0 \neq 0$,

$$O_{\mathscr{P}}(F') = O_{\mathscr{P}}(\lambda_0 F') = O_{\mathscr{P}}((F + \lambda_0 F') - F) = O_{\mathscr{P}}(F)$$

for all $\mathscr{P}$ on C, and therefore $F . [C] = F' . [C]$. This completes the proof of the theorem.

1.2. Traces on C of rational functions in S_d

We now extend the notion of trace to rational functions.

DEFINITION. Let $F(\mathbf{x})/G(\mathbf{x})$ be a rational function of a point $\mathbf{x}$ of S_d, i.e. a quotient of two K-forms of the same degree N, and let us suppose that $F(\xi) \neq 0$, $G(\xi) \neq 0$. Then the *trace on C of the rational function F/G*, which we denote by $F/G . [C]$, is the set—in general virtual—with index function $\mu_{\mathscr{P}} = O_{\mathscr{P}}(F) - O_{\mathscr{P}}(G)$.

Since $\sum\limits_{\mathscr{P}} O_{\mathscr{P}}(F)$ and $\sum\limits_{\mathscr{P}} O_{\mathscr{P}}(G)$ are both equal to qN, the order of the set $F/G.[C]$ is necessarily zero.

We can write $F/G.[C]$ as a formal difference of effective sets thus

$$F/G.[C] = F.[C] - G.[C];$$

but it should be noted that the effective sets $F.[C]$ and $G.[C]$ are not necessarily disjoint.

1.3. Traces on C of rational functions on the curve

We now pass from rational functions in S_d to the much more important rational functions on the curve C.

In terms of a chosen generic point ξ of C, we may identify the rational functions on C, to within isomorphism over K, with the elements

$$\chi = F(\xi)/G(\xi) \quad (G(\xi) \neq 0)$$

of the field $\Sigma = K(\xi)$. In order to change over to the alternative representation of such rational functions by congruence classes $\{F(\mathbf{x})/G(\mathbf{x})\} \pmod{C}$ we need only define these classes as the classes of rational functions $F(\mathbf{x})/G(\mathbf{x})$ in S_d which reduce to the several elements χ of Σ on substitution of ξ for $\mathbf{x}$.

A rational function χ on C has a *value* $\chi(\mathscr{P})$, belonging to $K \cup \{\infty\}$, at each place $\mathscr{P}$ on C, this value being given by the formula

$$\chi(\mathscr{P}) = [F(\mathbf{x}(u))/G(\mathbf{x}(u))]_{u=0},$$

where $\mathbf{x}(u)$ is some standard parametric representation of $\mathscr{P}$. It is easily seen that the right-hand side of this equation is invariant with respect to regular substitution for the parameter.

The *zero-places* and *pole-places* of χ are those places at which χ takes the value 0 or ∞, that is to say the places at which $O_{\mathscr{P}}(\chi) > 0$ or $O_{\mathscr{P}}(\chi) < 0$ respectively (cf. p. 169).

DEFINITION. The *trace* $\chi[C]$ *of any non-zero rational function* χ *on* C is the set of places defined by the index function $\mu_{\mathscr{P}} = O_{\mathscr{P}}(\chi)$.

By Theorem 6 on p. 91, the order $\sum\limits_{\mathscr{P}} \mu_{\mathscr{P}}$ of the set so defined is zero. It may be seen that this set is the trace on C of every rational function $F(\mathbf{x})/G(\mathbf{x})$ belonging to the congruence class modulo C that corresponds to the element χ of Σ.

There is one very special case that can arise, namely that in which the trace of χ on C is the null set; and we can show that the functions with a null trace are the non-zero constants. For suppose that $\chi[C] = 0$. Then $O_{\mathscr{P}}(\chi) = 0$ for every place $\mathscr{P}$ on C, and therefore, if we choose any fixed place $\mathscr{P}_0$, $\chi(\mathscr{P}_0)$ is some non-zero element c of K. $\chi-c$ is then a rational function χ' on C, and if it is different from zero it has an order $O_{\mathscr{P}}(\chi')$ such that $O_{\mathscr{P}}(\chi') \geqslant 0$ for all $\mathscr{P}$ on C and $O_{\mathscr{P}_0}(\chi') > 0$. This means, however, that $\sum_{\mathscr{P}} O_{\mathscr{P}}(\chi') > 0$, which we already know to be impossible; and therefore χ' cannot be different from zero. Thus $\chi-c = 0$, and so $\chi = c$. This proves that a rational function χ on C can only have the null set as its trace if it is a non-zero constant; and it is at once obvious that, conversely, the trace of every non-zero constant function is the null set.

Now suppose that χ_1 and χ_2 are any two non-zero rational functions with the same trace. Then χ_1/χ_2 is also a non-zero rational function, and since

$$\chi_1/\chi_2[C] = \chi_1[C] - \chi_2[C] = 0,$$

it follows by what we have just proved that χ_1/χ_2 is a constant. We thus have the following theorem.

THEOREM 3. *The traces of two non-zero rational functions χ_1 and χ_2 on C are identical if and only if χ_1/χ_2 is a constant.*

Since the trace $\chi[C]$ of any non-zero χ is of order zero, we can represent it uniquely as a difference

$$\chi[C] = Z_\chi - P_\chi$$

of two disjoint effective sets of equal order. These sets Z_χ and P_χ will be referred to as the *positive and negative components* of $\chi[C]$. The effective point-sets $\delta(Z_\chi)$ and $\delta(P_\chi)$ are respectively the set of centres of zero-places and the set of centres of pole-places of χ.

We note finally that, if $F(\mathbf{x})/G(\mathbf{x})$ is any one of the rational functions in S_d that reduce to χ on C—i.e. if, in the notation of Chapter III, § 2.4, $\{F(\mathbf{x})/G(\mathbf{x})\} = \chi$—then the traces of $F(\mathbf{x})$ and $G(\mathbf{x})$ on C must be of the form

$$F.[C] = Z_\chi + E, \qquad G.[C] = P_\chi + E,$$

where E is some effective set.

2. The relation of equivalence between sets on C

Apart from the preliminary definitions and properties that we have given in § 1, the basic structure of the aggregate of sets of places on C depends almost entirely on a certain relation of equivalence between such sets, and we shall now define this relation.

DEFINITION. Two sets of places A and B on C are said to be *equivalent* ($A \equiv B$) if and only if $A - B = \chi[C]$, where χ is some non-zero rational function on C.

We can readily verify that the relation $A \equiv B$ possesses the three characteristic properties of an equivalence relation.

(i) It is reflexive, since $A - A = c[C]$, where c is any non-zero element of K.

(ii) It is symmetrical, since $A - B = \chi[C]$ implies $B - A = \chi^{-1}[C]$.

(iii) It is transitive, since $A - B = \chi_1[C]$ and $B - D = \chi_2[C]$ together imply $A - D = \chi_1 \chi_2[C]$.

It now follows that the relation $A \equiv B$ distributes all the sets on C into mutually exclusive *equivalence classes*. Every set A determines a unique equivalence class, which we shall denote by $\{A\}$.

The relation of equivalence between sets is compatible with addition of sets; for if $A \equiv A'$ and $B \equiv B'$ we have

$$A - A' = \chi_1[C] \quad \text{and} \quad B - B' = \chi_2[C],$$

from which it follows that

$$(A+B) - (A'+B') = \chi_1 \chi_2[C],$$

so that $A + B \equiv A' + B'$. We may therefore define *addition of equivalence classes* by putting $\{A\} + \{B\} = \{A+B\}$; and subtraction may be defined similarly. We can then assert the following theorem, which is easily verified.

THEOREM 4. *Every set of places A on C belongs to a unique equivalence class $\{A\}$, consisting of mutually equivalent sets on C, all of the same order; and, when addition of equivalence classes is defined in the natural way, the set of equivalence classes is an abelian group.*

2.1. Equivalence of effective sets

It follows from the observation made at the end of § 1.3 that, for effective sets, the definition of equivalence can be expressed in the following alternative forms. The condition for two effective sets A and B to be equivalent is that the sets are of the form

$$A = Z_\chi + E, \qquad B = P_\chi + E,$$

where Z_χ and P_χ are the positive and negative components of the trace of some rational function χ on C and E is some effective set on C. In other words, *two effective sets are equivalent if and only if* *they are traced on C, residually to some effective set E, by two primals of the same order in S_d.*

EXAMPLES. (i) In S_2, the complete sets traced on an irreducible curve C by any two curves of the same order, neither of which has C as a component, are equivalent; and thus the aggregate of (effective) sets traced on C by all curves of any given order n is contained in an equivalence class $\{A\}$ on C.

(ii) If C is a plane cubic, and (L_1, L_2) is any general pair of lines through a simple point P_0 of C, then L_1 and L_2 trace equivalent sets $(\mathscr{P}_1, \mathscr{P}_1')$ and $(\mathscr{P}_2, \mathscr{P}_2')$ on C, residual to the single place $\mathscr{P}_0$ at P_0. If C has a double point D, at which there are two places $\mathscr{D}_1$ and $\mathscr{D}_2$ then any two places on C, being each residual to the pair $(\mathscr{D}_1, \mathscr{D}_2)$, are equivalent sets of order 1 on C.

We often wish, instead of considering an entire equivalence class $\{A\}$, to confine our attention to the *effective* sets in $\{A\}$, and it is accordingly convenient to give a name to the aggregate of effective sets in any equivalence class.

DEFINITION. If an equivalence class $\{A\}$ on C has at least one effective set among its members, then the aggregate of effective sets in $\{A\}$ is called the *effective kernel* of $\{A\}$ and is denoted by $|A|$.

In other words, $|A|$ is the aggregate of all effective sets that are equivalent to A. If an operation of addition of effective kernels is introduced by the definition

$$|A|+|B| = |A+B|,$$

which is readily seen to be legitimate, the totality of effective kernels acquires the structure of an additive semigroup.

In the next phase of our investigation we shall be working towards a basic result, obtained in § 4.1, which tells us that every linear series on a curve C can be extended to a maximal or 'complete' linear series on C, and that every such complete series is in fact the kernel $|A|$ of some equivalence class $\{A\}$ on C. Before addressing ourselves to this task, however, we need to study the general properties of linear systems of rational functions on C and linear systems of sets of places on the curve.

3. Linear systems of rational functions on C

The field $K_C = \Sigma$ of all rational functions on C is a vector space over K, and any given set of such functions determines a subspace of the vector space. If $\chi_0, ..., \chi_r$ are $r+1$ rational functions on C that are linearly independent over K, we shall refer to the set of all functions of the form

$$\chi_\lambda = \lambda_0 \chi_0 + \ldots + \lambda_r \chi_r,$$

where $\lambda_0, \ldots, \lambda_r$ are any elements of K that are not all zero, as an *$(r+1)$-dimensional linear system* (χ) *of rational functions on C*. The linear system thus consists of all the functions of the vector subspace spanned by $\chi_0, \ldots, \chi_r$ *except for the one function* 0, which we shall always exclude. Any basis of the vector subspace (i.e. any set of $r+1$ linearly independent functions which belong to it) will be said to be a *basis of the linear system*. In particular, (χ) has the basis $(\chi_0, \ldots, \chi_r)$, and in terms of this basis every function χ_λ of the system has a well defined non-zero coefficient vector $\boldsymbol{\lambda} = (\lambda_0, \ldots, \lambda_r)$. By a *stalk* of the linear system (χ) we shall understand a linear sub-system which consists of all functions $\lambda\chi$, where χ is a fixed element of (χ) and λ can be any non-zero element of K.

The members of (χ) may be mapped by means of their coefficient vectors $\boldsymbol{\lambda}$ on the points, excluding the origin, of an affine space A_{r+1}; and the stalks are then mapped on the rays through the origin. Alternatively, the stalks, being given by *homogeneous* coordinate vectors $\boldsymbol{\lambda}$, may be mapped directly on the points of a projective space S_r.

A second linear system (χ') will be said to be *similar* to the system (χ) if its elements are obtainable by multiplying all the elements of (χ) by a fixed rational function $\bar{\chi}$ on C, i.e. if $(\chi') = \bar{\chi}(\chi)$. This condition implies (since a field can have no divisors of zero) that (χ) and (χ') are of the same dimensionality. The relation of similarity between linear systems is clearly symmetrical.

A linear system (χ) will be said to be *normal* if it has the constant 1 among its members. When (χ) is normal it has a basis of the special form $(1, \chi_1, \ldots, \chi_r)$. Every linear system is similar to a normal system, since, if (χ) has a basis $(\chi_0, \chi_1, \ldots, \chi_r)$, $\chi_0^{-1}(\chi)$ has a basis $(1, \chi_0^{-1}\chi_1, \ldots, \chi_0^{-1}\chi_r)$.

Two linear systems will be said to be *conormal* if (i) they are similar to each other, and (ii) each is separately normal. The relation between two such systems is symmetrical, and each system can be obtained from the other by dividing each member of the latter by a fixed member of itself.

In what follows we shall be largely concerned with the properties of normal linear systems (χ).

3.1. Linear systems of null-equivalent sets on C

We are not so much interested in linear systems (χ) of rational functions themselves as in the systems of sets of places on C to which they give rise; and we shall denote the set of traces on C of all the members of a given linear system (χ) by the symbol $(\chi)[C]$. We note first of all that the sets that are obtainable in this way, being traces of rational functions, are of a special kind. If χ is any rational function on C, it follows from the definition of equivalence of sets (p. 235) that $\chi[C] \equiv 0$; and every set traced by a rational function may accordingly be said to be *null-equivalent*.

By Theorem 3, two functions χ_1 and χ_2 have the same trace if and only if they differ by a constant factor; and therefore *the functions which have the same trace on C as any given function χ are those functions which make up the stalk through χ in any linear system to which χ belongs*. If we take any particular $(r+1)$-dimensional system (χ) of rational functions on C, there is a $(1, 1)$ correspondence between the stalks of (χ) and the sets of $(\chi)[C]$; and since the stalks can be mapped without exception on the points of a projective space S_r, the same is true of the sets of $(\chi)[C]$. We shall therefore say that $(\chi)[C]$ is an *r-dimensional linear system N_r of null-equivalent sets on C*.

A system N_r will be called *normal* if and only if it contains the null set; for then and only then is it derivable from a normal system (χ) of rational functions. Further, two systems N_r and N'_r will be called *conormal* if and only if they can be derived from conormal systems (χ) and (χ'); and this means that each of them is normal and the sets of N'_r are obtainable from those of N_r by subtracting one particular set of N_r from them all.

We now prove an important lemma.

LEMMA 1. *If a system N_r, as defined above, is normal, then its (null-equivalent) sets can all be written as differences $X - P$ of effective sets X and P such that* (i) *P is fixed, and* (ii) *there is no place on C that belongs to every X.*

Proof. We may suppose that $N_r = (\chi)[C]$, where (χ) is normal and therefore has a basis $(\chi_0, \chi_1, ..., \chi_r)$, with $\chi_0 = 1$. We may then express $\chi_1, ..., \chi_r$ in the form

$$\chi_i = F_i(\boldsymbol{\xi})/F_0(\boldsymbol{\xi}) \quad (i = 1, ..., r),$$

where $F_0(\mathbf{x}), F_1(\mathbf{x}), ..., F_r(\mathbf{x})$ are $r+1$ K-forms of the same degree M.

Then if
$$\chi_\lambda = \sum_{i=0}^{r} \lambda_i \chi_i, \quad F_\lambda(\mathbf{x}) = \sum_{i=0}^{r} \lambda_i F_i(\mathbf{x}),$$
we have
$$\chi_\lambda[C] = F_\lambda/F_0 \cdot [C] = F_\lambda \cdot [C] - F_0 \cdot [C].$$

Now let E be the maximum effective set common to all the effective sets $F_\lambda \cdot [C]$. By taking $\lambda_0 = 1$, $\lambda_i = 0$ $(i = 1,...,r)$, we see that E is contained, in particular, in the set $F_0 \cdot [C]$. Hence if we write

$$X = F_\lambda \cdot [C] - E, \qquad P = F_0 \cdot [C] - E,$$

we obtain the required expression for $\chi_\lambda[C]$ in the form $X - P$.

DEFINITION. The *polar set* of a normal linear system N_r is the set P (evidently unique) associated with N_r by Lemma 1.

We now prove a further lemma.

LEMMA 2. *If the sets of a normal linear system N_r are expressed in the form $X - P$, P being the polar set of N_r, and if P' is any one of the (effective) sets X so arising, then the sets $X - P'$ are the sets of a linear system N'_r conormal with N_r; and every system N'_r conormal with N_r is obtainable in this way.*

Proof. Adopting the notation of the preceding proof, and excluding the trivial case $P' = P$, we may suppose that the basis for (χ) is chosen in such a way that $P' - P = \chi_1[C]$. Then

$$X - P' = (X - P) - (P' - P) = \chi_\lambda[C] - \chi_1[C] = \chi'_\lambda[C],$$

where $\chi'_\lambda = \chi_\lambda/\chi_1$. Hence the sets $X - P'$ make up the linear system of sets N'_r generated by the system of rational functions $\chi_1^{-1}(\chi)$; and N'_r is plainly conormal with N_r. The converse follows at once, and this completes the proof of the lemma.

3.2. Linear series on C

We see from the proof of Lemma 2 of § 3.1 that P' is the polar set of N'_r. We can indeed express the result obtained by saying that *the aggregate of effective sets X is the same for every system N'_r conormal with N_r, and each set of this aggregate is the polar set of one and only one of the conormal systems*. Plainly, then, the aggregate of sets X (all of them effective) is characterized by its property of arising equally from every member of a family of conormal linear systems N_r. We shall say, in conformity with the following slightly more general definition, that this aggregate is a *linear series* on C.

DEFINITION. A *linear series* Γ_r^n on an irreducible curve C is any aggregate of effective sets of places that can be obtained by adding a fixed effective set L of order n to all the null-equivalent sets of a normal linear system N_r, of dimensionality r, the polar set of which is contained in L. The integers n and r are called respectively the *order* and the *dimensionality* of the linear series.

The order n of Γ_r^n may be thought of as the number of places in each set of the linear series. For every null-equivalent set is of order zero, and therefore the sets of Γ_r^n are effective sets of order n, i.e. sets of n places on C, when due account is taken of multiplicity. Γ_r^n thus consists of ∞^r sets of n places on C.

Reverting to our formal development, we note that if L is identical with the polar set P of N_r, then the sets of Γ_r^n have no place common to them all. In this case Γ_r^n is said to be *base-free*. If, on the other hand, the effective set $B = L - P$ is not null, then all the sets of Γ_r^n have the fixed set B as effective component, and we say that Γ_r^n has B as its *base set*.

The fundamental properties of linear series, which may be inferred at once from the preceding analysis, may now be formulated in the following terms, Γ_r^n being any fixed linear series.

(i) If G is an arbitrary set of Γ_r^n and G_0 is any fixed set of Γ_r^n, then the sets $G - G_0$ constitute a linear system N_r of null-equivalent sets on C; and any two linear systems that arise in this way from the same linear series Γ_r^n are conormal.

(ii) The sets of Γ_r^n are all mutually equivalent, and Γ_r^n is therefore contained in the effective kernel $|A|$ of some equivalence class $\{A\}$ on C.

(iii) Γ_r^n has the invariant structure of a projective space S_r.

In addition, we shall now show that any given linear series on the curve C can be traced directly on C by a linear system of primals of S_d.

THEOREM 5. *Every linear series on C is the aggregate of (effective) sets traced on C, residually to a fixed effective set H, by primals of a linear system (F); and conversely, every aggregate of effective sets so constructed is a linear series on C.*

Proof. We suppose first that (χ) is a normal linear system of rational functions on C with basis $(1, \chi_1, ..., \chi_r)$, that N_r is the associated system of null-equivalent sets, and that Γ_r^n is a linear series obtained by adding the same effective set L to every member of N_r. We define a K-form $F_\lambda(\mathbf{x})$ and a set E as in the proof of Lemma 1.

If Γ_r^n is base-free, so that L is the polar set P of N_r, then the primals of the system $(F) \equiv (F_\lambda)$ trace the sets of Γ_r^n on C residually to the effective set E, this latter being the complete fixed component of all the traces in question. Identifying H with E in this case, we have the required type of construction for Γ_r^n.

Now suppose that $L - P = B$, where B is effective but not null. If B is contained in E then we have only to identify H with $E - B$, and the system (F) gives the required construction as before. If B is not contained in E we can always find a primal F^*, if we allow its order to be sufficiently high, which traces on C a set E^* that contains B; and then the sets of Γ_r^n will be traced on C, residually to the effective set $H = (E^* - B) + E$, by the primals of the linear system $F^*(F)$ with F^* as a fixed component. The required construction for Γ_r^n is therefore possible in all cases.

We now suppose that, conversely, H is any given effective set on C and $(\overline{F})$ is any linear system of primals such that all those of its members which do not contain C have traces $\overline{F}.[C]$ which include H. We have to show that the residual sets $G = \overline{F}.[C] - H$ constitute a linear series on C. If the sets $\overline{F}.[C]$ all have in common a set E which has H as a proper part, then the sets G will, of course, have an effective base set $B = E - H$.

Since the condition for a primal of any given order N to contain a given curve is equivalent to a finite set of linear conditions on the coefficients in its equation (as may be inferred at once from Bézout's Theorem) it follows that the primals in the set $(\overline{F})$ which contain C form a linear subsystem (Φ) of $(\overline{F})$. We may therefore choose a basis $(F_0, F_1, ..., F_{\overline{r}})$ for $(\overline{F})$ in such a way that its members other than the first $r+1$ constitute a basis $(F_{r+1}, F_{r+2}, ..., F_{\overline{r}})$ for (Φ). The equation of any primal $\overline{F}$ in $(\overline{F})$ is then of the form

$$\overline{F}_\lambda \equiv F_{\lambda'} + H_{\lambda''} = 0,$$

where
$$F_{\lambda'} = \sum_{i=0}^{r} \lambda_i F_i, \quad H_{\lambda''} = \sum_{i=r+1}^{\overline{r}} \lambda_i F_i.$$

A necessary and sufficient condition for $\overline{F}_\lambda$ to contain C is then $\lambda_0 = \lambda_1 = ... = \lambda_r = 0$, i.e. $\boldsymbol{\lambda'} = \mathbf{0}$. Also, if $\overline{F}_\lambda$ does not contain C we shall have

$$O_{\mathscr{P}}(\overline{F}_\lambda) = O_{\mathscr{P}}(F_{\lambda'} + H_{\lambda''}) = O_{\mathscr{P}}(F_{\lambda'})$$

for all places $\mathscr{P}$ on C; and this means that $\overline{F}_\lambda$ and $F_{\lambda'}$ trace the same set on C. Thus the linear system (F) given by

$$F_{\lambda'} \equiv \sum_{i=0}^{r} \lambda_i F_i = 0$$

is such that:

(i) no primal of (F) contains C;

(ii) every set traced on C by a primal of $(\overline{F})$ is also traced by a primal of (F);

(iii) no two primals of (F) trace the same set on C (for, by Theorem 2, if they did then a primal of the pencil determined by them would contain C, in contradiction to (i)).

It follows that we are at liberty to replace $(\overline{F})$ by (F) as far as generation of sets of places on C is concerned.

We now observe that, by (i),

$$\sum_{i=0}^{r} \lambda_i F_i(\boldsymbol{\xi}) \neq 0$$

for every choice of the non-zero parameter vector $(\lambda_0,...,\lambda_r)$. Thus the $r+1$ rational functions

$$\chi_0 = 1, \quad \chi_i = F_i(\boldsymbol{\xi})/F_0(\boldsymbol{\xi}) \quad (i = 1,...,r)$$

on C are linearly independent. They define a normal linear system (χ); and if N_r is the associated system of null-equivalent sets $(\chi)[C]$, the sets $G+H$ traced on C by primals of (F) are the sets of N_r, each augmented by the fixed set $P+E$, where P is the polar set of N_r. It thus appears that the sets G are the sets of N_r, each augmented by the effective set

$$L = P+E-H = P+B;$$

and this completes the proof of the theorem.

In the course of the above proof we have established an additional important result which we may enunciate as follows.

COROLLARY. *Given a linear series Γ_r^n, we can always choose a linear system of primals (F) which traces Γ_r^n on C, residually to a fixed set H, in such a way that (i) every primal of (F) traces a set of Γ_r^n on C residually to H, and (ii) every set of Γ_r^n is traced on C, residually to H, by a unique primal of (F).*

If (F) satisfies the conditions of this corollary, it will be said to trace Γ_r^n, residually to H, *non-redundantly* on C.

4. Complete linear series

Every linear series, as we have already remarked (p. 240), is embedded in the kernel $|A|$ of some equivalence class $\{A\}$. In this section we propose to show that every kernel $|A|$ is itself a 'complete' linear series. Our first step is to prove the following theorem.

THEOREM 6. *If Γ_r^n is any linear series on a curve C, then $r \leqslant n$.*

Proof. If the theorem holds for base-free linear series, it will certainly hold in general. Let us suppose, then, that Γ_r^n is a base-free linear series on C, and that it is traced non-redundantly on C, residually to a fixed (effective) set H, by a linear system of primals (F). Then there exists, by the linearity of the conditions involved, at least one primal F_0 of (F) which passes through any r assigned points of C, remote from the centres of places of H; and since F_0 cannot contain C (because of non-redundancy) it must trace on C a set, residual to H, of order not less than r. It follows, therefore, that $r \leqslant n$; and the theorem is proved.

The next theorem is an addendum to Theorem 6.

THEOREM 7. *A rational curve C carries a series Γ_n^n for every $n \geqslant 0$; and, conversely, if a curve carries a series Γ_n^n for some $n \geqslant 1$, then it is rational.*

Proof. Let C be a given rational curve. Since linear series, being defined by linear systems of rational functions, are invariant over birational transformation, we may take C to be a line, and we may suppose that X is a non-homogeneous coordinate for the points of this line. Then, for any $n \geqslant 1$, the equation

$$\lambda_0 X^n + \lambda_1 X^{n-1} + \dots + \lambda_n = 0$$

determines a Γ_n^n on C; and this proves the first part of the theorem.

To prove the second part, we suppose that there exists, on a curve C, a Γ_n^n with $n \geqslant 1$. Then, by Theorem 6, this series is necessarily base-free. We may suppose that it is traced non-redundantly on C, residually to an effective set H, by an n-dimensional linear system of primals (F).

If $n > 1$, and if $\mathscr{P}_0$ is any fixed place on C which has its centre P_0 distinct from the centres of the places in H, the primals of (F) that pass through P_0 form an $(n-1)$-dimensional linear subsystem $(F)_1$ of (F); and $(F)_1$ traces non-redundantly on C a linear series Γ_{n-1}^{n-1} residual to $H + \mathscr{P}_0$. By repeating this argument a sufficient number of times we can show that if C carries a Γ_n^n, for some $n > 1$, then it carries a Γ_1^1. We need therefore only consider the case $n = 1$.

If, now, C carries a Γ_1^1, traced non-redundantly, residually to H, by a linear system of primals (F), this system is a pencil

$$\lambda_0 F_0(\mathbf{x}) + \lambda_1 F_1(\mathbf{x}) = 0,$$

or $$F_1(\mathbf{x}) = Y F_0(\mathbf{x})$$

where $Y = -\lambda_0/\lambda_1$; and the primals of the pencil trace the individual places $\mathscr{P}$ on C, residually to H. We now interpret Y as an affine coordinate for the points of a line L, writing η for the coordinate of a generic point of this same line. We obtain in this way a $(1, 1)$ correspondence between the places $\mathscr{P}$ on C and the places (or equally well the points) on L. Thus the unirational correspondence between C and L defined by the equation

$$\eta = F_1(\boldsymbol{\xi})/F_0(\boldsymbol{\xi})$$

is in fact birational, and C is therefore a rational curve, as was to be proved.

4.1. Extensions of linear series

As we noted in § 3.2, the sets of any linear series Γ_r^n can be mapped invariantively on the points of a projective space S_r. When such a mapping $\Gamma_r^n \to S_r$ is set up, every linear series $\Gamma_{r'}^n$ $(r' < r)$ entirely contained in Γ_r^n is mapped on a subspace $S_{r'}$ of S_r, and, conversely, every such subspace $S_{r'}$ is the image of a subseries $\Gamma_{r'}^n$. It follows, in particular, that we can give an obvious meaning to the join and intersection of two or more of the linear subseries of Γ_r^n.

When one linear series Γ_r^n is a subseries of another linear series $\Gamma_{\bar{r}}^n$, we say that $\Gamma_{\bar{r}}^n$ is an *extension* of Γ_r^n; and for extensions of linear series we have the following theorem.

THEOREM 8. *If a linear series Γ_r^n on C is contained in an equivalence class $\{A\}$, and if G is any effective set of $\{A\}$ that does not belong to Γ_r^n, then there exists an extension Γ_{r+1}^n of Γ_r^n which contains G.*

Proof. We suppose as usual that Γ_r^n is traced non-redundantly on C, residually to an effective set H, by a system of primals (F) with equation

$$F_\lambda \equiv \sum_{i=0}^r \lambda_i F_i = 0,$$

and we denote by G_λ and G_0 the sets of Γ_r^n traced on C by F_λ and F_0 respectively. By hypothesis, then, $G_0 \equiv G$; and the difference $G - G_0$ is therefore the trace on C of a rational function $P(\mathbf{x})/Q(\mathbf{x})$.

Hence
$$P(\mathbf{x}).[C] = G+E, \quad Q(\mathbf{x}).[C] = G_0+E,$$
where E is effective.

Consider now the trace on C of the $(r+1)$-dimensional linear system (F^*) with equation

$$F^*_{\lambda\cdot} \equiv Q(\lambda_0 F_0+\ldots+\lambda_r F_r)+\lambda_{r+1} PF_0 = 0.$$

Since $Q(\lambda_0 F_0+\ldots+\lambda_r F_r)$ traces the set $G_0+E+G_\lambda+H$ on C, while PF_0 traces the set $G+E+G_0+H$, it follows that $F^*_{\lambda\cdot}$ traces a set of the form $G^*_{\lambda\cdot}+E+H+G_0$, where $G^*_{\lambda\cdot}$ is of the same order as G and G_0, namely n. Thus the system (F^*) traces on C, residually to the fixed set $E+H+G_0$, a Γ^n_{r+1} which includes all the sets of Γ^n_r (for $\lambda_{r+1} = 0$) and also the set G (for $\lambda_0 = \ldots = \lambda_r = 0$). This proves the theorem.

Combining Theorems 6 and 8, we can now infer that, not only is every linear series contained in the kernel $|A|$ of some equivalence class, but every kernel $|A|$ is also itself a linear series.

THEOREM 9. *All the effective sets (if there are any) in any equivalence class $\{A\}$ on C constitute a linear series on C.*

Proof. If, as may well happen, $\{A\}$ contains only one effective set, then this set constitutes a Γ^n_0 $(n \geqslant 0)$. If $\{A\}$ contains two effective sets then, by Theorem 8, it contains a Γ^n_1 to which they both belong. If it contains a set not in this Γ^n_1 then, again by Theorem 8, it contains a Γ^n_2 which itself contains the Γ^n_1 and also the further set. Proceeding in this way, we must eventually exhaust $\{A\}$ since, by Theorem 6, the maximum dimensionality of a Γ^n_r is n. The aggregate $|A|$ of all effective sets in $\{A\}$ is therefore a linear series on C.

COROLLARY. *Any effective kernel $|A|$ of an equivalence class is a linear series that has no proper extension.*

Proof. Any extension of $|A|$, being a linear series, is contained in some kernel; and this kernel can only be $|A|$ itself. The extension is therefore not proper.

DEFINITION. A linear series on C which is not contained in any linear series of higher dimensionality (i.e. which has no proper extension) is said to be a *complete linear series* on C.

THEOREM 10. *Every linear series on C is contained in a complete linear series.*

Proof. Any linear series Γ_r^n is contained in a kernel $|A|$, and $|A|$ is a complete linear series by the corollary just proved.

This last theorem may well be regarded as the culmination of the first stage in the development of invariantive geometry on a curve. It suggests to us, as a fundamental undertaking in relation to any given one-dimensional algebraic function field, *the identification, classification, and investigation of the properties of all the complete linear series of each successive order $n \geqslant 1$ on any arbitrary model C of the field.* This problem, as appears from the statement and proof of Theorem 7, is trivial when the field in question is a field $K(u)$ where u is an indeterminate, that is to say when C is a rational curve. In this case any two sets of the same order are equivalent, and the aggregate of all effective sets of any given order n is the unique complete Γ_n^n on the curve.

4.2. The language of point-sets on C

We conclude the present section by referring briefly to a highly convenient alternative way of talking about geometry on a curve, using a language of *point-sets* and *linear series of point-sets* instead of the language of sets of places and linear series of sets of places that we have adhered to consistently so far. Although, being less precise, the alternative language is theoretically inferior to the one that we have been using, it has considerable advantages of brevity and simplicity, and these become especially important when we wish to discuss particular examples rather than the general theory. The more accurate language of sets of places is then often excessively laboured. The weakness of the language of point-sets is, of course, that whereas a set of places A always determines a unique point-set δA, the point-set does not determine the set of places uniquely unless each of its points happens to be the centre of only one place on C. In cases where we shall use the more elementary language, however, the strict invariantive interpretation of our statements will never be in doubt; and we may accordingly look upon use of this language as principally a literary device.

DEFINITION. If each set of places A of a linear series Γ_r^n on C is replaced by the associated point-set δA, the aggregate of effective sets of points so arising will be called a *linear series of point-sets on C*, and it will be denoted by the symbol g_r^n.

Plainly, a g_0^n need not define a unique Γ_0^n, but, since C cannot have more than a finite number of multiple points, any base-free

g_r^n with $r \geqslant 1$ does define a unique Γ_r^n. Also, there is always one, and in general only one, set of a g_r^n that contains r assigned points of C.

A g_r^n which is derived from a complete Γ_r^n will be said to be a *complete linear series of point-sets*.

Finally, the analogue for point-sets of Theorem 5 runs as follows. *Every g_r^n on C can be obtained as the aggregate of effective sets cut on C, residually to a fixed effective set P, by primals of a linear system (F); and conversely, any aggregate of sets so constructed is a g_r^n, for some choice of the integers n and r.*

5. Noether's Theorem

At the stage we have now reached in the development of the present chapter we have to make an important digression before we can go on, in the next section, to establish a general method for constructing complete linear series on a curve. This digression will at the same time serve the purpose of introducing the reader to a topic of the first importance for algebraic geometry as a whole which has not so far received any mention in this book. Briefly, and in its most general form, the topic in question is concerned with the condition imposed on an arbitrary polynomial H of a ring $\mathscr{R} = K[X_1,...,X_n]$ when it is required to be expressible as a linear combination

$$H = A_1 F_1 + A_2 F_2 + ... + A_l F_l \quad (A_i \in \mathscr{R})$$

of a given set of polynomials $F_1,..., F_l$ in the same ring, that is to say when it is required to belong to a given ideal $(F_1,..., F_l)$ of $\mathscr{R}$. Since the degree of H is not supposed to be prescribed, we cannot envisage the imposed condition as a set of conditions on some finite set of coefficients; but we may hope that it will be expressible in terms of the local properties of H at the common zeros of $F_1,..., F_l$, in amplification of the obviously necessary condition on H that it must have a zero at each of these points. The general problem, as thus conceived, is one of fundamental importance, but also one of great complexity and with very wide ramifications. References to the literature are given in Appendix C, and so all that we shall attempt to do here is to introduce the reader to Noether's basic case of the problem, that in which $\mathscr{R}$ is the ring $K[X, Y]$ of K-polynomials in two indeterminates and H is required to be representable as a combination $AF + BG$ of two given polynomials $F(X, Y)$ and $G(X, Y)$ of this ring. Although, following Noether, we have stated the problem in terms of polynomials, its translation into an equivalent problem for forms is straightforward, as the reader may verify.

Let us suppose, then, that F and G are two given polynomials in $\mathscr{R} = K[X, Y]$, and let us consider the condition that a third polynomial H in this ring shall be representable in the form

$$H = AF + BG \quad (A, B \in \mathscr{R}).$$

We assume, for simplicity, that F and G have no non-constant common factor.

DEFINITION. If (X_0, Y_0) is any common zero of F and G, the *Noether condition* on H at (X_0, Y_0) with respect to F and G is the condition that there shall exist formal power series

$$A', B' \in K\{X - X_0, Y - Y_0\}$$

such that $$H = A'F + B'G, \tag{1}$$

F, G, H being expressed as (finite) power series in $X - X_0$, $Y - Y_0$.

If $H = h_{00} + h_{10}(X - X_0) + h_{01}(Y - Y_0) + h_{20}(X - X_0)^2 + \ldots$ it can be shown without much difficulty that the above Noether condition on H at (X_0, Y_0) always reduces in the end to the condition that a certain finite set of the coefficients h_{ij} must satisfy a certain finite set of linear homogeneous K-equations. In other words, in order to show that the Noether condition is satisfied it is sufficient to establish the existence of series A' and B' which satisfy equation (1) up to terms of sufficiently high degree† in $X - X_0$, $Y - Y_0$.

Thus, for example, if we consider the common zero at the origin O of the polynomials

$$F = X^2 + Y^3, \quad G = XY^2 + X^4 + Y^4,$$

then the Noether condition on H at O, requiring the existence of A' and B' such that

$$h_{00} + h_{10}X + h_{01}Y + \ldots = A'(X^2 + Y^3) + B'(XY^2 + X^4 + Y^4),$$

can be seen to reduce to the set of equations

$$0 = h_{00} = h_{01} = h_{10} = h_{11} = h_{02} = h_{20} - h_{03} = h_{21} + h_{12} - h_{04}.$$

---

† It was shown by Bertini, *Math. Ann.* **34** (1889), 447 and *Rend. Inst. Lomb.* (2) **24** (1891), 1095, that if (X_0, Y_0) is an r-fold point of the curve $F = 0$ and an s-fold point of the curve $G = 0$, and if its multiplicity as an intersection of these curves is α, then the agreement of both sides in the Noether condition (1) need only be shown up to and including terms of degree $\alpha - rs + r + s - 2$ in $X - X_0$ and $Y - Y_0$.

The remarkable theorem proved by Noether, which provided the starting-point for numerous subsequent developments, can now be stated as follows.

THEOREM 11 (*Noether's Theorem*). *If F and G are two polynomials in $K[X, Y]$ such that the curves $F = 0$ and $G = 0$ have no common component and no intersection at infinity, then in order that a third polynomial H should be of the form*

$$H = AF + BG \quad (A, B \in K[X, Y]),$$

it is both necessary and sufficient that H should satisfy the Noether conditions with respect to F and G at all the intersections of the curves $F = 0$ and $G = 0$.

Since we shall not use this theorem we do not propose to give any proof of it. We may remark, however, that the subsequent investigations aimed for the most part at replacing Noether's severely formal conditions by other sufficient (though not necessary) conditions of a much simpler and more geometrical character. In § 5.2 below we shall establish directly one of the most useful of these simplified versions of Noether's Theorem.

5.1. The alternative approach to Noether's Theorem

In this section we shall indicate, for the sake of completeness, the general lines of a second approach to Noether's problem which leads to an alternative form of the basic theorem and a somewhat simpler derivation of the various geometric variants of Noether's result.† This treatment is based on the formulation of the problem in terms of forms instead of polynomials. We suppose, in fact, that F and G are given K-forms in x_0, x_1, x_2, and that we have to find conditions under which an arbitrary form H of the same kind can be represented by an expression $AF + BG$, where A and B are further forms of the appropriate degrees in x_0, x_1, x_2. To this end, we first define the analogue of a Noether condition in the following way.

We assume in the first place that F and G have no common factor, that $F(0, 0, 1) \neq 0$, and that **a** is an intersection of the curves $F = 0$ and $G = 0$ that does not lie on the line joining any other intersection of the curves to the reference point $X_2 = (0, 0, 1)$. Further, we denote by σ the multiplicity of intersection of the

---

† For a very full and excellent account of the whole theory on this basis the reader should consult van der Waerden's *Einführung*, chapter viii.

curves at **a**, i.e. the greatest positive integer s such that $(a_0 x_1 - a_1 x_0)^s$ is a factor of the x_2-resultant $R(x_0, x_1)$ of F and G. Writing R, as we may, in the form

$$R = UF + VG,$$

where U and V are forms, we define the form T to be the remainder when VH is divided, as a polynomial in x_2, by F. Then the *alternative Noether condition on H at the point* **a** *with respect to F and G* is that T should be divisible by $(a_0 x_1 - a_1 x_0)^\sigma$.

The corresponding alternative form of Noether's Theorem runs as follows.

THEOREM 12 (*Noether's Theorem, alternative form*). *Let F and G be K-forms in* x_0, x_1, x_2, *having no common factor, and such that F is not zero at* $X_2 \equiv (0, 0, 1)$ *and* X_2 *is not collinear with any pair of intersections of the curves* $F = 0$ *and* $G = 0$. *Then, in order that a third form H should admit of a representation* $H = AF + BG$, *it is necessary and sufficient that H should satisfy the alternative Noether conditions with respect to F and G at all the intersections of the two curves.*

Here once again, since we make no direct application of this theorem, we shall omit the proof. We pass on instead to a direct proof of the more specialized theorem that we shall need in § 6.

5.2. The specialized Noether theorem

It is wholly immaterial whether, in the statement and proof of the following theorem, we adopt the language of affine coordinates and polynomials or that of homogeneous coordinates and forms; and we shall choose the first alternative.

THEOREM 13. *Let the equations* $F(X, Y) = 0$ *and* $G(X, Y) = 0$ *represent two curves F and G of* S_2, *with no common component, and let every intersection of the curves be either a simple point or an ordinary multiple point of F. Let P be any one of these intersections, of multiplicity* m_P *for F, and let* $\mathscr{P}$ *be any one of the* m_P *places on F at P. Then if another curve H, with equation* $H(X, Y) = 0$, *is such that*

$$O_\mathscr{P}(H) \geqslant O_\mathscr{P}(G) + m_P - 1$$

for every pair $(P, \mathscr{P})$ *as defined above, there exist polynomials* $A(X, Y)$ *and* $B(X, Y)$ *such that* $H = AF + BG$.

Although Theorem 13 is only a sufficiency theorem, and although its scope is limited by the restriction on the behaviour of F at the intersections of this curve with G, it has nevertheless a quite remarkable range of immediate geometrical applications. A major application of it will be made in § 6, and various other geometrical applications are outlined in the exercises at the end of the chapter. The proof of the theorem makes use of two lemmas, which we begin by establishing.

LEMMA 1. *Let F, G, H be polynomials in X and Y, and let F have no factor that involves X only. Further, let the Y-resultant of F and G be expressed in the form $R(X) = UF + VG$, where U, $V \in K[X, Y]$. Then a sufficient condition for H to be of the form $AF + BG$ is that there should exist a polynomial Q such that $VH - QF$ is divisible by R.*

Proof. Suppose the condition is satisfied, so that

$$T \equiv VH - QF = BR.$$

Then

$$HR = H(UF + VG)$$
$$= HUF + (QF + BR)G$$
$$= F(HU + GQ) + BRG.$$

Hence R is a factor of $F(HU + GQ)$; and since F has no factor independent of Y, $HU + GQ = AR$, where $A \in K[X, Y]$. If we now substitute AR for $HU + GQ$ in the equation already obtained, and then divide out the factor R, we get the required relation

$$H = AF + BG.$$

LEMMA 2. *If P is an ordinary m-fold point of a curve F and if, for some $m' \leqslant m$, another curve E has the property $O_{\mathscr{P}}(E) \geqslant m'$ for every place $\mathscr{P}$ on F at P, then the multiplicity of P on E is not less than m'.*

Proof. The proof follows from the fact that, if α is any linear branch at P, and $O_{\alpha}(E)$ exceeds the multiplicity of E at P, then one of the branch tangents of E at P must coincide with the tangent to α at P. We leave the completion of this proof to the reader.

Proof of Theorem 13. Let n denote the order of the curve F. We begin by choosing the affine coordinate system, as is evidently permissible, in such a way that:

(i) Y_{∞} is not a point of F,
(ii) the intersections of F and G are all finite points,
(iii) no two of the intersections lie on the same ordinate,

(iv) no branch tangent of F at any of these intersections is parallel to OY,

(v) no line drawn through any such intersection to touch F elsewhere, or to pass through a multiple point of F elsewhere is parallel to OY.

The effect of (iv) and (v) is to ensure that *the ordinate through any intersection P of F and G meets F m_P times at P and also in a set of $n-m_P$ distinct points (P') remote from P.*

By virtue of (i), the coefficient of Y^n in F is not zero. Hence, in the notation of Lemma 1, we may divide VH by F (as polynomials in Y) to obtain
$$VH = QF + T,$$
where T is of degree $n-1$ at most in Y. By the same lemma, the theorem will be proved if we can show that $R = R(X)$ is a factor of T.

By virtue of (i) and (iii), R is a product of factors of the form $(X-a)^\sigma$, one for each intersection P of F and G, the abscissa of P being a and its multiplicity as an intersection being σ (Theorem 5, p. 40). We have only to show, therefore, that L^σ is a factor of T, L being written for $X-a$.

Suppose that, on the contrary,
$$T = L^{\sigma_1} T_1,$$
where $\sigma_1 < \sigma$ and T_1 is not divisible by L. The degree of T_1 in Y, being the same as that of T, is again $n-1$ at most. Our method of deriving a contradiction will be to prove that the curve $T_1 = 0$ has a point of multiplicity m_P at least at P and that it passes through each of the $n-m_P$ further points of F on the same ordinate L, thus meeting this ordinate in more than $n-1$ points.

We consider first of all any place $\mathscr{P}$ on F with centre P. From the equation $T = VH - QF$ we deduce that
$$O_{\mathscr{P}}(T) = O_{\mathscr{P}}(V) + O_{\mathscr{P}}(H)$$
$$\geqslant O_{\mathscr{P}}(V) + O_{\mathscr{P}}(G) + m_P - 1;$$
and from the equation $R = UF + VG$ we deduce that
$$O_{\mathscr{P}}(V) + O_{\mathscr{P}}(G) = O_{\mathscr{P}}(R) = \sigma,$$
because the relevant factor of R is L^σ and $O_{\mathscr{P}}(L) = O_{\mathscr{P}}(X-a) = 1$ by virtue of (iv). Thus
$$O_{\mathscr{P}}(T_1) = O_{\mathscr{P}}(T) - \sigma_1$$
$$\geqslant \sigma + m_P - 1 - \sigma_1 \geqslant m_P.$$

Since this holds for each place $\mathscr{P}$ on F at P it follows, by Lemma 2, that the multiplicity of P on the curve T_1 is not less than m_P.

Now consider any residual intersection P' of F with the ordinate L through P. There is a single place $\mathscr{P}'$ of order 1 on F at P'; and

$$O_{\mathscr{P}'}(G) = 0, \quad O_{\mathscr{P}'}(L) = 1, \quad O_{\mathscr{P}'}(R) = \sigma.$$

From the formulae $R = UF + VG$ and $T = VH - QF$ we deduce that

$$O_{\mathscr{P}'}(V) = O_{\mathscr{P}'}(R) = \sigma,$$

and

$$O_{\mathscr{P}'}(T_1) = O_{\mathscr{P}'}(T) - \sigma_1 = \sigma + O_{\mathscr{P}'}(H) - \sigma_1 \geqslant 1;$$

and this proves that the curve T_1 passes through each of the $n - m_P$ points P' on the ordinate through P.

We have now obtained all the results that are needed to derive a contradiction from our assumption that R is not a factor of T, and Theorem 13 is accordingly established.

When the curve F is irreducible, the set of conditions imposed on H in the above theorem can be combined in a useful and suggestive way in a single formal condition, as we shall now show.

DEFINITION. *If C is any irreducible plane curve, the local set of adjunction D_P on C at any ordinary m-fold point P of the curve is the effective set*

$$D_P = (m-1)(\mathscr{P}_1 + \mathscr{P}_2 + \ldots + \mathscr{P}_m),$$

where the $\mathscr{P}_i$ are the m places on C at P.

Using the notion of the local set of adjunction, we can now state the following corollary to Theorem 13.

COROLLARY. *If the curve F in Theorem 13 is irreducible, then the conditions there imposed on H may be expressed in the form*

$$H.[F] \supset G.[F] + \sum_P D_P,$$

where D_P is the local set of adjunction on F at P, and the summation is over all the intersections P of G with F.

6. Construction of complete linear series

We now return, after the necessary digression of § 5, to the discussion of complete linear series on an irreducible curve C. The critical step now before us, if we are to make progress with the project proposed at the end of § 4.1, is to devise a refinement of Theorem 5 that will enable us to construct *complete* linear series on any given curve C, and, more particularly, to construct the complete linear series $|A|$ determined by any given effective set A on C. It might be supposed, at first sight, that the linear series traced on C by the complete system of primals of any given order N of the space S_d would be complete; but this is manifestly untrue in general since, for example, the lines of S_2 trace a Γ_2^3 on a nodal cubic while, since the curve is rational, any Γ_2^3 on it is contained in a Γ_3^3. We must therefore look deeper for the solution of the problem.

Since linear series are by definition invariant over birational transformation, we may, as a preliminary simplification, take C to be a plane curve; and further, by Theorem 11 of Chapter VI, this plane curve may be supposed to have only ordinary multiple points. *We shall accordingly assume throughout this section that our chosen model C of the given algebraic function field Σ is an irreducible plane curve of order q with ordinary multiple points $O_1,...,O_s$ of multiplicities $k_1,...,k_s$, and no other multiple points.*

For a plane curve C of this restricted kind, the curves which were called in Chapter VI, § 5, the sub-adjoints A^N of order N are called† simply the *adjoints A^N* of C. Thus by an adjoint A^N of C we shall understand a curve of order N with a point of multiplicity not less than k_i-1 at O_i $(i = 1,...,s)$. Every such curve, if it does not have C as a component, will be such that its trace on C includes the fixed set

$$D = \sum_{\mathscr{P}} (k-1)\mathscr{P},$$

where k is the multiplicity on C of the centre of the place $\mathscr{P}$ and the summation extends formally over all places on C. We call D the *set of adjunction* on C, noting that it is the sum

$$D = \sum_{i=1}^{s} D_{O_i} = \sum_{i=1}^{s} (k_i-1)(\mathscr{P}_{i,1}+\mathscr{P}_{i,2}+...+\mathscr{P}_{i,k_i})$$

of the local sets of adjunction of C at its multiple points (cf. p. 253).

Conversely, by Lemma 2 on p. 251, *any curve of order N in S_2 which is such that its trace on C contains the set of adjunction D, is an adjoint A^N of C.*

We shall now introduce a slight extension of our previous use of the term 'residual'. If Γ is any linear series and B is any fixed effective set on C, then those sets of Γ (if there are any) which

---

† The reasons for this change of nomenclature, as also for the substitution of 'genus' for 'deficiency' in the same circumstances, are not immediately relevant. They are, however, related to the fact that a curve with multiple points that are not ordinary may have 'infinitely near' multiple points, of which the definitions of deficiency and sub-adjointness take no account.

contain B will form a subordinate linear series Γ^*, and the residual
sets obtained by subtracting B from all the sets of Γ^* will form a
linear series Γ'. We shall then say that Γ' is *residual to B in Γ*, and
we shall put $\Gamma' = \Gamma - B$. Similarly, if the primals of a linear system
(F) trace Γ on C, we shall say that (F) *traces Γ' on C residually to B*
(as an imposed base set). The symbol $\Gamma - B$, in other words, is to
be interpreted as meaning the set of all *effective* sets of the form
$X - B$ for $X \in \Gamma$. For complete series the notation takes on added
significance, since *the residual $|A| - B$ of a complete series $|A|$
with respect to an effective set B is the complete series $|A - B|$*. For if
E is any member of the latter series, so that $E \equiv A - B$, then
$E + B$ is a member A' of $|A|$; and hence $E = A' - B$ is a member of
$|A| - B$.

After these preliminaries, we enunciate in the following terms
the main theorem to be proved.

THEOREM 14. *If C is an irreducible plane curve, with only ordinary
multiple points and with set of adjunction D, then its adjoints A^N of
any given order N trace, residually to D, a complete linear series on C.
More particularly, if A_0 is any effective set on C, and if the set traced
by some adjoint A_0^N is of the form $D + A_0 + L$, where L is effective,
then the complete linear series $|A_0|$ is traced on C, residually to $D + L$,
by the adjoints A^N of C.*

Before proving this theorem, we give a few illustrations of its
significance, using for this purpose the simpler terminology of
series g_r^n of point-sets (cf. § 4.2).

(i) *A nodal cubic of S_2.* In this case the unique g_1^1 on C is determined by lines through the node O. The unique g_2^2 on C is cut out
by conics through O and any pair of fixed points on C remote from
O. The unique g_3^3 is cut out by conics through O and one other fixed
point of C; and so on.

(ii) *A non-singular cubic of S_2.* In this case all curves of S_2 are
adjoint to C. Each point of C is a complete g_0^1. Each point-pair of
C belongs to the complete g_1^2 cut on C by lines through a fixed point
of the curve. Each point-triad of C belongs to a complete g_2^3 cut
on C by conics through three fixed points of the curve; and so on.

(iii) *A uninodal quartic of S_2.* In this case, if O is the node, each
point of C (other than O) is a complete g_0^1. Each point-pair (P, Q)
of C $(P, Q \neq O)$ such that O, P, Q are not collinear is a complete g_0^2;
but if O, P, Q are collinear then (P, Q) belongs to a complete g_1^2

cut on C by lines through O. A point-triad on C, remote from O, belongs always to a complete g_1^3, cut on C by conics through O and three fixed simple points of C; and so on.

EXERCISE. Show that, if C is a non-singular quartic curve in S_2, and (P, Q, R, S) is a tetrad of points of C such that P, Q, R are collinear but not collinear with S, then the tetrad belongs to a *complete* g_1^4 which has S as a base point.

For the proof of Theorem 14 we first establish a lemma.

LEMMA. *If adjoints $\bar{A}^N$ and $\bar{A}'^N$ trace sets $D + \bar{L} + A$ and $D + \bar{L} + A'$ on C, and if an adjoint A^N traces a set $D + L + A$, then there exists an adjoint A'^N which traces the set $D + L + A'$ on C.*

Proof. Let C have equation $F = 0$, and let the equations of $\bar{A}^N$, $\bar{A}'^N$, A^N be $\bar{G} = 0$, $\bar{J} = 0$, $G = 0$ respectively. Writing $H = \bar{J}G$, and identifying F, $\bar{G}$, H with the polynomials (or forms) F, G, H in Theorem 13, we observe that H satisfies the condition there imposed on it. For

$$H . [F] = (D + \bar{L} + A') + (D + L + A) \supset (D + \bar{L} + A) + D;$$

and hence $$H . [F] \supset \bar{G} . [F] + \sum_P D_P,$$

which is the form of the condition given in the corollary to Theorem 13. It follows, therefore, that

$$H \equiv \bar{J}G = AF + B\bar{G},$$

where A and B are polynomials, and B in particular is of degree N.† Further, by taking the traces of both sides of the equation on C, we see at once that the trace of B on C is $D + L + A'$. Thus the curve $B = 0$ is the required adjoint A^N which traces $D + L + A'$ on C; and this proves the lemma.

Proof of Theorem 14. We need to show that if $A \equiv A_0$, where A is effective, then there exists an adjoint A^N which traces $D + A + L$ on C. Since $A \equiv A_0$, then $D + A \equiv D + A_0$; and hence there exist adjoints $\bar{A}^N$ and $\bar{A}_0^N$ which have traces $D + A + L'$ and $D + A_0 + L'$ (L' effective) on C. It follows by the lemma that, since the given adjoint A_0^N traces $D + A_0 + L$ on C, there exists an adjoint A^N which traces $D + A + L$ on C; and this proves the theorem.

---

† In so far as we work with polynomials (instead of forms) B may of course be only formally of degree N, and actually of lower degree; but the curve $B = 0$ must then be supposed to have the line at infinity as a component of appropriate multiplicity.

Having thus solved the fundamental problem concerning the construction of complete linear series, we may now consider some important features of the internal structure of such series.

7. The structure of linear series

In considering the internal structure of linear series on a curve C we may evidently discard base sets, contained in every set of the series. *We shall therefore assume, except where the contrary is clearly implied, that the linear series considered are base-free and of dimensionality $r \geqslant 1$.*

The structure of a Γ_r^n $(r \geqslant 1)$ on C is best elucidated by constructing its projective model, which is defined as follows.

DEFINITION. *A projective model of a linear series Γ_r^n $(r \geqslant 1)$ on a curve C of S_d is a curve C' of S_r into which C can be transformed, either birationally or unirationally, in such a way that the sets on C' which arise from the sets of Γ_r^n on C are traced on C' by the primes of S_r.*

To construct such a model of a series Γ_r^n, and also to show that it is unique to within projective transformation of S_r, we suppose Γ_r^n to be derived, after the fashion of § 3.2, from a normal linear system (χ) of rational functions on C; that is to say, each set of Γ_r^n is to be of the form $\chi[C] + P$, where P is the polar set of (χ). If $(1, \chi_1, ..., \chi_r)$ is a basis for (χ), we take as C' the curve in S_r with generic point $\boldsymbol{\eta} = (1, \chi_1, ..., \chi_r)$. Then C' is a birational or a unirational transform of C (regarding the adjectives in this context as mutually exclusive) according as $K(\boldsymbol{\eta}) = K(\chi_1, ..., \chi_r)$ is identical with $\Sigma = K(\boldsymbol{\xi})$ or is a proper subfield of it, $\boldsymbol{\xi}$ being a generic point of C. Further, we see at once that the set of Γ_r^n which corresponds to any rational function $\lambda_0 + \lambda_1 \chi_1 + ... + \lambda_r \chi_r$ of (χ) is transformed into the set traced on C' by the prime with coordinates $(\lambda_0, ..., \lambda_r)$. Thus C' is a projective model of Γ_r^n according to our definition; and we shall leave as an exercise for the reader the proof that C' *is uniquely defined† by Γ_r^n to within projective transformation of S_r.*

The distinction between the two types of linear series for which the correspondence between C and C' is $(1, 1)$ or $(\mu, 1)$ with $\mu > 1$

---

† If Γ_r^n is traced non-redundantly on C, residually to some fixed set E, by the primals of a linear system $\sum_{i=0}^{r} \lambda_i F_i(\mathbf{x}) = 0$, then the equations of the transformation which carries C into C' may be taken to be $\mathbf{y}_i = F_i(\mathbf{x})$, $(i = 0, ..., r)$.

is of fundamental significance, and we shall devote the next section to an elucidation of this distinction.

7.1. Simple and compound linear series

We begin with a definition of the terms that we shall use.

DEFINITION. A linear series Γ_r^n on C is said to be *simple* when the basic correspondence between C and the projective model C' of Γ_r^n is birational. A linear series is said to be *compound* if it is not simple.

To interpret the distinction between simple and compound linear series, and particularly the properties of compound series, we may refer to the basic properties of unirational correspondences which we developed in detail in Chapter VII and extended by Theorem 5 of Chapter VIII. If the correspondence between C and C' is $(\mu, 1)$, then the places on C distribute themselves into the mutually exclusive sets of an involution I_μ of order μ, and each place $\mathscr{P}'$ on C' corresponds to a set $(\mathscr{P}_1, ..., \mathscr{P}_\mu)$ of I_μ. If C' is of order n', so that any prime λ of S_r traces on it a set of order n', it follows that the corresponding set of Γ_r^n must be compounded of n' sets of I_μ and must therefore be of order $n'\mu$. Thus $n = n'\mu$; and we have the following theorem.

THEOREM 15. *Every linear series Γ_r^n ($r \geqslant 1$) on C has a projective model C' which lies in a space S_r (and not in any space of lower dimensionality) and is unique to within projective transformation of S_r. If Γ_r^n is simple, so that the correspondence between C and C' is birational, then C' is of order n. If Γ_r^n is compound, then each of its sets is composed of the same number n' of sets of an involution I_μ ($\mu \geqslant 2$) on C, so that $n = n'\mu$; and in this case C' is of order n/μ.*

In brief, the characteristic property of a compound series Γ_r^n is that all the sets of the series that contain any given place $\mathscr{P}$ on C necessarily contain a whole set of order $\mu > 1$ that is uniquely determined by $\mathscr{P}$.

In the special case $r = 1$, the generic point $\boldsymbol{\eta} = (1, \chi_1)$ in S_1 determines a line L (the entire S_1), and each prime $\boldsymbol{\lambda} = (\lambda_0, \lambda_1)$ then traces a unique place $\mathscr{P}'$ on L. In this case, therefore, the sets of Γ_1^n on C are mapped unirationally on the individual places of L, and Γ_1^n is accordingly a rational involution I_n on C. Conversely (by Theorem 7, p. 169), every rational involution I_n on C is a Γ_1^n.

We thus have the following theorem on one-dimensional linear series on a curve.

THEOREM 16. *The one-dimensional linear series Γ_1^n on any irreducible curve C are identical with the rational involutions I_n on C.*

It follows from this theorem that every linear series Γ_1^n for which $n > 1$ is trivially compound.

When $r > 1$, a linear series Γ_r^n on C may be either simple or compound. If it is compound, and its sets are compounded each of n' sets of an involution I_μ, we say that Γ_r^n is *compounded of I_μ*. The involution in question may be rational or irrational, depending on whether the projective model of Γ_r^n is or is not a rational curve.

Suppose first that Γ_r^n is compounded of a rational involution $I_\mu = \Gamma_1^\mu$. Then each set of Γ_r^n is made up of a certain number n' $(n' \geqslant r)$ of sets of the involution, so that $n = \mu n'$. Furthermore, the aggregate of *all* sets made up of n' sets of the involution is a $\Gamma_{n'}^n$, in which Γ_r^n is contained. If, in fact, χ is any rational function on C which generates I_μ, then the series $\Gamma_{n'}^n$ is generated on C by the linear system of rational functions $\lambda_0 + \lambda_1 \chi + \ldots + \lambda_{n'} \chi^{n'}$. We thus have the following theorem on compound series.

Any Γ_r^n on C which is compounded of a Γ_1^μ is of the type $\Gamma_r^{\mu n'}$ $(n' \geqslant r)$, and it is contained in the $\Gamma_{n'}^{\mu n'}$ generated on C by the system of rational functions

$$\lambda_0 + \lambda_1 \chi + \ldots + \lambda_{n'} \chi^{n'},$$

χ being any rational function such that the system of functions $\lambda_0 + \lambda_1 \chi$ generates Γ_1^μ on C.

A simple example of this special type of compound series is the Γ_2^4 traced on a conic k by the ∞^2 linear system of line-pairs with a fixed point not on k as vertex.

In the general case, when the involution I_μ is not rational, we say that Γ_r^n is *compounded of the irrational involution I_μ*. If, for example, K is a cubic cone in S_3, with O as vertex and a non-singular plane cubic curve k as base, and C is the section of K by a quadric surface which does not pass through O, then the generators of the cone determine an irrational I_2 on C, with k as its model; and planes through O trace on C a Γ_2^6 which is evidently compounded of I_2.

7.2. Normal curves

We shall show in this section how the facts established in Theorem 15 enable us in theory to classify all curves, in spaces of all dimensionalities, into families in a way that proves to be of fundamental significance in projective geometry. We shall show, in fact, that there exist certain *normal curves* from which all other curves can be derived by suitable birational projection.

Every curve possesses a well-defined *ambient space*, or space of lowest dimensionality in which it is contained. If C is any irreducible curve, the primes of the ambient space trace a linear series on C, and we shall refer to this series as the *principal linear series on C*.

We have seen already that the sets of any simple linear series on a curve C are carried, by a birational transformation of C, into the sets of the principal linear series on the projective model C' of the given series; and we now observe that, conversely, any birational transform C' of a given curve C is the projective model of a linear series on C, namely of the inverse image of the principal linear series on C'. Birational transformation may therefore be looked upon (if we think of any curve as defined only to within projective transformation of its ambient space) as a transfer of principality from one simple linear series to another.

Suppose, now, that the principal linear series on C is a Γ_r^n, so that C is a curve of order n in an ambient space S_r, and let C be projected from a subspace S_{k-1} of S_r as vertex on to a suitable subspace S_{r-k}, its projection being a curve C'. Those primes of S_r that contain S_{k-1} will then trace on C a linear series Γ_{r-k}^n contained in Γ_r^n. We suppose that this series has a base set B of order h (which we may refer to as the trace of S_{k-1} on C). It then follows readily, by use of the theory of projection developed in Chapter VIII, § 9, that the sets of the residual series $\Gamma_{r-k}^{n-h} = \Gamma_{r-k}^n - B$ will project into the sets of the principal linear series on C'. The projection may be birational, in which case the projected sets will all be of order $n-h$, or it may be a $(\mu, 1)$ unirational correspondence, when the projected sets will all be of order $(n-h)/\mu$. The series Γ_{r-k}^{n-h} will be simple in the first case and compounded of an involution I_μ in the second.

We are now in a position to introduce the notion of normal curve and to make clear its significance.

DEFINITION. An irreducible curve C is *normal* if its principal linear series is complete.

THEOREM 17. *A curve is normal if and only if it is not a projection of any other curve of the same order in an ambient space of dimensionality higher than that of its own ambient space.*

Proof. Let C be of order n, and let its ambient space be an S_r. If C is a projection of a curve $\bar{C}$, also of order n, in an ambient space $S_{\bar{r}}$ ($\bar{r} > r$) containing S_r then, since the orders of $\bar{C}$ and C are equal, the projection is birational. Further, the principal series Γ_r^n on C is the projection of a proper linear subseries $\overline{\Gamma_{\bar{r}}^n}$ of the principal series $\Gamma_{\bar{r}}^n$ on $\bar{C}$; and since $\overline{\Gamma_{\bar{r}}^n}$ must project into a linear series $\Gamma_{\bar{r}}^n$ on C in which Γ_r^n is contained, it follows that Γ_r^n is not complete. Thus C is not normal.

If, conversely, the principal series Γ_r^n on C is contained in a linear series $\Gamma_{\bar{r}}^n$ ($\bar{r} > r$) on C, it is easy to arrange matters so that C is a proper projection of a projective model of $\Gamma_{\bar{r}}^n$, this being a curve of order n in an ambient space $S_{\bar{r}}$ which properly contains S_r. The proof of the theorem is then complete.

It follows from Theorem 17 that every subnormal curve of order n is a birational projection of a normal curve $\bar{C}$ of the same order, and that $\bar{C}$ is uniquely determined by C to within projective transformation. If the vertex of projection is a space Π (which does not meet $\bar{C}$) then all the projective properties of C can evidently be interpreted as projective properties of $\bar{C}$ relative to Π. On the other hand, every normal curve $\bar{C}$ of a given order n gives rise, for different choices of the dimensionality of Π and its relationship to $\bar{C}$, to many projectively distinct types of subnormal curve C of order n. It will thus be seen that normal curves must figure centrally in all problems relating to the projective classification of curves in spaces of arbitrary dimensionality. The most familiar example of a normal curve is the projectively unique *rational normal curve* $C^{(n)}$ of order n in S_n, of which every type of rational curve of order n in a space of lower dimensionality is a projection from a space Π that is related to C^n in some specific way.

8. The canonical system on C

The further development of geometry on a curve C is centred very largely round a certain unique equivalence system $\{X\}$ which we call the *canonical system of equivalence* on C, and also round the effective kernel $|X|$ (when it exists) of this system. We call $|X|$ the *canonical series* on C. The canonical system of equivalence and the canonical series between them furnish us, above all, with the first and most important numerical character of the function field Σ, namely its *genus p*, which is a birational invariant of every curve C of the field.

We have already seen that it is implied by our definition of equivalence of sets on an irreducible curve C (p. 235) that the totality of non-zero rational functions χ on C determines (or traces) on the curve a totality of sets which is in fact the unique equivalence class $\{0\}$. What we shall now show is that the canonical system $\{X\}$ on C is determined in a rather similar manner by the totality of *differentials* $d\chi$ of all the non-constant rational functions χ on C. Our first step, therefore, must be to give precise meaning to the term 'differential' as it will be used in this context.

8.1. Differentials of rational functions on C

If $\boldsymbol{\xi} = (1, \xi_1, ..., \xi_d)$ is a generic point of a curve C, then our concept of the invariance of places on C with respect to birational transformation of the curve arises from the fact (discussed at length in Chapter VII, § 5) that any such place $\mathbf{x}(u)$ defines a minimal parametrization τ of the whole field $\Sigma = K(\boldsymbol{\xi})$; and this parametrization of Σ defines in turn a place $\mathbf{y}(u)$ on any birational transform C' of C, given by a generic point $(1, \eta_1, ..., \eta_q)$ such that $\Sigma = K(\boldsymbol{\eta})$.

Now let us introduce a symbol du, to be called the *differential of the parameter u*, which is to be a new indeterminate. This differential is an entirely formal symbol, serving to suggest formal relationships familiar from analysis, but not possessing, from the point of view of the present theory, any functional connexion with the indeterminate u. We can now associate with any extended formal power series

$$h(u) = \sum_{i=0}^{\infty} a_i u^{N+i}$$

in the field $K|u|$ a formal derivative

$$h'(u) = \sum_{i=0}^{\infty} (N+i)a_i u^{N+i-1},$$

which is again an element of $K|u|$; and we then define the *differential* $dh(u)$ *of the power series* $h(u)$ as $h'(u)\,du$.

Turning back now to the field Σ and its parametrization τ, we have corresponding to every element χ of Σ a power series $h(u)$, and this series possesses a differential $dh(u) = dh$ in accordance with the definition just given. We shall say that *dh corresponds in the parametrization* τ *to the differential* $d\chi$ *of* χ. We do not need, for our present very limited purposes, to define what $d\chi$ *is*, or to attempt to extend the field Σ to include differentials $d\chi$ as well as the functions χ themselves, since it is sufficient to treat the differentials $d\chi$ as mere devices to be used in making concise statements about the differentials dh that we have defined. *Any statement involving a differential* $d\chi$ *is to be interpreted as standing for the whole class of statements to which it gives rise in terms of the possible minimal parametrizations of* Σ. This convention is legitimate because the only statements that we shall make about differentials $d\chi$ will be statements about their orders relative to minimal parametrizations τ of Σ; and we can show that the order of the differential dh that corresponds to $d\chi$ in τ is the same as that of the differential $d\bar{h}$ that corresponds to $d\chi$ in any parametrization $\bar{\tau}$ which is derived from τ by regular substitution for the parameter. Suppose, in fact, that

$$h(u) = a_0 u^\mu + a_1 u^{\mu+1} + \ldots \quad (a_0 \neq 0),$$

and that the parameter is changed from u to v by the regular substitution

$$u \to s(v) = k_1 v + k_2 v^2 + \ldots \quad (k_1 \neq 0).$$

Then

$$h(u) \to \bar{h}(v) = a_0(s(v))^\mu + a_1(s(v))^{\mu+1} + \ldots$$

$$= a_0 k_1^\mu v^\mu + \text{higher terms}.$$

If $\mu \neq 0$,

$$h'(u) = a_0 \mu u^{\mu-1} + \ldots$$

and

$$\bar{h}'(v) = a_0 k_1^\mu \mu v^{\mu-1} + \ldots,$$

and $h'(u)$ and $\bar{h}'(v)$ are of the same order $\mu - 1$.

If $\mu = 0$,

$$h(u) = a_0 + a_1 u + \ldots$$

and

$$\bar{h}(v) = a_0 + a_1(k_1 v + k_2 v^2 + \ldots) + \ldots$$

$$= a_0 + a_1 k_1 v + (a_1 k_2 + a_2 k_1^2)v^2 + \ldots.$$

In this case

$$h'(u) = a_1 + 2a_2 u + \ldots$$

and

$$\bar{h}'(v) = a_1 k_1 + 2(a_1 k_2 + a_2 k_1^2)v + \ldots,$$

and since we do not know which is the first non-zero coefficient among $a_1, a_2, \ldots$ we cannot specify the order of $h'(u)$ or $\bar{h}'(v)$. We can see, however, that since the coefficient of v^{i-1} in $\bar{h}'(v)$ is of the form $i(a_i k_1^i + \text{terms in } a_1, ..., a_{i-1} \text{ only})$, the orders of $h'(u)$ and $\bar{h}'(v)$ are the same. Thus $O_u(h'(u)) = O_v(\bar{h}'(v))$ in all cases, and we may therefore define $O_u(h'(u))$ as the order $O_{\mathscr{P}}(d\chi)$ of $d\chi$ at the place $\mathscr{P}$ on C represented by $\mathbf{x}(u)$. We can ignore the factor du that occurs in the equation $dh = h'(u)\,du$ as, being an indeterminate distinct from u, it makes no contribution to the order.

For any choice of χ, the order $O_{\mathscr{P}}(\chi)$ is zero at all but a finite number of places $\mathscr{P}$ on C (the zero-places and pole-places of χ) and thus, as we have already seen, $\mu_{\mathscr{P}} = O_{\mathscr{P}}(\chi)$ is the index function of a set on C. Provided that χ is not a constant, its differential $d\chi$ also has a finite order at every place $\mathscr{P}$ on C, as we have just shown, and this order $\mu'_{\mathscr{P}}$ has the value $\mu_{\mathscr{P}} - 1$ whenever $\mu_{\mathscr{P}} \neq 0$. We can as yet say nothing about the value of $\mu'_{\mathscr{P}}$ at any of the (infinitely many) places $\mathscr{P}$ where $\mu_{\mathscr{P}} = 0$, beyond the fact that this value is well defined; but we shall prove in the next section that $\mu'_{\mathscr{P}} = 0$ at all but a finite number of the places in question. Thus $\mu'_{\mathscr{P}}$, like $\mu_{\mathscr{P}}$, is the index function of a set. We shall call the set $\sum_{\mathscr{P}} \mu'_{\mathscr{P}} \mathscr{P}$ with this index function the *trace of the differential $d\chi$ on C*, and we shall denote it by $d\chi[C]$.

To establish the result just referred to, we shall have to study the structure of the Jacobian set of any rational involution Γ_1^n on C; and in doing so we shall obtain at the same time a significant relation between this Jacobian set J and the trace $d\chi[C]$ of the differential of a rational function χ which defines the linear series Γ_1^n.

8.2. The Jacobian set of a Γ_1^n

Let Γ_1^n be any base-free involution of sets of n places on C; and let us suppose, simplifying appropriately the procedures of §§ 3.1 and 3.2, that Γ_1^n arises from a linear system of rational functions on C of the form

$$\chi_\lambda = \lambda + \chi \quad (\chi_\infty = 1).$$

The sets G_λ of the Γ_1^n will then be such that

$$\chi_\lambda[C] = G_\lambda - G_\infty,$$

where G_∞ is a fixed set of Γ_1^n; and since G_λ and G_∞ are disjoint, they are respectively the whole positive and negative components of $\chi_\lambda[C]$ $(\lambda \neq \infty)$. In particular, the negative component of $\chi_\lambda[C]$ is independent of λ. This implies that when $O_{\mathscr{P}}(\chi_\lambda) > 0, \mathscr{P}$ is a place of multiplicity $O_{\mathscr{P}}(\chi_\lambda)$ in G_λ $(\lambda \neq \infty)$, and when $O_{\mathscr{P}}(\chi_\lambda) < 0$, $\mathscr{P}$ is a place of multiplicity $-O_{\mathscr{P}}(\chi_\lambda)$ in G_∞. Thus generally, if $\mathscr{P}$ is any place on C, and if $\lambda_{\mathscr{P}}$ is the parameter of the unique set of Γ_1^n to which $\mathscr{P}$ belongs, then the multiplicity $\sigma_{\mathscr{P}}$ of $\mathscr{P}$ in this set is given by

$$\sigma_{\mathscr{P}} = \begin{cases} O_{\mathscr{P}}(\lambda_{\mathscr{P}}+\chi) & \text{if } \lambda_{\mathscr{P}} \neq \infty \\ -O_{\mathscr{P}}(\chi) & \text{if } \lambda_{\mathscr{P}} = \infty. \end{cases} \tag{1}$$

By the general properties of unirational correspondences (cf. Chapter VII, § 6) we know that the places on C for which $\sigma_{\mathscr{P}} > 1$ are finite in number, so that $\sigma_{\mathscr{P}}-1$ is the index function of an effective set

$$J = \sum_{\mathscr{P}} (\sigma_{\mathscr{P}}-1)\mathscr{P} \tag{2}$$

on C. This is, in fact, the *Jacobian set* of the Γ_1^n, as previously defined in Chapter VII, p. 168, and it may be thought of as the set of double places of the involution, so weighted as to make a σ-fold place count as $\sigma-1$ double places. We have now to examine the structure of J.

In the first place, if $\mathscr{P}$ does not belong to G_{∞} then it belongs to a set of Γ_1^n, with parameter $\lambda_{\mathscr{P}} \neq \infty$, such that $O_{\mathscr{P}}(\lambda_{\mathscr{P}}+\chi) = \sigma_{\mathscr{P}} > 0$ by (1). Hence, if $\mathbf{x}(u)$ is any standard minimal representation of $\mathscr{P}$, the substitution $\boldsymbol{\xi} \to \mathbf{x}(u)$ carries $\chi(\boldsymbol{\xi})$ into a formal power series of the form

$$\chi(\mathbf{x}(u)) = -\lambda_{\mathscr{P}}+au^{\sigma_{\mathscr{P}}}+..., \quad a \neq 0;$$

and this gives on differentiation, since $\sigma_{\mathscr{P}} \neq 0$,

$$O_u(d\chi(\mathbf{x}(u))) = \sigma_{\mathscr{P}}-1. \tag{3}$$

If, on the other hand, $\mathscr{P}$ belongs to G_{∞}, then $O_{\mathscr{P}}(\chi) = -\sigma_{\mathscr{P}} < 0$, by (1), and we then have

$$\chi(\mathbf{x}(u)) = au^{-\sigma_{\mathscr{P}}}+..., \quad a \neq 0.$$

It now follows by differentiation that

$$O_u(d\chi(\mathbf{x}(u))) = -\sigma_{\mathscr{P}}-1 = \sigma_{\mathscr{P}}-1-2\sigma_{\mathscr{P}}. \tag{4}$$

Combining (3) and (4), we may now write

$$O_{\mathscr{P}}(d\chi) = \begin{cases} \sigma_{\mathscr{P}}-1 & \text{if } \mathscr{P} \notin G_{\infty} \\ \sigma_{\mathscr{P}}-1-2\sigma_{\mathscr{P}} & \text{if } \mathscr{P} \in G_{\infty}, \end{cases} \tag{5}$$

a result which at once implies that $O_{\mathscr{P}}(d\chi)$ is zero at all but a finite number of places on C. We are therefore at liberty to say that the differential $d\chi$ traces a set on C, namely the set

$$d\chi[C] = \sum_{\mathscr{P}} O_{\mathscr{P}}(d\chi)\mathscr{P}.$$

Furthermore, from (2) and (5) we see that

$$d\chi[C] = J-2G_{\infty}.$$

We have thus proved the following theorem.

THEOREM 18. *If χ is any non-constant rational function on C, then $O_{\mathscr{P}}(d\chi)$ is the index function of a set $X = d\chi[C]$ on C; and, if Γ_1^n is the base-free rational involution generated on C by the system of rational functions $\lambda + \chi$, then*

$$X = d\chi[C] = J - 2G, \tag{6}$$

where J is the Jacobian set of Γ_1^n and G, being the negative component of $\chi[C]$, is a set of Γ_1^n.

It may be added that our use in the above discussion of the non-homogeneous system of rational functions $\chi_\lambda = \lambda + \chi$ in preference to the homogeneous system $\chi_\lambda = \lambda_0 + \lambda_1 \chi$ was purely a matter of convenience; and further, that the only effect of replacing χ by any bilinear transform of itself

$$\chi' = \frac{a\chi + b}{c\chi + d} \quad (a, b, c, d \in K; \ ad - bc \neq 0)$$

would be to replace (6) by an equation

$$X' = d\chi'[C] = J - 2G',$$

where G' is some other set of Γ_1^n.

8.3. The equivalence of all sets $d\chi[C]$

Our final step now, having proved the existence of a set $d\chi[C]$ for every non-constant rational function χ on C, is to prove that all such sets are equivalent.

Suppose, then, that χ and $\bar{\chi}$ are any two non-constant rational functions on C. By Theorem 3, p. 151, there exists an irreducible K-polynomial $P(X, Y)$ such that $P(\chi, \bar{\chi}) = 0$; and this implies that, for any place $\mathbf{x}(u)$ on C,

$$P(\chi(\mathbf{x}(u)), \ \bar{\chi}(\mathbf{x}(u))) = 0.$$

Hence, by differentiation,†

$$P_X(\chi(\mathbf{x}(u)), \ \bar{\chi}(\mathbf{x}(u)))d\chi(\mathbf{x}(u)) + P_Y(\chi(\mathbf{x}(u)), \ \bar{\chi}(\mathbf{x}(u)))d\bar{\chi}(\mathbf{x}(u)) = 0,$$

so that

$$\frac{d\chi(\mathbf{x}(u))}{d\bar{\chi}(\mathbf{x}(u))} = -\frac{P_Y(\chi(\mathbf{x}(u)), \ \bar{\chi}(\mathbf{x}(u)))}{P_X(\chi(\mathbf{x}(u)), \ \bar{\chi}(\mathbf{x}(u)))} = \chi^*(\mathbf{x}(u)),$$

† The application here of a familiar rule of the differential calculus to the formal differentiation of power series needs justification. This is left to the reader.

where χ^* is a rational function on C. From this last result it follows that
$$O_{\mathscr{P}}(d\chi) - O_{\mathscr{P}}(d\bar{\chi}) = O_{\mathscr{P}}(\chi^*),$$
and hence, by the definition of equivalence, that
$$d\chi[C] \equiv d\bar{\chi}[C].$$
We thus have the following theorem.

THEOREM 19. *All the sets traced on C by differentials $d\chi$ of rational functions χ on C belong to one and the same system of equivalence $\{X\}$.*

The system $\{X\}$, as we have already said, will be called the *canonical system of equivalence* on C. Combining Theorem 19 with Theorem 18, we have the following further result for canonical sets.

COROLLARY 1. *If X is a canonical set on C, if J and $\bar{J}$ are the Jacobian sets of any pair of base-free rational involutions on the curve, and if G and $\bar{G}$ are arbitrary sets of these involutions, then*
$$X \equiv J - 2G \equiv \bar{J} - 2\bar{G}.$$

Since, by § 8.1, the orders of differentials are invariant over birational transformation of C, we have a further corollary as follows.

COROLLARY 2. *The canonical system $\{X\}$ is invariant over birational transformation of C.*

The kernel $|X|$ of $\{X\}$, when it exists, will be called the *canonical series* on C. Its order $n(X)$ and its dimensionality $r(X)$ are birationally invariant numerical characters of C, i.e. numerical characters of the field Σ. We shall see that there is only one case in which $\{X\}$ has no effective kernel $|X|$, namely that in which C is a rational curve (Theorem 21, p. 269).

8.4. Properties of the canonical series

For the closer investigation of the canonical system $\{X\}$ or the canonical series $|X|$ on a curve C we may confine our attention, in view of Corollary 2 above, to the case in which C is a plane curve of order n with only ordinary multiple points $O_1, \ldots, O_s$ of multiplicities $k_1, \ldots, k_s$; and we begin by evaluating the order $n(X)$ of the canonical series on such a curve.

We proceed by applying the second part of Theorem 18 to the involution Γ_1^n traced on C by lines through a point A of S_2, choosing A for convenience in such a way that it does not lie on C, nor on any branch tangent of C at one of the points O_i, nor on any inflexional tangent of C. It is readily seen that, in these circumstances, the only places on C that count more than once in the sets of Γ_1^n to which they belong are those with centres at the points of contact $P_1,\ldots,P_m$—simple on C—of the tangents from A to the curve; and, moreover, each of these counts exactly twice in the set that contains it. Hence the order of the Jacobian set of Γ_1^n is equal to the class m of C; and by equating the orders of both sides of equation (6) on p. 266 we obtain the relation

$$n(X) = m - 2n.$$

Applying then the formula for m given by Theorem 8, p. 125, we have

$$\begin{aligned}
n(X) &= n(n-1) - \sum_{i=1}^{s} k_i(k_i-1) - 2n \\
&= 2\left(\tfrac{1}{2}(n-1)(n-2) - \tfrac{1}{2}\sum_{i=1}^{s} k_i(k_i-1)\right) - 2 \\
&= 2D - 2,
\end{aligned} \tag{7}$$

where D is the deficiency of C. This is the formula that we set out to obtain; and, prompted by it, we now lay down the following definition of the genus of a curve.

DEFINITION. The *genus* of an irreducible curve C is the number p defined by the equation $2p - 2 = n(X)$, where $n(X)$ denotes the common order of the canonical sets on C.

THEOREM 20. *The genus of an irreducible curve C is equal to the deficiency of any birationally equivalent plane curve with only ordinary multiple points.*

This theorem is essentially a restatement of equation (7). It has the following important consequence.

COROLLARY 1. *The genus p of an irreducible curve C is always a non-negative integer.*

Since, further, any plane curve of deficiency zero is rational (Theorem 10, p. 128), and since any rational curve (being transformable birationally into a line) is necessarily of genus zero, we see that $p = 0$ is a necessary and sufficient condition for rationality (unlike $D = 0$, which is only a sufficient condition). In view of the importance of this result we now state it as a formal corollary.

COROLLARY 2. *An irreducible curve C is rational if and only if its genus p is zero.*

We now observe that the argument leading up to equation (7)

will take us much further than the computation of $n(X)$. In the notation there used, and under the conditions there imposed, the first polar of A is an adjoint A^{n-1} of C, and it meets C in the m points P_j $(j = 1,...,m)$, each counted once, and in the multiple points O_i $(i = 1,...,s)$, each counted exactly $k_i(k_i-1)$ times. Hence the trace of A^{n-1} on C is

$$A^{n-1}[C] = J+D,$$

where J is the Jacobian set of the Γ_1^n traced on C by lines through A, and D is the set of adjunction on C. Since, by Theorem 19, Corollary 1, $J \equiv X+2G$, where G is any set traced on C by a line of the plane, and since adjoint curves of any given order trace a complete linear series on C (Theorem 14) it follows that *adjoints A^{n-1} of C trace on C, residually to the set of adjunction D, the complete series $|X+2G|$, where X is a canonical set and G is the set traced on C by a line.*

Further, since any adjoint A^{n-3} (if such a curve exists), augmented by any pair of lines of S_2, forms a composite A^{n-1}, it follows by the same argument that *adjoints A^{n-3} of C, if any such exist, trace the complete canonical series on C, residually to the set of adjunction D.*

Finally, as regards the existence of curves A^{n-3}, we note that the virtual freedom $\bar{r}^{(n-3)}$ of such curves is given by

$$\bar{r}^{(n-3)} = \tfrac{1}{2}n(n-3)-\tfrac{1}{2}\sum_{i=1}^{s} k_i(k_i-1) = p-1,$$

since the genus is here equal to the deficiency by Theorem 20. This result implies, by Corollary 2 to the same theorem, that $\bar{r}^{(n-3)} \geqslant 0$ as long as C is not rational, and therefore that in such a case there always exists at least one A^{n-3} of C. In fact, if $r^{(n-3)}$ is the effective freedom of A^{n-3} we must have $r^{(n-3)} \geqslant p-1$; and from this, by the invariance of $|X|$, we have the following general theorem.

THEOREM 21. *Any non-rational irreducible curve C of genus p possesses an (effective) canonical series $|X|$ of dimensionality not less than $p-1$. If C is a plane curve of order n with only ordinary multiple points, then $|X|$ is traced on C, residually to its set of adjunction D, by the adjoints A^{n-3} of C.*

For a rational curve, with $p = 0$, we have $n(X) = -2$; and hence the canonical system of equivalence $\{X\}$ has no effective kernel. In this case $\{X\}$ consists trivially of all sets of order -2 on C.

When $p = 1$, the curve C is said to be *elliptic*. In this case the canonical series $|X|$ is of dimensionality zero, having the null set 0 as its only member.

Now, in the final section of this chapter, we shall deal with the most fundamental problem of all, namely that of determining the precise dimensionality of any complete linear series $|A|$, defined by a given effective set A on C.

9. The Riemann-Roch Theorem

The theorem that we propose to prove in this section can properly be described as the central theorem of the invariantive geometry of curves. Since it will be trivially true, as we state it, for complete series on rational curves ($p = 0$), we may suppose throughout the proof that the curves under consideration are of genus $p \geqslant 1$, so that they possess—as we have just seen—effective canonical series $|X|$ of order $2p-2$ and dimensionality not less than $p-1$. We are concerned, then, with finding the dimensionality r of any complete linear series $|A|$, of order n, on such a curve C.

9.1. Index of speciality

The value of r depends essentially, as will appear, on the relation between $|A|$ and the canonical series $|X|$.

Consider any given effective set A on C. We shall say that A is a *special* set on C if and only if it is contained in at least one effective canonical set X, that is to say if and only if there exists an effective X such that $X-A$ is also effective. The maximum number i of linearly independent effective canonical sets in which A is contained ($i \geqslant 0$) will be called the *index of speciality* of A and will be denoted by $\mathrm{sp}(A)$. If $\mathrm{sp}(A) = 0$, we shall say that A is *non-special*.

We observe next that *every set of the complete linear series* $|A|$ *determined by* A *has the same index of speciality*. For suppose that A_1 and A_2 are any two sets of $|A|$. If $\mathrm{sp}(A_1) = i > 0$, then the sets of $|X|$ that contain A_1 as a fixed part form an effective linear series of dimensionality $i-1$. This means that $i-1$ is the dimensionality of the residual series $|X|-A_1$, i.e. the series $|X-A_1|$ (cf. p. 255), and as such it is independent of the choice of A_1 in $|A|$. Thus if either of $\mathrm{sp}(A_1)$ and $\mathrm{sp}(A_2)$ is different from zero the other one is equal to it; and it follows from this that if one of the two indices is zero then so also is the other. Thus $\mathrm{sp}(A_1) = \mathrm{sp}(A_2)$, and the common value of $\mathrm{sp}(A)$ for all the sets of $|A|$ is a character of the linear series $|A|$ itself. We accordingly lay down the following definition.

DEFINITION. The *index of speciality* $i = \mathrm{sp}|A|$ of an (effective) linear series $|A|$ on a curve C is the maximum number of linearly independent effective canonical sets X that contain any given set of $|A|$.

If $i = 0$, the series $|A|$ is said to be *non-special*. If $i > 0$, $|A|$ is *special*; and in this case $|X-A|$ exists and is of dimensionality $i-1$.

Since every canonical set X is of order $2p-2$, a series $|A|$ of order n is certainly non-special if $n > 2p-2$. Equally, since the dimensionality of $|X|$ is not less than $p-1$, $|A|$ is necessarily special if $n \leqslant p-1$. The index of speciality of the canonical series itself is 1.

On a rational curve, every series $|A|$ is trivially non-special, for $|X|$ does not exist in this case. On an elliptic curve $(p = 1)$ the only special series is the canonical series, which in this case reduces to the null series $|0|$.

EXAMPLE. Let C be a plane non-singular quartic curve, so that $|X|$ is the Γ_2^4 traced on C by the lines of the plane. Then every effective set of order 1 on C constitutes by itself a complete Γ_0^1 with index of speciality 2, because two linearly independent lines pass through any given point of C. Similarly, every effective set of order 2 on C constitutes a complete Γ_0^2 with index of speciality 1. An effective set of order 3 is either special (with $i = 1$) or non-special according as it is or is not part of the trace of a line on C. All effective sets of order $n \geqslant 4$ on C, excepting only the canonical sets themselves, are non-special.

9.2. Proof of the Riemann-Roch Theorem

We can now state and prove the fundamental theorem already alluded to at the beginning of § 9.

THEOREM 22 (*The Riemann-Roch Theorem*). *The dimensionality r of any complete linear series of order n and index of speciality i on an irreducible curve of genus p is given by the formula*

$$r = n-p+i.$$

The proof of this theorem will be built up in four stages.

I. *Proof that $r \geqslant n-p$.* To establish the inequality $r \geqslant n-p$ for any complete linear series $|A|$ on C we suppose, as we always may, that C is a plane curve of order m with ordinary multiple points O_i of multiplicities k_i $(i = 1,...,s)$ as its only singularities.

We consider first the case in which $|A|$ is the complete series traced on C, residually to the set of adjunction D of the curve, by all the adjoints A^M of some fixed order $M \geqslant m$. If d is the order of D, then we have the relations

$$d = \sum_{i=1}^{s} k_i(k_i-1), \quad n = mM-d; \tag{1}$$

and the dimensionality ρ_M of the linear system of curves A^M satisfies the inequality

$$\rho_M \geqslant \tfrac{1}{2}M(M+3)-\tfrac{1}{2}d.$$

The dimensionality r of $|A|$ is then given by

$$r = \rho_M-\sigma,$$

where σ is the maximum number of linearly independent curves of the system (A^M) that have C as a component. Since C forms an A^M when taken in conjunction with any curve of order $M-m$, we have

$$\sigma = \tfrac{1}{2}(M-m+1)(M-m+2),$$

and hence

$$\begin{aligned}
r &\geqslant \tfrac{1}{2}M(M+3)-\tfrac{1}{2}d-\tfrac{1}{2}(M-m+1)(M-m+2) \\
&= Mm-\tfrac{1}{2}d-\tfrac{1}{2}(m-1)(m-2) \\
&= Mm-\tfrac{1}{2}d-p-\tfrac{1}{2}d\dagger \\
&= n-p
\end{aligned}$$

by (1).

Now consider the general case in which $|A|$ is the complete residual $\Gamma_{r'}^{n'}$ of a Γ_r^n, such as the one just considered, with respect to a fixed effective set L of order l. Then $n' = n-l$ and $r' \geqslant r-l$, and we have at once the required inequality

$$r' \geqslant n'-p.$$

II. LEMMA (*The Reduction Theorem*). *If A is any effective set and $\mathscr{P}$ is any place on C, then either* $\mathrm{sp}(A+\mathscr{P}) = \mathrm{sp}(A)$ *or $\mathscr{P}$ is a fixed place of* $|A+\mathscr{P}|$.

Proof. We suppose C to be chosen as in I, with the further stipulation (which we can always fulfil by use, if necessary, of a standard quadratic transformation of the plane) that the centre of $\mathscr{P}$ is a simple point P of C.

Assume, then, that $\mathrm{sp}(A+\mathscr{P}) \neq \mathrm{sp}(A)$. This implies that there exists an adjoint A^{m-3} such that its trace on C, residual to D, is a canonical set of the form $A+B$, where B is effective and $\mathscr{P} \notin B$.

---

† If m' denotes the class of C, we have $n(X) = 2p-2 = m'-2m$ (from § 8.4) and $m' = m(m-1)-d$, from which $(m-1)(m-2) = 2p+d$.

Now consider any line L which passes through P and meets C residually in $m-1$ distinct points $Q_1, ..., Q_{m-1}$; and denote the trace of L on C by $Q+\mathscr{P}$, where Q stands for the sum of the places on C with centres at the points $Q_1, ..., Q_{m-1}$. We observe then that the composite curve $A^{m-3}+L$ is an adjoint A^{m-2} with trace

$$D+A+B+Q+\mathscr{P}$$

on C; and from this it follows, by Theorem 14, that the complete series $|A+\mathscr{P}|$ is traced on C, residually to the set $D+B+Q$, by adjoint curves A^{m-2}. Any such adjoint, however, having Q as part of its trace on C, must contain the $m-1$ centres Q_i of the places in Q; and hence, containing $m-1$ distinct points of L, it must have L as a component. It therefore also contains $\mathscr{P}$; and this proves that $\mathscr{P}$ is a fixed place of $|A+\mathscr{P}|$. The lemma is accordingly established.

EXAMPLE. Let A be the triad of places at three collinear points L, M, N of a plane non-singular quartic curve C, and let T be the fourth intersection of the line LMN with C. Further, let $\mathscr{P}$ be a place on C at any point P other than L, M, N. Then (i) if $P = T$, we have $\mathrm{sp}(A+\mathscr{P}) = \mathrm{sp}(A) = 1$, while the dimensionalities of $|A|$ and $|A+\mathscr{P}|$ are 1 and 2 respectively; and (ii) if $P \neq T$, then $\mathrm{sp}(A+\mathscr{P}) = 0$, and $\mathscr{P}$ is a fixed place of $|A+\mathscr{P}|$.

III. *Proof of the theorem for $i = 0$.* The third stage of our proof consists in showing that $r = n-p$ for any complete non-special series on C, thus proving the theorem for the special case $i = 0$. Since $r \geqslant n-p$ for any complete series on C, as was proved in I, we have only to show that $|A|$ is always special when $r > n-p$. We do this by induction with respect to r.

In the first place, then, when $r = 0$ the inequality $r > n-p$ gives $n \leqslant p-1$; and in this case, as already remarked in § 9.1, $|A|$ is necessarily special.

Now suppose that, for some given value of $r \geqslant 0$, every series $|A|$ for which $r > n-p$ is special; and let $|A'|$ be any complete series, of order $n' = n+1$ and dimensionality $r' = r+1$, such that $r' > n'-p$. Further, let $\mathscr{P}$ be any place on C which is not fixed in $|A'|$. Then $|A| = |A'-\mathscr{P}|$ is a series of order n and dimensionality r for which $r > n-p$, and therefore, by the induction hypothesis, $|A|$ is special. But then it follows by the lemma just proved that, since $\mathscr{P}$ is not a fixed place of $|A+\mathscr{P}| = |A'|$, $\mathrm{sp}|A'| = \mathrm{sp}|A| > 0$; and thus $|A'|$ is special. The basis of the induction is now established, and the Riemann-Roch Theorem accordingly proved for $i = 0$.

IV. *Proof of the theorem in the general case.* We shall prove the theorem generally by a further induction with respect to i. The initial case $i = 0$ has already been dealt with, and we have only to show that if the theorem is true for any given value of i then it is also true for the next higher value. Suppose, then, that for every complete linear series Γ_r^n on C with index of speciality i, we have $r = n - p + i$; and let $|A|$ be any complete $\Gamma_{r'}^{n'}$ with index of speciality $i+1$. Further, let $\mathscr{P}$ be any place on C that is not fixed for $|X-A|$, so that $\mathrm{sp}|A+\mathscr{P}| = i$.

We then know, by the lemma, that $\mathscr{P}$ must be a fixed place of $|A+\mathscr{P}|$, so that this series is a $\Gamma_{r'}^{n'+1}$ with index of speciality i; and we know further, by the induction hypothesis as applied to the same series, that

$$r' = (n'+1) - p + i = n' - p + (i+1).$$

Thus the theorem holds for the series $|A|$; and the argument by induction therefore applies.

We have tacitly assumed in the course of the preceding argument that $p > 0$, since the concept of speciality has to be interpreted conventionally for rational curves, which possess no effective canonical sets. For a rational curve, however, every complete series is such that $r = n$ and $i = 0$; and the Riemann-Roch Theorem is therefore valid also in this very special case. The proof of the theorem is now complete.

9.3. Applications of the Riemann-Roch Theorem

We shall conclude this chapter by noting a few of the more important immediate applications of the Riemann-Roch Theorem, at the same time referring the reader for additional information to the exercises which follow.

We begin by applying the theorem to the canonical series $|X|$ itself, for which $n = 2p - 2$ and $i = 1$, and therefore $r = p - 1$.

COROLLARY 1. *The dimensionality of the canonical series is $p-1$.*

Thus $|X|$ is a Γ_{p-1}^{2p-2}; and the reader may readily verify that $|X|$ is the only Γ_{p-1}^{2p-2}, complete or incomplete, that exists on C.

COROLLARY 2. *Any set of a special Γ_r^n imposes precisely $n-r$ conditions on a canonical set X required to contain it.*

This follows at once from Corollary 1.

COROLLARY 3. *(Clifford's Theorem). Every special Γ_r^n on C is such that $n \geqslant 2r$.*

Proof. If the result is true for complete series, then it must hold *a fortiori* for incomplete series. Suppose, then, that Γ_r^n is a special complete series $|A|$, and that $|X| = |A+A'|$, where A' is effective; and let the indices of speciality of $|A|$ and $|A'|$ be i and i' respectively. Since i independent sets of $|X|$ contain A, and only one such set contains $A+A'$, it follows that A' imposes at least $i-1$ linearly independent conditions on sets of $|X|$ that are required to contain it. In fact, however, the actual number of conditions so imposed is $(p-1)-(i'-1) = p-i'$; and therefore $p-i' \geqslant i-1$. If we now write $r = n-p+i$ and $i' = r+1$, we obtain the inequality $p-r-1 \geqslant r-n+p-1$, i.e. $n \geqslant 2r$.

COROLLARY 4. *The canonical series X has no fixed place.*

Proof. If $\mathscr{P}$ were a fixed place of $|X|$, then $|X-\mathscr{P}|$ would be a Γ_{p-1}^{2p-3}, in contradiction to Corollary 3.

NOTES AND EXERCISES ON CHAPTER X

1. If C has the equation $XY = (X^2+Y^2)^2$ and $\mathscr{P}_1$, $\mathscr{P}_2$ are the two (inflexional) places at O on C, with tangents $Y = 0$ and $X = 0$, show that (i) the line $Y = 0$ traces the set $3\mathscr{P}_1+\mathscr{P}_2$ on C, (ii) the line $Y = X$ traces $\mathscr{P}_1+\mathscr{P}_2+\mathscr{P}_3+\mathscr{P}_4$ on C, where $\mathscr{P}_3$, $\mathscr{P}_4$ are the places with centres $(\frac{1}{2}, \frac{1}{2})$ and $(-\frac{1}{2}, -\frac{1}{2})$, and (iii) the line $Y = iX$ traces $\mathscr{P}_1+\mathscr{P}_2+\mathscr{P}_3'+\mathscr{P}_4'$, where $\mathscr{P}_3'$, $\mathscr{P}_4'$ are the places at one of the nodes of C on the line at infinity.

Exhibit in a similar way the sets traced on C by (a) the line at infinity, (b) the circle $X^2+Y^2 = X$, (c) the cubic $Y^2 = X^3$, and (d) the quartic $2XY = (X^2+Y^2)^2$.

2. If $\mathscr{P}$ and $\mathscr{P}_1$ are the places at $(0, 0)$ and $(0, 1)$ on the curve C with equation $Y^2 = X^3+Y^3$, and if E is the trace of the line at infinity on C, show that each of $(1-Y)/X^2$ and $2X/Y^2$ traces the same set $E+\mathscr{P}_1-4\mathscr{P}$ on C, and verify that (in agreement with Theorem 3) the ratio of the rational functions which they define on C is constant.

If χ is the rational function on C defined by $(1-Y)/X^2$, show that, for every finite value of the parameter λ, the set $(\chi+\lambda)[C]$ is of the form $A_\lambda-4\mathscr{P}$, where A_λ is effective of order 4.

3. Show that the set traced by the cubic $X^2+Y^2 = X(1-Y^2)$ on the parabola $Y^2 = X$ is $4\mathscr{P}+2\mathscr{P}'$, where $\mathscr{P}$ and $\mathscr{P}'$ are the places at $(0, 0)$ and at X_∞ on the parabola.

4. If $\mathscr{P}$ is the place at O on the curve $Y^2 = X^3$, show that $\mathscr{P}$ cannot have multiplicity greater than 3 in the set traced on this curve by any other curve with a simple point at O.

5. Verify that the set traced on a Plücker curve C by its Hessian (cf. Chapter V, Exercises 15 and 16, Chapter VI, Exercise 10) is

$$\sum \mathscr{I}_\alpha + \sum (3\mathscr{D}_\beta+3\mathscr{D}_\beta') + \sum 8\mathscr{K}_\gamma,$$

where $\mathscr{I}_\alpha$ is the place on C at an inflexion, $\mathscr{D}_\beta$ and $\mathscr{D}_\beta'$ are the places on C at a node, and $\mathscr{K}_\gamma$ is the place on C at a cusp.

6. If C is the cubic with equation $yz^2 + zx^2 + xy^2 = 0$, and χ_1, χ_2, χ_3 are the rational functions on C defined by x/z, y/z, xy/z^2, show that the linear system N_3 of (null-equivalent) sets traced on C by rational functions of the normal system $\lambda_0 + \lambda_1\chi_1 + \lambda_2\chi_2 + \lambda_3\chi_3$ has the polar set $P = 3\mathscr{P}_X + \mathscr{P}_Y$, where $\mathscr{P}_X$ and $\mathscr{P}_Y$ are the places on C at the reference points X and Y.

Show also that the trace N_3' of the conormal linear system

$$\lambda_0 \chi_1^{-1} + \lambda_1 + \lambda_2 \chi_2 \chi_1^{-1} + \lambda_3 \chi_3 \chi_1^{-1}$$

has the polar set $P' = \mathscr{P}_X + 2\mathscr{P}_Y + \mathscr{P}_Z$.

Show further that the linear series Γ_3^4 obtained by adding P (P') to every set of N_3 (N_3') is that traced on C, residually to $\mathscr{P}_X + \mathscr{P}_Y$, by conics through X and Y.

7. Show that a projective model of the Γ_3^4 in Exercise 6 is the elliptic quartic curve of intersection of the quadrics

$$x_0 x_3 = x_1 x_2 \quad \text{and} \quad x_1^2 + x_2(x_0 + x_3) = 0.$$

8. *Noether's Theorem: the 'simple' case.* Deduce from Theorem 13 the following result:

If two plane curves C, C', with no common component, have equations $F = 0$ and $G = 0$, and if each intersection P of these curves, being an ordinary s-fold point of C and an ordinary t-fold point of C', is such that the two sets of branch tangents at P have no common member, then any curve C'' which has multiplicity $s + t - 1$ at least at each intersection P as above described, has an equation of the form $AF + BG = 0$.

This implies, in particular, that if a C^m and a C^n meet in mn distinct points, then any other curve through these mn points has an equation of the Noether form $AF + BG = 0$.

9. Show that the condition of Theorem 13 relevant to an intersection P which is a simple point on each of the two curves C, C' is that C'' should have multiplicity of intersection with C at P not less than that of C' with C at P.

10. If a C^m and a C^n in the plane meet in mn distinct points, of which mp lie on a C^p, show that the remaining intersections lie on a C^{n-p}.

11. *Cayley–Bacharach Theorems.* Prove the theorem:

If a C^{m+n-3} passes through all but one of the mn distinct intersections of a C^m and a C^n, then it passes also through the last intersection.

Prove also the extension:

If a $C^{m+n-\gamma}$ ($\gamma > 3$) passes through all but $\frac{1}{2}(\gamma-1)(\gamma-2)$ of the mn distinct intersections of a C^m and a C^n, then it passes also through the remaining intersections except only in the case when these lie on a $C^{\gamma-3}$.

Formulate appropriate generalizations of these results on the basis of the 'simple' case of Noether's Theorem given in Exercise 8.

12. Verify the following applications of the preceding Exercise:

(i) Eleven of the intersections of a variable quartic curve with a given non-singular cubic determine the twelfth.

(ii) If A, B, C are three of the sixteen intersections of two quartic curves, then any other quartic through the remaining thirteen intersections will pass through A, B, C if these points are not collinear (but will not in general do so if A, B, C are collinear).

(iii) If two quartics with a common node A meet in twelve further distinct points, then these twelve impose only eleven independent linear conditions on quintic curves with A as triple point that are required to contain them.

Discuss (ii) in detail.

13. Discuss the Jacobian set of the Γ_1^{n-k} traced on a plane curve $^pC^n$ by lines through a k-fold point A on C, showing the different ways in which the $2(n-k)+2p-2$ members of this set may arise.

Show, in particular, that if the k-fold point at A is strictly ordinary, and none of the branch tangents at other multiple points pass through A, then the number of tangents (properly counted) that can be drawn from C to touch the curve elsewhere is $m-2k$, where m is the class of C.

14. Show that any irreducible non-singular (α, β) curve on a quadric surface ψ is of genus $p = (\alpha-1)(\beta-1)$, and find the number of generators of each system (properly counted) which touch the curve.

15. *Geometry on an elliptic curve.* Show that all the sets of n places $(n \geqslant 1)$ on any elliptic curve C distribute themselves into ∞^1 complete linear series Γ_{n-1}^n.

Taking C to be a non-singular cubic, show how to construct the point-series g_{n-1}^n associated with the Γ_{n-1}^n in question. Show, in particular, that the ∞^1 series g_2^3 on C arrange themselves in pairs g, g' in such a way that the conics through any set of g (g') meet C residually in the triads of g' (g), the series cut on C by lines being paired in this way with itself.

Show, however, that the projective model of **any** g_2^3 on the cubic curve C is not only birationally but also projectively equivalent to C.

16. *Normal elliptic curves.* Show that every normal elliptic curve is a $^1C^n[n-1]$ for some $n \geqslant 3$, and that it projects from any point of itself $(n \geqslant 4)$ into a normal $^1C^{n-1}[n-2]$. Show also that every $^1C^n[n-1]$ is non-singular.

Discuss in this connexion the normal curves $^1C^4[3]$ and $^1C^5[4]$, and the subnormal curve $^1C^5[3]$, already obtained in Exercise 9 on p. 205.

17. *Structure of the canonical series.* By Corollary 4 on p. 275, the canonical series Γ_{p-1}^{2p-2} on a curve C of genus p has no fixed place. We now ask when it is simple and when compounded of an involution. For $p = 0$ or 1 the question does not arise, and for $p = 2$ the canonical series, being a Γ_1^2, is trivially compounded of this Γ_1^2.

Suppose, then, that $p \geqslant 3$ and that Γ_{p-1}^{2p-2} is compounded of an involution I_μ ($\mu > 1$). The projective model C' of the series is then a curve of order $(2p-2)/\mu$ with an S_{p-1} as its ambient space, and C' is a model of the sets of I_μ. These properties of C' imply that $(2p-2)/\mu \geqslant p-1$ (C' being rational normal in case of equality). This gives $\mu \leqslant 2$, whence, since $\mu > 1$, we have $\mu = 2$, and C' is rational. The only possibility, therefore, is that Γ_{p-1}^{2p-2} may be compounded of a rational involution Γ_1^2.

On the other hand, if $p \geqslant 2$ and there exists a Γ_1^2 on C (so that C, by definition, is hyperelliptic), then this Γ_1^2 is special. It follows therefore by the Reduction Theorem (p. 272) that every canonical set that contains one place of a set of Γ_1^2 necessarily contains the other also, so that Γ_{p-1}^{2p-2} is compounded of the Γ_1^2. We therefore have the following result:

For $p \geqslant 2$, the canonical series of a curve C is simple excepting only when C is hyperelliptic, in which case it is compounded of a Γ_1^2.

Thus, for example, if C is a plane hyperelliptic curve of order n with an $(n-2)$-fold point A and d further double points D_i $(i = 1,...,d)$, then its adjoints $A^{(n-3)}$ are sets of $n-3$ lines through A, of which d are the joins AD_i, and each canonical set consists of $n-3-d$ sets of the involution Γ_1^2 traced on C by lines through A.

18. Show that, if $q \geqslant 3$, an irreducible non-singular $(2, q)$ curve on a quadric surface in S_3 is always hyperelliptic, and give an appropriate construction for its canonical sets.

Explain, by examples, how this result must be modified if C has multiple points.

19. *Neutral sets of a Γ_r^n.* An effective set N is said to be *neutral* for a Γ_r^n on C if every set of this series that contains any one place of N contains the whole set N.

For $r = 1$, every set or sub-set of a Γ_1^n without base is trivially neutral; and, more generally, if a Γ_r^n is compounded of an I_μ, then every set of I_μ is trivially neutral for the series. But if Γ_2^n is the series traced on a plane curve C by the lines of S_2, then the pair of places on C at an ordinary double point forms an *isolated* neutral set for Γ_2^n; and if $\mathscr{P}$ is the place on C at a simple cusp, then $2\mathscr{P}$ is an isolated neutral set for Γ_2^n.

Prove that *the singularity of any curve C at a k-fold point O can be interpreted primarily (though not completely) as an isolated neutral set N of order k for the series traced on C by the primes of its ambient space.*

Define the composition of N in terms of the places on C at O and the orders of these places.

20. *Curves of genus 2.* Classify the complete linear series of all orders $n \leqslant 5$ on a uninodal quartic C in S_2. Comment in particular on the projective model $^2C^5[3]$ of a Γ_3^5 on the curve (cf. Exercise 10, p. 205).

21. *Curves of genus 3.* Show that every non-hyperelliptic curve of genus 3 is birationally transformable into a plane non-singular quartic curve C, and classify all the complete series of orders $n \leqslant 6$ on C.

Show also that every hyperelliptic curve of genus 3 is birationally transformable into a plane quintic with a triple point.

Discuss in this connexion the non-hyperelliptic and hyperelliptic curves $^3C^6[3]$ defined in Exercise 12 on p. 205.

22. *Curves normal in S_2.* If $s \geqslant 0$ is the number of linearly independent adjoints A^{n-4} of a plane curve $^pC^n$ with only ordinary multiple points, show that the index of speciality of the Γ_2^n traced on C by the lines of S_2 is equal to s.

If $s = 0$, deduce that $^pC^n$ is normal in S_2 if and only if $n = p+2$.

If $s > 0$, show that $s = p+2-n+\alpha$, where α is the superabundance of the system of adjoints $A^{(n-4)}$ with respect to their assigned base; and deduce that in this case $^pC^n$ is normal in S_2 if and only if $\alpha = 0$.

23. *Curves* $^4C^6$ *normal in* S_2 *and* S_3. Show that a plane 6-nodal sextic curve $^4C^6$ is normal in S_2 unless its six nodes lie on a conic. When this last condition holds, show that the curve is the projection of a normal $^4C^6[3]$— intersection of a quadric and a cubic surface.

[This implies, incidentally, that the six chords of such an intersection curve that pass through a general point of S_3 must lie on a quadric cone.]

Show further that a $^4C^6$ of S_2 with two ordinary triple points is always the projection of a normal $^4C^6[3]$ from a point on the quadric containing it.

24. *A normal* $^3C^6[3]$ *with a node.* If C is a 7-nodal $^3C^6$ in S_2, show that cubics through six of the nodes trace (residually) a *complete* Γ_3^6 on C, and that the projective model of this series is a normal $^3C^6[3]$ with a node at the transform of the seventh node of C. Verify, then, that this $^3C^6[3]$ is the intersection of a quadric and a cubic surface that touch at one point.

Three quadrics of S_4 that have a line L in common meet residually in a normal $^3C^7[4]$ with L as trisecant line. Show that this curve projects from any one of its intersections with L into a nodal $^3C^6[3]$ of the type described above.

25. *Postulation of a* $^pC^n[r]$. The number of linear conditions imposed on the primals F^l of any given order l of S_r by requiring them to contain a given curve $^pC^n[r]$ is called the *postulation* ϕ_l *of the curve for primals of order* l. [The definition is not usually restricted, as here, to irreducible curves.]

If $i \geqslant 0$ is the index of speciality of the series Γ_ρ^{ln} traced on the curve by primals F^l, and if $\delta \geqslant 0$ is the deficiency from completeness of the same series, then the dimensionality ρ is given by

$$\rho = ln - p + i - \delta,$$

and we deduce that $\phi_l = ln - p + i - \delta + 1.$

Thus, in particular, if $ln > 2p - 2$, so that the series Γ_ρ^{ln} is certainly non-special, then we may infer that $\phi_l \leqslant ln - p + 1$.

[It can be shown that if C is non-singular then there exists always an l_0 such that $\phi_l = ln - p + 1$ for $l \geqslant l_0$; while if C has singular points, then there exist integers l_0 and k such that $\phi_l = ln - p + 1 - k$ for $l \geqslant l_0$.]

26. *Canonical curves.* We may define a *canonical curve of genus* p to be any curve of this genus such that the primes of its ambient space trace on it the complete canonical series. It is, therefore, a $^pC^{2p-2}[p-1]$.

If C is any non-hyperelliptic curve of genus $p \geqslant 3$, then the projective model of its canonical series—since this is simple and without fixed points —is a canonical curve, uniquely defined to within projective transformation. Conversely, since the canonical series is the only Γ_{p-1}^{2p-2} on the curve (cf. p. 274), it follows that every $^pC^{2p-2}[p-1]$ is canonical.

As examples of such curves we may mention (i) for $p = 3$, the plane non-singular quartic, (ii) for $p = 4$, the $^4C^6[3]$, intersection of a quadric and a cubic surface, (iii) for $p = 5$, the $^5C^8[4]$, complete (non-singular) intersection of three quadrics in S_4; etc.

27. *Property of canonical curves.* Show that every canonical curve is non-singular.

[This can be proved in two stages: by showing first that for non-hyperelliptic curves the sign of equality in Clifford's Theorem (p. 274) holds uniquely for the canonical series; and then by applying this result in connexion with the Γ^{2p-2-k}_{p-2} traced residually on a canonical curve $^pC^{2p-2}[p-1]$ by primes through a k-fold point of the curve, from which it appears that $k=1$.]

28. *Dilatation of a point of S_r.* A basic operation for use in the analysis of singular points of curves and other algebraic varieties in a space S_r is the so-called *dilatation of a point of S_r.* This is essentially a birational transformation of the whole space S_r into a non-singular variety V_r in a higher space S_N, of such a kind that the neighbourhood of one particular point A of S_r is 'blown up' into a space Π_{r-1} on V_r, while every other point of S_r is transformed 'regularly' into a unique point of V_r not on Π_{r-1}. We define such a transformation as follows.

Let A be taken as the reference point $(1, 0,..., 0)$ in S_r, and let a minimal basis for quadrics through A be taken in the form

$$(x_0x_1, x_0x_2,..., x_0x_r, x_1^2, x_1x_2,..., x_{r-1}x_r, x_r^2),$$

the number of its elements being $N+1 = \frac{1}{2}(r+1)(r+2)-1$. The equations

$$y_i = x_0x_{i+1} \quad (i = 0,...,r-1),$$

$$y_r = x_1^2, \quad y_{r+1} = x_1x_2, \quad ..., \quad y_{N-1} = x_{r-1}x_r, \quad y_N = x_r^2$$

then transform S_r birationally into a variety V_r such that if $(1, u_1,..., u_r)$ is a generic point of S_r then

$$(u_1, u_2,..., u_r, u_1^2, u_1u_2,..., u_r^2)$$

is a generic point of V_r. [The birationality is seen by dividing all the coordinates of this last point by u_1, and then noting that $r+1$ of the modified coordinates have the values $1, u_1,..., u_r$.]

The reader may now easily verify for himself the following properties of the above transformation of S_r into V_r:

(i) If P is any point of S_r other than A, then P has a unique transform Q on V_r. Moreover, the transformation is *regular* at the pair (P, Q), in the sense that directions at P (regarded as potential tangents to curve-branches at P) correspond *homographically* to directions at Q, in a certain space T_r, regarded as tangents to branches on V_r at Q, the space T_r being in fact the *tangent space* to V_r at Q. More particularly, a branch of order ν at P transforms always to a branch of order ν at Q; and if the tangents of two branches at P are distinct, so are those of the transformed branches on V_r at Q.

(ii) The point A is dilated by the transformation into a space Π_{r-1} on V_r in the sense that each direction b at A (tangent to a class of branches β at A) transforms to a unique point B in Π_{r-1} (centre of the transforms of all the branches β); and, moreover, this correspondence between directions b at A and points B of Π_{r-1} is homographic (projective). More particularly, a branch β of order ν at A transforms always to a branch β' of order $\nu' \leqslant \nu$ at B, and if the tangents to two branches at A are distinct then their transforms have different centres on Π_{r-1}.

(iii) Every point of V_r is either the transform of a unique point of S_r other than A, or it corresponds to a unique direction at A, these alternatives being mutually exclusive.

We record also, though it does not immediately concern us, the following property:

(iv) Every point of V_r (whether on Π_{r-1} or not) is *simple* on V_r (such that V_r has a proper tangent space T_r at the point).

A point-dilatation, as thus described, is the simplest of a special category of transformations—often called *monoidal*—which are of fundamental importance in the discussion of singularities of algebraic varieties.

29. *Desingularization of a curve.* As for curves in S_2, an s-fold point A of a curve C in S_r ($r \geqslant 2$) will be said to be ordinary if C has s linear branches (simple places) with distinct branch tangents at A.

Suppose, then, that the only singularities of C are a set of k ordinary multiple points $A_1,...,A_k$ with multiplicities $s_1,...,s_k$, and consider the effect of a dilatation applied to A_k in the sense of the preceding note.

This transforms C birationally into a curve C' in a higher space S_N in such a way that (i) the s places on C at A_k are transformed into s_k simple places with distinct centres $A_{k,1},...,A_{k,s_k}$ on C', (ii) the correspondence between the ground points of C other than A_k and those of C' other than the $A_{k,i}$ is one-one without exception, (iii) if points P, P' so correspond, then each place at P, being simple, corresponds to a simple place on C' at P', and hence (iv) if P is simple on C then P' is simple on C', and if P is one of the points A_i ($i = 1,...,k-1$), then P' is an ordinary s_i-fold point A_i' of C' (by the final clause of (i) in the preceding note). In short, the multiple points of C' are again ordinary, but one fewer than those of C. Thus by k successive dilatations we shall obtain a non-singular birational transform C^* of C.

Since any irreducible curve C is birationally transformable into a plane curve C_1 with only ordinary multiple points (cf. Noether's Theorem, p. 133) and the above procedure is applicable to C_1, we obtain the result:

Every irreducible curve C can be birationally transformed into a nonsingular curve C^*.

This process is sometimes referred to as the *desingularization* of C.

A careful argument, concerning birational projections of C^* on to S_2, leads to the further useful result:

Every irreducible curve C can be birationally transformed into a plane curve C whose only singularities are a finite number of ordinary double points.

30. *Algebraic series.* Let C be a non-singular model, in N-dimensional space S_N, of a given one-dimensional function field Σ, places and ground points of C being then in unexceptional $(1, 1)$-correspondence. We now assert that all the effective sets of n points (or places) on C can be mapped without exception on the points of an irreducible algebraic variety Ω_n of dimensionality n. [The coordinates of a generic point of Ω_n may be taken to be the coefficients in the product $\prod_1^n \left(u_0 + u_1 \overset{i}{\xi_1} + ... + u_N \overset{i}{\xi_N} \right)$ of the left-hand sides of the equations of n independent generic points $\overset{i}{\xi}$ ($i = 1,...,n$) of C.] We then define a d-*dimensional algebraic series* γ_d^n of sets of n places on C by the condition that its map on Ω_n is a d-dimensional algebraic variety W_d.

Among such algebraic series we refer particularly to complete linear series Γ_r^n represented by irreducible rational varieties L_r which together cover Ω_n without overlapping. Thus, for example, if C is of genus p and $n > 2p-2$, then Ω_n is simply generated by ∞^p varieties L_{n-p}—all in this case of the same dimensionality $n-p$.

Algebraic series γ_d^n are of two main kinds, those that are contained in some linear series Γ_r^n and those that are not; or, in other words, those whose sets are all mutually equivalent and those which do not have this property. A γ_d^n of the first kind can be mapped directly on a d-dimensional algebraic subvariety of the space S_r which is the normal map of the Γ_r^n.

31. *Conditions for a γ_1^n to be a Γ_1^n.* Any irreducible γ_1^n on C is represented on Ω_n (cf. the preceding note) by an irreducible curve W. It defines an involution I_N on C if and only if it is of *index* 1, by which we mean that it generates a unirational $(n, 1)$ correspondence between C and W, so that each place on C belongs to only one set of the γ_1^n. Further, if γ_1^n has this property, then, by Theorem 16, the resulting involution I_n is a Γ_1^n if and only if it is rational (i.e. W is rational). Thus we have the result:

An irreducible γ_1^n on C is a Γ_1^n if and only if it is rational and of index 1.

An example of a γ_1^2 which is rational but not of index 1 is given by the pairs of points in which a conic C is met by the tangents to another conic. An example of a γ_1^2 which is of index 1 but not rational is given by one of the cyclic involutions, such as that with elliptic parametric equation

$$u' \equiv u + \tfrac{1}{2}\omega \quad (\mathrm{mod}\,\omega, \omega'),$$

on a plane non-singular cubic.

CHAPTER XI

LOCAL GEOMETRY IN S_2

1. The intention of the chapter

OUR principal object in this concluding chapter of our book is to introduce the reader to a new range of ideas, based largely on the concept of infinitely near points in the plane, by which we are enabled to describe in concise and expressive terminology the basic structure of branches and, more generally, the local geometry of the plane at any given point O. Historically, the so-called doctrine of infinitely near points arose out of an intuitive geometrical mode of thought which was found to be very useful in practice, even though it led not infrequently, in default of proper control, to erroneous conclusions. When once its foundations had been properly laid, however, the conception of infinitesimal neighbourhoods became fully acceptable, both as a convenience in giving simple expression to complicated ideas and also as a valuable stimulus to reasoning.†

The outline of the theory which we shall now present is of necessity condensed in form and limited in scope. Urgent considerations of space, no less than our wish to avoid obscuring the main development by too much detail, compel us now to put much more responsibility on the reader for the filling in of proofs than would have been justified in the earlier systematic chapters of the book. The present chapter, indeed, can be regarded more as an introduction to a major development that is related to our main programme than as a completion of that programme itself.

Although we shall deal for the most part only with the local geometry of the plane, developing this geometry mainly by classical methods, we may remark that the same theory also applies, when suitable local coordinates have been defined, to local geometry on any algebraic surface F at a simple point of this surface. Further, we have appended to this chapter two sections dealing with alternative methods of handling the same or more general problems.

---

† The classical theory of infinitely near points and of the analysis of singularities of algebraic curves is discussed comprehensively in volume II of the book *Teoria geometrica delle equazioni e delle funzioni algebriche* by Enriques and Chisini (Bologna, 1918). The reader is also referred to the account given by van der Waerden in the last chapter of his *Einführung* and to the admirable though highly condensed summary given by Zariski on pp. 5–17 of his book *Algebraic Surfaces* (Berlin, 1935).

The first of these methods, that of Zariski, depends on the representation of infinitely near points of the plane by suitable classes of polynomial ideals; and the second method, which is not confined to S_2, derives the invariant properties of any branch from the structure of the ring of power series which it generates.

2. Linear branch elements E_r

Local geometry at a point of S_2 is concerned with the behaviour of branches with that point as centre; and in all that follows, except where the contrary is stated, the branches that we shall deal with will all have their centres at the same fixed point O of S_2, and the systems of reference that we shall use will all be affine systems with O as origin. We now consider first of all, before turning to the more general problem of the local structure of branches of arbitrary order, the relatively simple local geometry of the aggregate of linear branches at O.

Every linear branch α at O, provided only that its tangent does not lie along OY, has an equation of the form

$$Y = a_1 X + a_2 X^2 + ... + a_r X^r + ..., \tag{1}$$

and is accordingly characterized by an infinite coefficient vector $(a_1, a_2, ..., a_r, ...)$. Now suppose that the same branch is represented in another affine coordinate system with O as origin by a vector $(a_1', a_2', ..., a_r', ...)$. It may be verified that, for each $r \geqslant 1$, the new coefficient a_r' is a rational function of $a_1, ..., a_r$ only, apart from the constants occurring in the transformation of coordinates. In view of this, any aggregate A_r of linear branches of the form (1) for which $a_1, ..., a_r$ have assigned values may properly be regarded as a local geometric object. Instead of referring directly to the aggregate A_r we shall prefer to speak of all the branches of this aggregate as *containing the same linear branch element E_r of rank r*, which is thereby assumed to be uniquely defined by A_r.

The linear branches which contain the unique element E_0 of rank zero are all those with centre O; those which contain a given E_1 at O are all those with an assigned branch tangent at O; those which contain a given E_2 at O are all those with an assigned tangent and an assigned 'curvature' at O; and so on. We see at once, moreover, that every linear branch at O contains a unique element E_r of each rank $r \geqslant 0$. Also every element E_r of rank $r \geqslant 1$ determines a unique *consecutive sequence of elements* $E_0, E_1, ..., E_r$ leading up to it, such that every linear branch which contains E_r contains the whole sequence $E_0,..., E_r$ as its first $r+1$ branch elements.

We now propose, when considering any simple consecutive sequence $E_0,..., E_r$ of the kind we have just been describing, to represent the members of the sequence by a set of progressive symbols of the type

$$O; \quad O,O_1; \quad O,O_1,O_2; \quad ...; \quad O,O_1,..., O_r;$$

where O still refers to the origin of coordinates, and the other individual components $O_1,..., O_r$ of the composite symbols are to be suitably interpreted as denoting fictitious points adjacent (infinitely near) to O in its successive neighbourhoods up to the rth. We may interpret *passing through O_i*, for this purpose, as *the condition on a linear branch α which already contains E_{i-1} that it should also contain E_i*; and our justification for ascribing to this condition something of the character of passing through an assigned point is that the minimum multiplicity of intersection of any pair of linear branches through E_i is precisely one less than the minimum multiplicity of intersection of any pair of linear branches through E_{i+1} (cf. Chapter V, § 8).

In brief, then, we have analysed any linear branch element E_r, regarded as a condition on linear branches α required to contain it, into $r+1$ separate† but necessarily consecutive conditions, each after the first being expressed as a condition on a linear branch which already satisfies all the preceding conditions; we then propose to describe these conditions as requiring a linear branch to have O as centre and to pass through r specified fictitious points $O_1,..., O_r$ in sequence after O; and finally we embody this analysis in the representation of any E_r in the form $O, O_1,..., O_r$.

In view of the remarks just made, *we can now define not only the multiplicity of intersection of any two linear branches at O, but also the actual intersection itself*; for this will consist of O and all the fictitious points $O_1,..., O_r$ consecutive to O that the branches have in common. Our preliminary account of the geometry of linear branches at O is now complete.

3. Branch elements in general

We now turn to the problem of defining, on any branch α of arbitrary order ν, a succession of branch elements that progressively

---

† The first condition, that α should have O as origin, is in an obvious sense of weight 2 as compared with the others which are each of weight 1.

characterize the branch, or, as we may say, a sequence of fictitious points that lie on it; and this is a problem of very much greater complexity in every sense than the problem which we have just considered in § 2. So true is this, indeed, that if we are to give the reader any real insight into the structure of an arbitrary branch we have no option but to make a rather different approach to this more general problem. The plan that we propose to adopt may be summarized in the following terms. (i) We shall first define branch elements in general, in relation to one particular affine coordinate system in S_2, and we shall do so by the classical procedure, that is to say by a geometrical method, using sequences of quadratic transformations. (ii) Then, having gained sufficient insight into the structure of the elements defined on this limited (and rather arbitrary) basis, we shall find it possible to revert to the direct method of § 2. We shall, in fact, be able to represent branch elements in general, without any extraneous aid, by *partially determined fractional equations* of the form $Y = P(X^{1/\nu})$, removing automatically in this way the ambiguities inherent in the geometrical definition. (iii) We shall then prove that the branch elements so represented are *locally invariant*, i.e. independent of the original choice of affine coordinates in S_2.

3.1. The method of special quadratic transformations

Our primary objective, as we have already indicated, is to define branch elements

$$\mathscr{E}_r = O, O_1, ..., O_r \quad (r = 0, 1, 2, ...)$$

in such a way that every branch α with its centre at the fixed point O of S_2 contains, and is progressively characterized by, a unique infinite sequence

$$\mathscr{E}_0 = O; \quad \mathscr{E}_1 = O, O_1; \quad \mathscr{E}_2 = O, O_1, O_2; ...$$

of such elements, each $\mathscr{E}_r$ being an extension in a well-defined sense of its predecessor $\mathscr{E}_{r-1}$ $(r > 0)$. As in § 2, $\mathscr{E}_0$ signifies only the common centre $O = O_0$ of all the branches considered; but the branches α which also contain a given $\mathscr{E}_1$ will now be all those (of arbitrary order) which have a given branch tangent OO_1 at O. The proposed method of special quadratic transformations is designed to reduce the definition of every $\mathscr{E}_r$ of higher rank to the successive choice of r elements of rank 1 at points of r different planes. We must now specify the particular quadratic transformations that we shall use for this purpose. These are two in number:

$$T_1: \quad X' = X, \qquad Y' = Y/X,$$
$$T_2: \quad X' = X/Y, \quad Y' = Y;$$

and the second is obtained from the first by interchanging the roles of X and Y. We regard each of these transformations as transforming a plane π into another (or the same) plane π', the origins of coordinates being O and O'. The transformations have inverses:

$$T_1^{-1}: \quad X = X', \qquad Y = X'Y',$$
$$T_2^{-1}: \quad X = X'Y', \quad Y = Y'.$$

3.2. Properties of the transformations T_1 and T_2

We now summarize the properties of T_1 and T_2, more especially in relation to the *affine* planes π and π'. It will be convenient, in doing this, to use the symbols δ, δ_X, δ_Y to stand respectively for a general direction at O, the direction of OX at O, and the direction of OY at O.

Properties of T_1

(i) T_1 transforms the neighbourhood of O (as a pencil of directions δ) into the fundamental line $O'Y'$ (as a range of points).

(ii) It transforms δ_X into O' and δ_Y into Y'_∞.

(iii) It transforms the line OX (exclusive of O) into the line $O'X'$ and the line OY (exclusive of O) into the point Y'_∞.

(iv) It is regular (cf. p. 130) at all finite points of π not on OY.

Properties of T_2

(i') T_2 transforms the neighbourhood of O into the fundamental line $O'X'$.

(ii') It transforms δ_X into X'_∞ and δ_Y into O'.

(iii') It transforms the line OX (exclusive of O) into the point X'_∞ and the line OY (exclusive of O) into the line $O'Y'$.

(iv') It is regular at all finite points of π not on OX.

Further, T_1 (T_2) transforms every branch at O, excepting only those with branch tangent along OY (OX), into a branch in π' with a finite centre; but T_1^{-1} (T_2^{-1}) transforms every branch at O', excepting only the line $O'Y'$ ($O'X'$), into a branch at O with tangent along OX (OY)—cf. (ii) and (ii').

3.3. General definition of an $\mathscr{E}_r$

We now give the construction by which we shall suppose any branch element $\mathscr{E}_r$, of arbitrary rank $r \geqslant 1$, to be defined.

We begin with a set of $r+1$ planes π, $\pi_1,..., \pi_r$, of which the first is our original S_2, and with a given affine coordinate system in π with O as origin. The choice of the coordinate systems in $\pi_1,..., \pi_r$ is initially arbitrary, although in each case, as will appear, we shall usually want to move the origin to a new point on one or other of the axes originally chosen.

We envisage now a sequence

$$T^{(1)}, T^{(2)},..., T^{(r)}$$

of transformations, each either a T_1 or a T_2, which respectively transform π into π_1, π_1 into $\pi_2,..., \pi_{r-1}$ into π_r. $T^{(1)}$ transforms the neighbourhood of O in π into a fundamental line $e_0^{(1)}$ in π_1, this being either the Y-axis or the X-axis in π_1 according as $T^{(1)}$ is a T_1 or a T_2. We now select a *finite* point O_1 on $e_0^{(1)}$, and we move the origin of coordinates in π_1 from its original position $\bar{O}_1$ to O_1, keeping the axes parallel to themselves, preparatory to applying the next transformation $T^{(2)}$. The choice of O_1, of course, is equivalent to selecting a particular direction δ_1 at O.†

In the same way, $T^{(2)}$ transforms the neighbourhood of O_1 into a fundamental line $e_1^{(2)}$ of π_2, which is again one or other of the axes; and again we choose a finite point O_2—corresponding to a direction δ_2 at O_1—on $e_1^{(2)}$, and move the origin of coordinates from its original position $\bar{O}_2$ to O_2 before applying $T^{(3)}$.

Continuing then in the same way, we end by choosing a finite point O_r on $e_{r-1}^{(r)}$ in π_r, corresponding to a direction δ_r at O_{r-1} in π_{r-1}. The whole operation, embracing the successive choices both of directions $\delta_1,..., \delta_r$ at $O,..., O_{r-1}$ and of transformations $T^{(1)},..., T^{(r)}$ which carry these directions into the points $O_1,..., O_r$, will be said to define an $\mathscr{E}_r$ in the original plane π, the basic connexion between branch elements $\mathscr{E}_r$, as so defined, and branches α being prescribed as follows.

DEFINITION. A branch α with centre O in π will be said to contain the $\mathscr{E}_r$ defined by the above construction if and only if it is transformed by the resultant transformation $T^{(r)}T^{(r-1)}... T^{(1)}$ into a branch in π_r with centre O_r.

We may say, expressing the matter loosely in order to give a

† Since O_1 is to be a finite point of $e_0^{(1)}$, the direction δ_1 must not be along OY if $T^{(1)}$ is a T_1 or along OX if $T^{(1)}$ is a T_2. The necessity of allowing both types of transformation T_1 and T_2 arises from the fact that here, as at each stage in the construction, we must be able to transform *any* given direction at O_{i-1} into a *finite* point in π_i.

rough intuitive idea of where the formal development is tending, that the effect of each transformation $T^{(i)}$ is to transform a general point of π_{i-1} (remote from O_{i-1}) into a general point of π_i, at the same time yielding an infinite magnification of the infinitesimal neighbourhood of O_{i-1} into a fundamental line $e_{i-1}^{(i)}$ of π_i which contains O_i. Thus the points $O_1,..., O_r$ may be interpreted as transforms of points near to O, belonging to infinitesimal neighbourhoods of higher and higher order. We shall accordingly say that $O_1,..., O_r$ are the transforms, in $\pi_1,..., \pi_r$ respectively, of a succession of *fictitious points* in π, in a nest of neighbourhoods of O; and we shall denote these fictitious points by the same symbols $O_1,..., O_r$ as the actual transformed points. Having introduced fictitious points in this way, we can afterwards make the new language rigorous by giving to all statements about fictitious points a precise meaning in terms of the actual transformed points to which they correspond. We shall then be able to interpret the branch element $\mathscr{E}_r$ just defined as a sequence of points $O, O_1,..., O_r$ (all of them fictitious except the first) which follow one another consecutively on every branch that contains the element $\mathscr{E}_r$.

The assumption underlying this conception of branch element is, of course, that any $\mathscr{E}_r$ can be shown to be a geometric object, independent alike of the original choice of coordinate system in π and of any permissible variation in the set of transformations used to define it; but we leave the proof of this assumption until a later stage.

DEFINITION. A set of $r+1$ consecutive points $O, O_1,..., O_r$ $(r \geqslant 1)$, defined as above, and together constituting a branch element $\mathscr{E}_r$ at O, will be called a *simplicial sequence* of $r+1$ infinitely near points.

4. The proximity relation

Having now laid down a procedure for the construction of branch elements $\mathscr{E}_r$, we shall next show that the elements that are obtainable in the prescribed manner differ widely among themselves in respect of their internal structure. We shall show, that is to say, that the permissible sequences of points $O, O_1,..., O_r$ in the respective planes $\pi, \pi_1,..., \pi_r$ are of many essentially different types, and we shall interpret these types of transformed sequence as representing essentially distinct types of simplicial sequence of $r+1$ points infinitely near to O in π. The basis of the proposed classification is a relation of *proximity* between points of a sequence, which we now elucidate.

In our process of construction, for each i ($1 \leqslant i \leqslant r$) the neighbourhood of O_{i-1} in π_{i-1} is transformed into a line $e_{i-1}^{(i)}$ in π_i, and we then require O_i to lie on this line. It is therefore natural to speak of O_i as being (directly) proximate to O_{i-1}, since it represents a direction δ_i at this point. It can happen, however, in circumstances that we shall consider, that O_i lies also on a finite line $e_{i-\alpha}^{(i)}$ which represents in π_i the neighbourhood of some previous point $O_{i-\alpha}$ ($2 \leqslant \alpha \leqslant i$), the original image $e_{i-\alpha}^{(i-\alpha+1)}$ of $O_{i-\alpha}$ in $\pi_{i-\alpha+1}$ having been carried into $e_{i-\alpha}^{(i)}$ by the intervening quadratic transformations. In these circumstances, we shall say that O_i is (remotely) proximate to $O_{i-\alpha}$. Our full definition of proximity accordingly runs as follows.

DEFINITION. If O, O_1,... is a simplicial sequence, defined by a sequence of quadratic transformations between planes π, π_1,..., a point O_β of the sequence is said to be *proximate* to another such point O_α ($\alpha < \beta$) if O_β, as a point of π_β, lies on a finite line of this plane which corresponds to the neighbourhood of O_α as a point of π_α.

We now consider in detail the particular circumstances in which a point O_β can be proximate to a point O_α. We may suppose, for definiteness, that $T^{(\alpha+1)}$ is a T_1, so that the line $e_\alpha^{(\alpha+1)}$ into which it transforms the neighbourhood of O_α is the Y-axis in $\pi_{\alpha+1}$. If $T^{(\alpha+2)}$ were also a T_1, then it would banish $e_\alpha^{(\alpha+1)}$ altogether to infinity in $\pi_{\alpha+2}$, and no further transformation $T^{(\alpha+i)}$ would ever make it reappear. We suppose, therefore, that $T^{(\alpha+2)}$ is a T_2, in which case it transforms $e_\alpha^{(\alpha+1)}$ into a line $e_\alpha^{(\alpha+2)}$ which is again the Y-axis in $\pi_{\alpha+2}$, the new fundamental line $e_{\alpha+1}^{(\alpha+2)} = T^{(\alpha+2)}O_{\alpha+1}$ being now the X-axis in $\pi_{\alpha+2}$. If $O_{\alpha+2}$ is taken to be the (existing) origin in $\pi_{\alpha+2}$—the intersection of $e_\alpha^{(\alpha+2)}$ with $e_{\alpha+1}^{(\alpha+2)}$—then it is proximate, according to our definition, to each of O_α and $O_{\alpha+1}$. Further, if the succeeding transformations $T^{(\alpha+3)}$,..., $T^{(\beta)}$ are all also of type T_2, and if each of the points $O_{\alpha+3}$,..., O_β is taken to be the (existing) origin of coordinates in the plane to which it belongs, then the neighbourhood of O_α will be represented by the Y-axis in each of the planes $\pi_{\alpha+1}$,..., π_β. In particular, $e_\alpha^{(\beta)}$ will be the Y-axis in π_β, and the image $e_{\beta-1}^{(\beta)}$ of the neighbourhood of $O_{\beta-1}$ will be the X-axis in π_β, thus making O_β proximate to both O_α and $O_{\beta-1}$.

From such considerations, the reader will have no difficulty in verifying the following general statements.

Laws of Proximity (*for plane simplicial sequences of points*)

    (i) *Every point* O_i $(i \geqslant 1)$ *is proximate to its immediate predecessor* O_{i-1}.

    (ii) *A point* O_i $(i \geqslant 2)$ *can also be proximate to at most one remote predecessor* $O_{i-\alpha}$ $(\alpha > 1)$.

    (iii) *The points of a simplicial sequence that are proximate to any given member* O_α *form a set* $O_{\alpha+1}, O_{\alpha+2}, ..., O_{\alpha+s}$ $(s \geqslant 1)$ *following without interruption after* O_α.

These three laws characterize completely the relation of proximity as it applies to the points of any simplicial sequence in the plane, and they provide a basis for the general analysis of the proximity structure of such sequences, which we shall now develop.

4.1. Free points and satellite points

The first step in the proposed analysis is a certain separation of all the points of a simplicial sequence into two categories.

DEFINITION. Excluding only the leading point O, every point O_i $(i \geqslant 1)$ of a simplicial sequence $O, O_1,...$ is either a *free point*, if it is proximate only to its immediate predecessor, or a *satellite point*, if it is proximate to two of its predecessors O_{i-1} and $O_{i-\alpha}$ $(\alpha > 1)$. The leading point O is to be regarded conventionally as free.

We now consider, in the light of this definition, the alternative possibilities in regard to the successor O_{i+1} of any point O_i.

If, in the first place, O_i is a free point, then it lies, as a point of the plane π_i, on only one line $e_{i-1}^{(i)}$ that represents the neighbourhood of a predecessor. We see then at once that its successor O_{i+1} can only be either a free point or a satellite proximate to O_{i-1} and O_i.

If, however, O_i is a satellite, proximate to O_{i-1} and $O_{i-\alpha}$ $(\alpha > 1)$, then it lies, as a point of π_i, at the intersection of two lines $e_{i-1}^{(i)}$ and $e_{i-\alpha}^{(i)}$ that represent the neighbourhoods of predecessors. The direction δ_{i+1} at O_i which is to determine O_{i+1} can lie along either or neither of these lines; and this means, as we can readily verify, that O_{i+1} can be either a free point proximate only to O_i or else one or other of two distinct satellite points, of which one is remotely proximate to O_{i-1} and the other to $O_{i-\alpha}$. We thus have the following general result.

THEOREM 1. *The possible types of successor O_{i+1} for any point O_i of a simplicial sequence of points in S_2 can be enumerated as follows:*

(i) *If O_i $(i > 0)$ is a free point, O_{i+1} may be any one of a simple infinity of free points proximate to O_i, or it may be a unique satellite point proximate to O_i and O_{i-1}.*

(ii) *If O_i is a satellite point, proximate to O_{i-1} and $O_{i-\alpha}$ $(\alpha > 1)$, then O_{i+1} may be any one of a simple infinity of free points proximate to O_i, or it may be one or other of two determinate satellite points, of which one is remotely proximate to O_{i-1} and the other is remotely proximate to $O_{i-\alpha}$.*

With the application of these results to branches in mind, we now find it convenient to write every simplicial sequence $O, O_1,...$ as an alternating succession $F_1 S_1 F_2 S_2 ...$ of subsequences F_i of consecutive free points and subsequences S_j of satellite points. Since the leading point O is free by convention, and the second point O_1 is always free, the opening subsequence must be F_1 and it must begin with O and O_1. None of the other subsequences F_i and S_j need contain more than one point. We shall call the F_i the *free stretches* and the S_j the *satellite clusters* of the sequence $O, O_1,....$. By a *linear simplicial sequence* we shall understand a sequence all of whose points are free, so that it consists entirely of the one free stretch F_1.

The proximity structure of a free stretch F_i is trivial, each of its points (except O itself, in the case $i = 1$) being proximate only to its immediate predecessor; but the structure of an arbitrary satellite cluster needs closer examination.

4.2. The typical satellite cluster

We now consider a typical satellite cluster

$$S = O_{i+1}, O_{i+2},..., O_{i+s},$$

preceded by a free point O_i. By Theorem 1 (i), O_{i+1} can be remotely proximate only to O_{i-1}; and, by the third law of proximity, all the points of S that are remotely proximate to O_{i-1} form a consecutive set

$$S^{(1)} = O_{i+1}, O_{i+2},..., O_{i+s_1} \quad (s_1 \leqslant s).$$

Supposing, then, that $s_1 < s$, we see by Theorem 1 (ii) that O_{i+s_1+1} must be remotely proximate to O_{i+s_1-1}; and all the points of S that are remotely proximate to this same point O_{i+s_1-1} will form a second consecutive set

$$S^{(2)} = O_{i+s_1+1}, O_{i+s_1+2},..., O_{i+s_1+s_2} \quad (s_1+s_2 \leqslant s).$$

Similarly, if $s_1 + s_2 < s$, we shall have a third set

$$S^{(3)} = O_{i+s_1+s_2+1},\ O_{i+s_1+s_2+2}, ...,\ O_{i+s_1+s_2+s_3} \quad (s_1+s_2+s_3 \leqslant s),$$

consisting of all the points of S that are remotely proximate to $O_{i+s_1+s_2-1}$; and so on until S is exhausted. We may thus describe the proximity structure of the typical satellite cluster in the following terms.

Any satellite cluster $S = O_{i+1}, ..., O_{i+s}$ has a unique decomposition of the form
$$S = S^{(1)},\ S^{(2)}, ...,\ S^{(h)}$$

into consecutive subsets $S^{(j)}$ $(j = 1, ..., h)$ such that all the points of $S^{(j)}$ are remotely proximate to the same predecessor. This predecessor, which is said to confront $S^{(j)}$, is the last point but one preceding $S^{(j)}$.

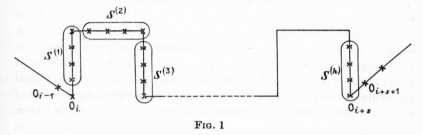

FIG. 1

The structure that we have thus described can conveniently be represented by a diagram of the type shown in Fig. 1. In this diagram:

   (i) certain points of the sequence $O, O_1, ...,$ and in particular all the points of the satellite cluster, are represented as discrete points on a continuous graph in the form of a broken line;

  (ii) all the points on any horizontal or vertical segment of the graph represent points of the sequence that are proximate to a common predecessor, namely the point represented by the immediately preceding point of the graph; and

(iii) points on the initial and final sloping lines represent free points of the sequence that precede or follow the satellite cluster.

To extend this form of diagrammatic representation to the whole simplicial sequence, we may denote the entire proximity diagram for each satellite cluster S_i $(i = 1, 2, ...)$ by a symbol $[S_i]$. Each symbol $[S_i]$ then stands for a partial diagram of the type set out in full above, and we may represent any simplicial sequence in π by a complete diagram of the form shown in Fig. 2, terminating on the right either with a sloping line segment or with a cluster symbol, according as the last subsequence of the simplicial sequence $O, O_1,..., O_r$ is a free stretch or a satellite cluster.

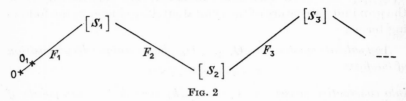

FIG. 2

We have now completed our general analysis of the structure—all based on the proximity relation—of branch elements $\mathcal{E}_r$ or their equivalent simplicial point-sequences $O, O_1,..., O_r$; and this has been accomplished solely on the basis of our original geometric definition of an $\mathcal{E}_r$ by means of a sequence of quadratic transformations. The next step, if further progress is to be made, must be to establish a general direct connexion between the elements $\mathcal{E}_r$ and the fractional equations $Y = P(X^{1/\nu})$ (or the equivalent parametric equations) of the branches α that contain them; and, more particularly, between the proximity structure of an $\mathcal{E}_r$ and certain common structural features of the power series, such as $P(X^{1/\nu})$, that appear in the equations of branches which contain that $\mathcal{E}_r$.

As a result of the somewhat detailed discussion of species of power series which now follows, we shall in due course be able (a) to establish the uniqueness of the succession of points on any branch α (i.e. its independence of possible variations in the resolving sequence of quadratic transformations); and (b) to show that the complete proximity structure and multiplicity sequence of the succession of points depend only on the sequence of exponents of powers of X that occur in the fractional equation of α.

The reader may find it advantageous, in his first reading of this chapter, to concentrate on understanding the results obtained in §§ 5 to 5.3, leaving the details of the proofs for later scrutiny.

5. Basic form of a power series

Before introducing the formal definitions of the next section, we must give some explanation of the principal concept on which these will be based. This is, effectively, a way of writing any fractional power series $P(X^{1/\nu})$, of given index ν, in such a way as to focus attention on certain features of its sequence of exponents; or, alternatively, of writing a formal power series $P(u)$ in such a way as to relate its exponent sequence in a systematic way to a particular power u^ν of the indeterminate u. We refer to this as the procedure of writing $P(X^{1/\nu})$ in *basic form*, or of writing $P(u)$ in *basic form over u^ν*, for a given index ν, the two procedures being essentially the same.

The idea of basic form for a fractional power series $S(X) = P(X^{1/\nu})$ of index ν (and of non-negative order) is that $S(X)$ should be written, with as many zero coefficients as may be necessary, but in a uniquely determined way, as a succession of maximal blocks of terms of progressively increasing indices:

$$S(X) = \sum_{i=0}^{k_1} a_{1,i} X^i + \sum_{i=0}^{k_2} a_{2,i} X^{(m_1+i)/n_1} + \sum_{i=0}^{k_3} a_{3,i} X^{(m_2+i)/n_1 n_2} + \dots$$

$$\dots + \sum_{i=0}^{k_s} a_{s,i} X^{(m_{s-1}+i)/n_1 n_2 \dots n_{s-1}} + \sum_{i=0}^{\infty} a_{s+1,i} X^{(m_s+i)/n_1 n_2 \dots n_s},$$

where $n_1 n_2 \dots n_s = \nu$, and only the s coefficients $a_{2,0}, \dots, a_{s+1,0}$ are required to be necessarily non-zero. In other words, the sets of integers n_i, m_i, k_i $(i = 1, \dots, s)$ are to be so chosen that $S(X)$ proceeds first, and as far as possible, by successive integral powers of X; then, as far as possible, by successive integral powers of X^{1/n_1} for the least possible $n_1 > 1$; then, as far as possible, by integral powers of $X^{1/n_1 n_2}$ for the least possible $n_2 > 1$; and so forth until it is proceeding formally by successive integral powers of $X^{1/\nu}$. The exponents of the leading terms in each block after the first—where the denominators of the exponents have to be stepped up—are termed the *characteristic exponents* of $S(X)$, and these alone determine the general form, or, as we shall say, the *species* of $S(X)$.

EXAMPLE. To represent in basic form the series

$$S(X) = X + X^{8/3} + X^3 + X^{11/3} + X^{47/12} + X^5,$$

which is of index 12, we write

$$S(X) = (0 + X + 0 . X^2) + (X^{8/3} + X^{9/3} + 0 . X^{10/3} + X^{11/3}) +$$

$$+ \left(X^{47/12} + \sum_{i=1}^{12} 0 . X^{(47+i)/12} + X^{60/12} + \sum_{i=1}^{\infty} 0 . X^{(60+i)/12} \right).$$

In this case $\nu = 12$, $n_1 = 3$, $n_2 = 4$, $m_1 = 8$, $m_2 = 47$, $k_1 = 2$, $k_2 = 3$. The characteristic exponents are 8/3 and 47/12; and the species to which $S(X)$ belongs is equally well represented by any two-term series of the form $aX^{8/3}+bX^{47/12}$, where $a \neq 0$, $b \neq 0$.

In passing over from the above to consideration of the basic form over u^ν of a formal power series $P(u)$, we need to ensure that the corresponding fractional series $P(X^{1/\nu})$ is effectively of index ν, or, in other words, that $P(u)$ *is not an element of* $K\{u^p\}$ *for any factor* $p > 1$ *of* ν. We shall say that any formal power series $P(u)$ is *minimal over* u^ν if it satisfies this condition.

5.1. Species and pseudo-species

In regard to this and the two following sections (§§ 5.1, 5.2, 5.3) the authors acknowledge their very substantial debt to Dr. D. Kirby, whose valuable suggestions as to the arrangement and proofs of the results have been freely adopted.

The terms we now propose to define are those expressed by saying that a given power series $P(u)$ (of non-negative order) is of a *certain species or pseudo-species* $\Omega^{(\nu)}$ over u^ν (*or with respect to the prescribed power* u^ν *of* u); and our procedure is as follows.

For $\nu = 1$, the concept is trivial, every series $P(u)$ (of non-negative order) being of the same species (or pseudo-species) $\Omega^{(1)}$. We therefore suppose that $\nu > 1$.

We first choose, then, any set of integers $n_1,...,n_s$ ($s \geqslant 1$), each greater than 1, such that $n_1 n_2 ... n_s = \nu$; and we write for convenience

$$\nu_1 = \nu, \qquad \nu_\lambda = n_\lambda n_{\lambda+1} ... n_s \quad (\lambda = 1,...,s), \qquad \nu_{s+1} = 1.$$

Next we write $m_0 = 0$, and choose a second set of integers $m_1,...,m_s$ such that m_λ is not divisible by n_λ ($\lambda = 1,...,s$), and $m_\lambda > n_\lambda m_{\lambda-1}$ ($\lambda = 1,...,s$); and we define the integers $k_1,...,k_s$ to be such that k_λ is the largest integer less than $m_\lambda/n_\lambda - m_{\lambda-1}$ ($\lambda = 1,...,s$).

The two chosen sets of integers then define a class $\Omega^{(\nu)}$ of power series, consisting of all the series (in any unspecified indeterminate u) which can be written in the form

$$P(u) = \sum_{i=0}^{k_1} a_{1,i} u^{i\nu_1} + \sum_{i=0}^{k_2} a_{2,i} u^{(m_1+i)\nu_2} + ... + \sum_{i=0}^{\infty} a_{s+1,i} u^{(m_s+i)\nu_{s+1}} \quad (1)$$

for suitable values (in K) of the coefficients $a_{j,i}$; and for any such series, the s coefficients $a_{\lambda,0}$ ($\lambda = 2,...,s+1$) are specially singled out as the *characteristic coefficients* in $P(u)$ as a member of $\Omega^{(\nu)}$.

A formal power series will then be said to be of *pseudo-species* $\Omega^{(v)}$ if and only if it belongs to the class $\Omega^{(v)}$ (i.e. admits of representation in the form (1)); and it will be said to be of *species* $\Omega^{(v)}$ if and only if it satisfies the further condition that each of its characteristic coefficients $a_{\lambda,0}$ ($\lambda = 2,...,s+1$), as a member of $\Omega^{(v)}$, is non-zero.

Further, a series such as $P(u)$ will be termed *unitary* if and only if its constant term $a_{1,0}$ is not zero.

We now note the following elementary properties of species and pseudo-species:

$E(1)$. *Every power series $P(u)$ that is minimal over u^v belongs to one and only one species $\Omega^{(v)}$ of index v.*

$E(2)$. *Any finite sum $\sum_1^n P_i(u)$ of series of a given pseudo-species $\Omega^{(v)}$ is again of pseudo-species $\Omega^{(v)}$. A similar result holds for infinite sums $\sum_1^\infty P_i(u)$, provided only that $O(P_n(u)) \to \infty$ as $n \to \infty$.*

$E(3)$. *Any finite product $\prod_1^n P_i(u)$ of series of a given pseudo-species $\Omega^{(v)}$ is again of pseudo-species $\Omega^{(v)}$.*

In amplification of $E(3)$, we suppose that $P(u)$, $Q(u)$ are both of the psuedo-species represented in equation (1), with coefficients $a_{\lambda,i}$, $b_{\lambda,i}$ respectively. Then

$$P(u)Q(u) = \sum_{i=0}^{k_1} c_{1,i} u^{iv_1} + ... \left.\begin{array}{l}\end{array}\right\}$$

where $\quad$ (a) $\quad c_{1,0} = a_{1,0} b_{1,0}$

$\qquad\qquad c_{\lambda,0} = a_{1,0} b_{\lambda,0} + a_{\lambda,0} b_{1,0} \quad (\lambda = 2,...,s+1)$

$\qquad$ (b) $\quad c_{\lambda,i} = a_{1,0} b_{\lambda,i} + a_{\lambda,i} b_{1,0} + f_{\lambda,i} \quad (i \neq 0)$ $\qquad\qquad$ (2)

and $f_{\lambda,i}$ is a function of those coefficients in $P(u)$ and $Q(u)$ which precede $a_{\lambda,i}$ and $b_{\lambda,i}$ respectively. From (2 a) we have:

$E(4)$. *If $P(u)$, $Q(u)$ are of pseudo-species $\Omega^{(v)}$, then the characteristic coefficients in $P(u)Q(u)$ are the same as those in $P(0)Q(u)+P(u)Q(0)$.*

More generally, the characteristic coefficients in the product $\prod_1^n P_i(u)$ in $E(3)$ are the same as those in

$$\sum_1^n P_1(0)...P_{i-1}(0)P_i(u)P_{i+1}(0)...P_n(0). \qquad (3)$$

5.2. The basic lemmas

The principal properties of species and pseudo-species that we shall need will now be proved.

It will be assumed, in what follows, that every series which is said to be of species or pseudo-species $\Omega^{(\nu)}$ is of the form (1), with coefficients which are denoted by some such set of symbols as $a_{\lambda,i}$ or $b_{\lambda,i}$.

LEMMA 1. *If $P(u)$ is non-unitary of species $\Omega^{(\nu)}$, and if $Q(u)$ is unitary of pseudo-species $\Omega^{(\nu)}$, then their product $P(u)Q(u)$ is of species $\Omega^{(\nu)}$.*

Proof. By $E(4)$, the characteristic coefficients in $P(u)Q(u)$ are the same as those in $P(0)Q(u)+P(u)Q(0)$, and the same therefore, since $P(0) = 0$, as those in $Q(0)P(u)$. Since $Q(0) \neq 0$, the result follows at once.

LEMMA 2. *Every rational non-zero power of a unitary series $P(u)$ of species $\Omega^{(\nu)}$ is again of species $\Omega^{(\nu)}$.*

Proof. (i) *Positive integral power.* By $E(3)$, if m is a positive integer, then $(P(u))^m$ is of pseudo-species $\Omega^{(\nu)}$. Also, by $E(4)$, the characteristic coefficients in $(P(u))^m$ are the same as those in $m(P(0))^{m-1}P(u)$; whence, since $P(0) \neq 0$, they are all non-zero. Thus $(P(u))^m$ is of species $\Omega^{(\nu)}$.

(ii) *Reciprocal.* If we put $c_{1,0}$ equal to 1 and the remaining $c_{\lambda,i}$ equal to 0 in equations (2) of § 5.1, then the resulting equations can be solved successively for the $b_{\lambda,i}$ to give $(P(u))^{-1}$. Thus $(P(u))^{-1}$ exists and is of pseudo-species $\Omega^{(\nu)}$. By $E(4)$, however, the product $P(u)(P(u))^{-1}$ has the same characteristic coefficients as $(P(0))(P(u))^{-1}+(P(u))(P(0))^{-1}$; whence it appears that the characteristic coefficients of $(P(u))^{-1}$—being the products of those in $P(u)$ by $\{-(P(0))^{-2}\}$—must all be non-zero. Thus $(P(u))^{-1}$ is of species $\Omega^{(\nu)}$.

(iii) *Integral power.* The truth of the lemma for any integral power $m \neq 0$ now follows from (i) and (ii).

(iv) *Fractional power.* For a fractional power $P^{p/q}$ ($p \neq 0$), we remark first that since P is necessarily minimal over u^ν (being of species $\Omega^{(\nu)}$), it follows readily that $P^{1/q}$ is also minimal over u^ν. By $E(1)$ then, since $P^{p/q}$ and P are both integral powers of $P^{1/q}$, (iii) is applicable; and it follows that $P^{p/q}$ is of species $\Omega^{(\nu)}$.

This completes the proof of the lemma.

Notes. (i) If $P(u)$ is unitary of pseudo-species $\Omega^{(\nu)}$, then any rational power of $P(u)$ is evidently of pseudo-species $\Omega^{(\nu)}$.

(ii) For any rational $m \neq 0$, the coefficients $b_{\lambda,i}$ in $(P(u))^m$ are given by

$$b_{1,0} = (a_{1,0})^m, \quad b_{\lambda,0} = m(a_{1,0})^{m-1}a_{\lambda,0} \quad (\lambda = 2,...,s+1),$$

$$b_{\lambda,i} = m(a_{1,0})^{m-1}a_{\lambda,i} + f_{\lambda,i},$$

where $f_{\lambda,i}$ is a function of the coefficients preceding $a_{\lambda,i}$ in $P(u)$. [These values are deduced for negative integral powers from those for positive integral powers and those for $(P(u))^{-1}$; and for fractional powers the coefficients in $(P)^{1/q}$ ($q > 0$) are found by inverting the formulae for positive integral powers.]

LEMMA 3. *If $P(u)$ is of species $\Omega^{(\nu)}$ and $S(u)$ is unitary of species $\Omega^{(\nu)}$, then $P(uS(u))$ is of species $\Omega^{(\nu)}$.*

(This result still holds if $S(u)$ is only of pseudo-species $\Omega^{(\nu)}$.)

Proof. If M is any positive integer, then $(S(u))^M$ is of species $\Omega^{(\nu)}$ by Lemma 2. Also, by $E(3)$, if $Q(u)$ is any series of pseudo-species $\Omega^{(\nu)}$, then $Q(u)(S(u))^M$ is of pseudo-species $\Omega^{(\nu)}$.

Now let M be any permissible exponent for series of pseudo-species $\Omega^{(\nu)}$. Then u^M is of pseudo-species $\Omega^{(\nu)}$; and so, therefore, as above, is $u^M(S(u))^M$.

If M is a characteristic exponent, the only non-zero characteristic coefficient in $u^M(S(u))^M$ is seen by $E(4)$ to be $(S(0))^M$.

If M is not a characteristic exponent, then all the characteristic exponents of $u^M(S(u))^M$—again by $E(4)$—are zero.

If $\sum_{(M)} d_M u^M(S(u))^M$ is any infinite sum taken over all permissible exponents M, then we see by $E(2)$ that this sum exists and is of pseudo-species $\Omega^{(\nu)}$; and, by the above, we see that the characteristic coefficients in the sum are $d_M(S(0))^M$ for each characteristic exponent M.

It follows therefore that $P(uS(u))$ is of pseudo-species $\Omega^{(\nu)}$; and that each characteristic exponent $b_{\lambda,0}$ ($\lambda = 2,...,s+1$) in this series, having the value $(S(0))^{m_{\lambda-1}\nu_\lambda} a_{\lambda,0}$, is non-zero. Thus $P(uS(u))$ is of species $\Omega^{(\nu)}$.

Notes. (i) The non-characteristic coefficients $b_{\lambda,i}$ in $P(uS(u))$ are of the form $b_{\lambda,i} = (S(0))^{(m_{\lambda-i+i)\nu_\lambda}} a_{\lambda,i} + f_{\lambda,i}$, where $f_{\lambda,i}$ is a function of the coefficients preceding $a_{\lambda,i}$ in $P(u)$ and of those preceding the corresponding coefficient $c_{\lambda,i}$ in $S(u)$.

(ii) If $P(u)$ and $S(u)$ in Lemma 3 are only required to be of pseudo-species $\Omega^{(\nu)}$, then $P(uS(u))$ will be also of pseudo-species $\Omega^{(\nu)}$.

LEMMA 4. *If $S(v)$ is unitary of species $\Omega^{(\nu)}$, and if the substitution $u \to vS(v)$ has inverse $v \to uT(u)$, then $T(u)$ is unitary of species $\Omega^{(\nu)}$.*

Proof. If we suppose S to be given, then T has to be found from the identity
$$v = vS(v)T(vS(v));$$
or, in other words, T is to be such that
$$T(vS(v)) = (S(v))^{-1}.$$

Now suppose that the coefficients in S are $a_{\lambda,i}$, and let T be an arbitrary series of pseudo-species $\Omega^{(\nu)}$ with coefficients $b_{\lambda,i}$.

By Lemma 2 (Note (ii)), the coefficients $c_{\lambda,i}$ in $(S(v))^{-1}$ are given by
$$c_{1,0} = (a_{1,0})^{-1}, \quad c_{\lambda,0} = -(a_{1,0})^{-2}a_{\lambda,0} \quad (\lambda = 2,...,s+1),$$
$$c_{\lambda,i} = -(a_{1,0})^{-2}a_{\lambda,i}+g_{\lambda,i} \quad (i \neq 0),$$
where $g_{\lambda,i}$ is a function of the coefficients preceding $a_{\lambda,i}$ in S.

By Lemma 3 (with Notes (i) and (ii)), the series $T(vS(v))$, being of pseudo-species $\Omega^{(\nu)}$, has coefficients $d_{\lambda,i}$ given by
$$d_{\lambda,0} = a_{1,0}^{m_{\lambda-1}\nu_\lambda}b_{\lambda,0}, \quad d_{\lambda,i} = a_{1,0}^{(m_{\lambda-1}+i)\nu_\lambda}b_{\lambda,i}+f_{\lambda,i},$$
where $f_{\lambda,i}$ is a function of the coefficients preceding $a_{\lambda,i}$ in S and $b_{\lambda,i}$ in T.

We can now solve the equations
$$\left. \begin{aligned} -(a_{1,0})^{-2}a_{\lambda,0} &= a_{1,0}^{m_{\lambda-1}\nu_\lambda}b_{\lambda,0} \\ -(a_{1,0})^{-2}a_{\lambda,i}+g_{\lambda,i} &= a_{1,0}^{(m_{\lambda-1}+i)\nu_\lambda}b_{\lambda,i}+f_{\lambda,i} \end{aligned} \right\} \tag{4}$$
successively for the $b_{\lambda,i}$, so defining $T(v)$, of pseudo-species $\Omega^{(\nu)}$, such that $T(vS(v)) = (S(v))^{-1}$.

By (4) the characteristic coefficients of T are $-a_{1,0}^{-(m_{\lambda-1}\nu_\lambda+2)}a_{\lambda,0} \neq 0$ ($\lambda = 2,...,s+1$); and hence T is of species $\Omega^{(\nu)}$. Further, the remaining coefficients $b_{\lambda,i}$ depend only on the coefficients in S up to $a_{\lambda,i}$ inclusive.

Note. If S in the above lemma is only of pseudo-species $\Omega^{(\nu)}$, then T is also of pseudo-species $\Omega^{(\nu)}$.

Besides the four basic lemmas thus established, we add here for convenience a fifth which is of a rather more specialized kind and only needed for the proof of the theorem to follow.

LEMMA 5. *If $P(u)$ is of pseudo-species $\Omega^{(\nu)}$ with coefficients $a_{\lambda,i}$, and if $S(v)$ is unitary of pseudo-species $\Omega^{(\nu)}$, with coefficients $b_{\lambda,i}$, then the substitution $u \to v S(v)$ carries $u^\nu P(u)$ into $v^\nu Q(v)$, where $Q(v)$ is of pseudo-species $\Omega^{(\nu)}$ with characteristic coefficients $c_{\lambda,0}$ given by*

$$c_{\lambda,0} = \nu a_{1,0} b_{1,0}^{\nu-1} b_{\lambda,0} + b_{1,0}^{m_{\lambda-1}\nu_\lambda + \nu} a_{\lambda,0}.$$

Proof. The proof follows much on the lines of the proof of Lemma 3. Thus, if M is any admissible exponent for $\Omega^{(\nu)}$, then the transform of $u^\nu P(u)$ will be an infinite sum of the form

$$\sum_{(M)} d_M v^{M+\nu} (S(v))^{M+\nu},$$

which gives $\qquad Q(v) = \sum_{(M)} d_M v^M (S(v))^{M+\nu}.$

Since each term of this summation is of pseudo-species $\Omega^{(\nu)}$, it follows then, by $E(2)$, that $Q(v)$ is of pseudo-species $\Omega^{(\nu)}$.

If M is a characteristic exponent, the only non-zero characteristic coefficient of $v^M (S(v))^{M+\nu}$ is $(S(0))^{M+\nu}$, the coefficient of v^M.

If M is a non-characteristic exponent other than 0, then all the characteristic coefficients of $v^M (S(v))^{M+\nu}$ are zero.

If $M = 0$, however, we now have the term $d_0 (S(v))^\nu$ which has characteristic coefficients $d_0 \nu b_{1,0}^{\nu-1} b_{\lambda,0}$ ($\lambda = 2,...,s+1$).

Putting $m_{\lambda-1} \nu_\lambda$ for the characteristic exponent M and $a_{1,0}$ for d_0, we see that

$$c_{\lambda,0} = b_{1,0}^{m_{\lambda-1}\nu_\lambda + \nu} a_{\lambda,0} + \nu b_{1,0}^{\nu-1} b_{\lambda,0} a_{1,0} \quad (\lambda = 2,...,s+1),$$

as stated in the lemma. This completes the proof.

5.3. Invariant species of a branch

We now consider any branch α about which we assume only that its centre is at the origin O and that its branch tangent is not along OY. We suppose then that the fractional equation of α is $Y = S(X)$, where $S(X)$ is a fractional power series of a determinate species $\Omega^{(\nu)}$ indicated (in the standard notation of § 5) by the basic form

$$S(X) = \sum_{i=1}^{k_1} a_{1,i} X^i + \sum_{i=0}^{k_2} a_{2,i} X^{(m_1+i)/n_1} + ... + \sum_{i=0}^{\infty} a_{s+1,i} X^{(m_s+i)/n_1 n_2 ... n_s} \quad (5)$$

$(k_1 \geqslant 1,\ \nu = n_1 n_2 ... n_s,\ a_{\lambda,0} \neq 0\ (\lambda = 2,...,s+1))$. The equivalent parametric equations of α will then be

$$X = u^\nu, \quad Y = P(u), \tag{6}$$

where $P(u)$ is the formal power series, of species $\Omega^{(\nu)}$ over u^ν, given by

$$P(u) = \sum_{i=1}^{k_1} a_{1,i} u^{i\nu_1} + \sum_{i=0}^{k_2} a_{2,i} u^{(m_1+i)\nu_2} + ... + \sum_{i=0}^{\infty} a_{s+1,i} u^{(m_s+i)\nu_{s+1}} \tag{7}$$

in the standard notation of § 5.1.

Always supposing, as above, that the branch tangent of α does not lie along OY, we may then say that α is itself a *branch of species* $\Omega^{(\nu)}$ relative to the given system of affine coordinates X, Y. The fundamental theorem we now prove asserts essentially that the species of α is invariant over any allowable transformation of X, Y to new affine coordinates X', Y' with the same origin O, provided only that the branch tangent of α does not lie along the new axis OY'. Thus:

THEOREM 2. *If α is any branch of order ν and centre O, then α is of the same fixed species $\Omega^{(\nu)}$ relative to every allowable system of affine coordinates X, Y with O as origin and with coordinate axis OY not along the branch tangent of α. Furthermore, if α has fractional equations $Y = S(X)$ and $Y' = S'(X')$ in any two such coordinate systems, and if corresponding coefficients in the basic forms of $S(X)$ and $S'(X')$ are $a_{\lambda,i}$ and $a'_{\lambda,i}$ respectively, then each coefficient $a'_{\lambda,i}$ is a function only of the coefficients in $S(X)$ up to and including $a_{\lambda,i}$, and of the coefficients in the equations of transformation from the one coordinate system to the other.*

Proof. Let α be given by the parametric equations (6) above, and let the equations

$$X' = \frac{p_1 X + q_1 Y}{1 + aX + bY}, \quad Y' = \frac{p_2 X + q_2 Y}{1 + aX + bY} \quad (p_1 q_2 \neq p_2 q_1) \quad (8)$$

define a transformation to new affine coordinates X', Y' with origin O.

Since $k_1 \geqslant 1$, we may write (6) in the form

$$X = u^\nu, \quad Y = u^\nu Q(u), \quad (9)$$

and denote the species (over u^ν) of $P(u)$ and $Q(u)$ by $\Omega^{(\nu)}$ and $\Omega'^{(\nu)}$ respectively.

Since $(p_1 + q_1 a_{1,1}) q_2 \neq (p_2 + q_2 a_{1,1}) q_1$, we may suppose that

$$(p_1 + q_1 a_{1,1}) q_2 \neq 0, \quad (10)$$

the alternative supposition $(p_2 + q_2 a_{1,1}) q_1 \neq 0$ requiring only an interchange of the roles of X' and Y'. Then, by Lemmas 1 and 2,

(i) $p_1 u^\nu + q_1 u^\nu Q(u)$ is non-unitary of pseudo-species $\Omega^{(\nu)}$, with a non-zero coefficient $p_1 + q_1 a_{1,1}$ of u^ν,

(ii) $p_2 u^\nu + q_2 u^\nu Q(u)$ is non-unitary of pseudo-species $\Omega^{(\nu)}$,

(iii) $1 + au^\nu + bu^\nu Q(u)$ is unitary of pseudo-species $\Omega^{(\nu)}$.

Hence α has the transformed parametric equations

$$X' = u^\nu S(u), \quad Y' = u^\nu Q'(u), \quad (11)$$

where

(i) $S(u)$ is unitary of pseudo-species $\Omega'^{(\nu)}$, with constant term $p_1+q_1 a_{1,1} \neq 0$ and characteristic coefficients $q_1 a_{\lambda,0}$ (coefficient of $u^{m_{\lambda-1}\nu_\lambda - \nu}$),

(ii) $Q'(u)$ is of pseudo-species $\Omega'^{(\nu)}$, with constant term $p_2+q_2 a_{1,1}$ and characteristic coefficients $q_2 a_{\lambda,0}$ (coefficient of $u^{m_{\lambda-1}\nu_\lambda-\nu}$).

Taking a νth root of $S(u)$, we write $v = uS^{1/\nu}$, so that, by the arguments used in proving Lemma 4, and in the notation of that lemma, $T(v)$ is of pseudo-species $\Omega'^{(\nu)}$, with constant term $(p_1+q_1 a_{1,1})^{-1/\nu}$ and with characteristic coefficients

$$\frac{-\nu^{-1}(p_1+q_1 a_{1,1})^{(1-\nu)/\nu} q_1 a_{\lambda,0}}{(p_1+q_1 a_{1,1})^{(m_{\lambda-1}\nu_\lambda-\nu+2)/\nu}} = -\nu^{-1} q_1 a_{\lambda,0}(p_1+q_1 a_{1,1})^{-(m_{\lambda-1}\nu_\lambda+1)/\nu}.$$

Substituting $u = vT(v)$ in $Y' = u^\nu Q'(u)$, and applying† Lemma 5, we find that $Y' = v^\nu Q''(v)$, where $Q''(v)$ is of pseudo-species $\Omega'^{(\nu)}$, with characteristic coefficients

$$\nu(p_2+q_2 a_{1,1})(p_1+q_1 a_{1,1})^{-(\nu-1)/\nu}(-\nu)^{-1} q_1 a_{\lambda,0}(p_1+q_1 a_{1,1})^{-(m_{\lambda-1}\nu_\lambda+1)/\nu} +$$

$$+ (p_1+q_1 a_{1,1})^{-m_{\lambda-1}\nu_\lambda/\nu} q_2 a_{\lambda,0}$$

$$= a_{\lambda,0}(p_1 q_2 - p_2 q_1)(p_1+q_1 a_{1,1})^{-(m_{\lambda-1}\nu_\lambda+\nu)/\nu} \neq 0.$$

It follows, then, that $Q''(u)$ is of species $\Omega'^{(\nu)}$; so that, writing $P'(u) = u^\nu Q'(u)$, the transformed equations of α are

$$X' = u^\nu, \quad Y' = P'(u),$$

where $P'(u)$ is of species $\Omega^{(\nu)}$. This proves the first part of the theorem.

For the second part, we need only note that, throughout all the calculations of coefficients, each non-characteristic coefficient in $P'(u)$ depends only—as was shown in the similar circumstances of each of the Lemmas 2, 3, and 4—on the coefficients up to and including the corresponding one in $P(u)$.

The theorem is therefore completely proved.

Note. With little modification, the above proof can be made to show that Theorem 2 is also valid for regular analytic transformations at O; so that the species of a branch is not only an affine invariant but also an analytic invariant of the branch.

---

† It should be noted that here, since we are dealing with a series $T(v)$ of pseudo-species $\Omega'^{(\nu)}$ (instead of $\Omega^{(\nu)}$ as in Lemma 5), the exponent $m_{\lambda-1}\nu_\lambda+\nu$ in the second term of the formula given in the lemma has to be replaced by

$$m_{\lambda-1}\nu_\lambda - \nu + \nu = m_{\lambda-1}\nu_\lambda.$$

6. Analysis of branches

We now consider a given branch α, and we suppose in the first instance that its (minimal) parametric equations are written in the natural form

$$X = u^\nu, \quad Y = k_1 u^{\nu_1} + k_2 u^{\nu_2} + \dots \quad (k_i \neq 0).$$

We suppose also for convenience (though this is not essential) that $\nu_1 \geqslant \nu$, so that the branch tangent is not along OY and the order of the branch is ν.

We then construct a succession of *resolutes* $\alpha_1, \alpha_2, \dots$ of α, in planes $\pi_1, \pi_2, \dots$, by applying successive quadratic transformations of types T_1 or T_2. These resolutes are to have finite centres $O_1, O_2, \dots$ which will stand for fictitious points, represented also by the symbols $O_1, O_2, \dots$, consecutive to O on α.

In simple cases this can be done forthwith. If, in particular, α is a linear branch ($\nu = 1$) we can take all the transformations to be of type T_1. The resolutes $\alpha_1, \alpha_2, \dots$ are then also all linear, and we say that the successive fictitious points $O_1, O_2, \dots$ on α are all free points of multiplicity 1 for α. If α is not linear ($\nu > 1$) we shall usually stop the sequence of transformations when we arrive at the resolute α_r (a linear branch) which has the image of the last satellite point O_r on α as its centre.

Before passing to the general case, we may first consider a simple example of a non-linear branch. Let α be the algebraic branch, of order 12, with equations

$$X = u^{12}, \quad Y = u^{18} + u^{22} + u^{25}.$$

The successive resolutes of α, up to α_8, are given in the table.

Resolute α_i	X	Y	Order	Points to which O_i is proximate
$\alpha_1 = T_1(\alpha)$	u^{12}	$u^6 + u^{10} + u^{13}$	6	O
$\alpha_2 = T_2(\alpha_1)$	$u^6 - u^{10} - u^{13} + \dots$	$u^6 + u^{10} + u^{13}$	6	O, O_1
$\alpha_3 = T_1(\alpha_2)$ with change of origin	$u^6 - u^{10} - u^{13} + \dots$	$2u^4 + 2u^7 + \dots$	4	O_2
$\alpha_4 = T_2(\alpha_3)$	$\frac{1}{2}u^2 - \frac{1}{2}u^5 + \dots$	$2u^4 + 2u^7 + \dots$	2	O_2, O_3
$\alpha_5 = T_1(\alpha_4)$	$\frac{1}{2}u^2 - \frac{1}{2}u^5 + \dots$	$4u^2 + 8u^5 + \dots$	2	O_3, O_4
$\alpha_6 = T_1(\alpha_5)$ with change of origin	$\frac{1}{2}u^2 - \frac{1}{2}u^5 + \dots$	$24u^3 + \dots$	2	O_5
$\alpha_7 = T_1(\alpha_6)$	$\frac{1}{2}u^2 - \frac{1}{2}u^5 + \dots$	$48u + \dots$	1	O_6
$\alpha_8 = T_2(\alpha_7)$	$u/96 + \dots$	$48u + \dots$	1	O_6, O_7

The last point O_8 of the sequence is the last satellite point on α.

When a resolute α_i ($i \geqslant 1$) is of order μ_i, we shall say that the associated fictitious point O_i is of *multiplicity* μ_i for α. Thus in the above example it is convenient to use the symbol

$$O^{12}O_1^6\,O_2^6\,O_3^4\,O_4^2\,O_5^2\,O_6^2\,O_7^1\,O_8^1\,O_{8+i}^1 \quad (i = 1, 2, \ldots)$$

to denote the composition of the succession of points on α. More briefly, we can denote the *multiplicity sequence* of these points by the symbol $(12)^1(6)^2(4)^1(2)^3(1)^\infty$. The reader may notice that it is a feature of this example that—as will be seen shortly to be the case in general—the multiplicity of each point O_i is equal to the sum of the multiplicities of all the points proximate to it.

6.1. The general branch of species $\Omega^{(\nu)}$

From the above example, we now proceed to the analysis of a general branch α, of species $\Omega^{(\nu)}$, with parametric equations

$$X = u^\nu, \quad Y = P(u) \tag{1}$$

where, in the standard notation of § 5.1 (with $a_{1,0} = 0$, $k_1 \geqslant 1$),

$$P(u) = \sum_{i=1}^{k_1} a_{1,i}\,u^{i\nu_1} + \sum_{i=0}^{k_2} a_{2,i}\,u^{(m_1+i)\nu_2} + \ldots + \sum_{i=0}^{\infty} a_{s+1,i}\,u^{(m_s+i)}. \tag{2}$$

This again implies, conveniently, that the branch tangent is not along OY.

We now write

$$P(u) = \sum_{i=1}^{k_1} a_{1,i}\,u^{i\nu_1} + u^{m_1\nu_2}Q(u),$$

where $Q(u)$ is a unitary series of the basic form

$$Q(u) = \sum_{i=0}^{k_2} a_{2,i}\,u^{i\nu_2} + \sum_{i=0}^{k_3} a_{3,i}\,u^{(m_2-m_1\nu_2+i)\nu_3} +$$

$$\ldots + \sum_{i=0}^{\infty} a_{s+1,i}\,u^{m_s-m_1\nu_2+i},$$

and belongs therefore to a well-defined species $\Omega^{(\nu_2)}$ over u^{ν_2}.

The origin O is ν-fold (i.e. of multiplicity ν) for α, and the first stage in the resolution of α consists in applying k_1 successive resolutions T_1 each followed where necessary by the appropriate change of origin. This exhibits a sequence of k_1 free fictitious points following O on α, of which the first k_1-1 are each of multiplicity ν, while the last, say $O_{(1)}$, is of multiplicity

$$m_1\nu_2 - k_1\nu_1 = (m_1-k_1 n_1)\nu_2 < n_1\nu_2 = \nu,$$

as follows from the definition of k_1 in § 5.1. Also, if we write

$\nu = n_1 \nu_2$ and define $n_{1,1}$ (relatively prime to n_1) by the equation

$$m_1 - k_1 n_1 = n_{1,1} < n_1,$$

then the last resolute so obtained, with centre at $O_{(1)}$, has equations

$$X = u^{n_1\nu_2}, \quad Y = u^{n_{1,1}\nu_2}Q(u), \tag{3}$$

and we may call this branch $\alpha_{(1)}$.

The next stage of the resolution consists in the application of alternate sets of transformations, of types T_2 and T_1 respectively, which have the effect of exhibiting the first satellite cluster on α (cf. § 4.1). None of these operations involves a change of origin; and the numbers and multiplicities of the successive sets composing the cluster (cf. § 4.2) depend solely on the algorithm which reduces $n_{1,1}/n_1$ to a continued fraction. At the end of this stage we reach a branch $\alpha_{(1)}^*$ whose centre O_1^* represents the last satellite point of the cluster. The equations of $\alpha_{(1)}^*$ will obviously be of the general form

$$X = u^{\nu_2}(Q(u))^{-p}, \quad Y = u^{\nu_2}(Q(u))^q, \tag{4}$$

where p and q are positive integers; and the tangent to $\alpha_{(1)}^*$ will not be along OX or OY.

We now use the lemmas of § 5.2, observing first that, by Lemma 2, the rational power $(Q(u))^{-p/\nu_2}$ (of which we take any one value) is of the same species $\Omega^{(\nu_2)}$ as $Q(u)$. We then make the substitution $v \to u(Q(u))^{-p/\nu_2}$, and observe that by Lemma 4 this has an inverse $u \to vT(v)$, where $T(v)$ is again of species $\Omega^{(\nu_2)}$. The parametric equations (4) of $\alpha_{(1)}^*$, if we first write $u^{\nu_2}(Q(u))^q$ in the form $u^{\nu_2}(Q(u))^{-p}(Q(u))^{p+q}$, are now seen to reduce to the form

$$X = v^{\nu_2}, \quad Y = v^{\nu_2}R(v), \tag{5}$$

where $R(v) = \{Q(vT(v))\}^{p+q}$; and we see then, by Lemmas 3 and 2, that $R(v)$ also is unitary of species $\Omega^{(\nu_2)}$.

The effect of all this is that these new equations (5) of $\alpha_{(1)}^*$ bring us to a position not essentially different from that with which we started, except that we are now dealing with a branch $\alpha_{(1)}^*$ of order ν_2 instead of with a branch of order $\nu = \nu_1$. We can proceed then, as before, to exhibit a second sequence of free points on α, followed (as may be) by a second satellite cluster; and we continue thus until, after the last satellite cluster has been exhibited, we are left with an infinite succession of free points on the branch. The essential fact, of course, is that *all the species that arise in the course of the resolution are derived from and directly related to the original species $\Omega^{(\nu)}$ from which we started.*

With the above indication of the mechanism that is used, we now give, in the form of a theorem, a detailed statement of the results that emerge from the resolution procedure.

THEOREM 3. *Let α be any branch of order ν, with centre O, with branch tangent not along OY, and with fractional equation $Y = S(X)$, where $S(X)$, being of a certain species $\Omega^{(\nu)}$, is written in the basic form*

$$S(X) = \sum_{i=1}^{k_1} a_{1,i} X^i + \sum_{i=0}^{k_2} a_{2,i} X^{(m_1+i)/n_1} + \ldots + \sum_{i=0}^{\infty} a_{s+1,i} X^{(m_s+i)/n_1 n_2 \ldots n_s}.$$

Further, let the infinite sequence of points on α, determined by a suitable succession of quadratic transformations, be $O, O_1, O_2, \ldots$. Then:

(i) *the sequence $O, O_1, O_2, \ldots$ is composed of an alternate succession of stretches F_λ ($\lambda = 1, \ldots, s+1$) of free points and clusters S_μ ($\mu = 1, \ldots, s$) of satellite points, ending with an infinite stretch F_{s+1} of free points;*

(ii) *the free points (excluding O) are each determined as they arise by the value of one of the coefficients in the basic form $S(X)$, the points of F_λ being determined successively in this way by the values of the coefficients $a_{\lambda,i}$, so that their number (if $\lambda \neq s+1$) is $k_\lambda+1$;*

(iii) *the multiplicities of the points of F_{s+1} are all 1;*

(iv) *the sequence of multiplicities of the points of F_λ ($\lambda \neq s+1$) is that indicated by the symbol*

$$(\nu_\lambda)^{k_\lambda} (n_{\lambda,1} \nu_{\lambda+1})^1,$$

where $\nu_i = n_i n_{i+1} \ldots n_s$ ($i = 1, \ldots, s$; $\nu_1 = \nu$), and

$$n_{\lambda,1} = m_\lambda - (m_{\lambda-1} + k_\lambda) n_\lambda < n_\lambda \quad (\lambda = 1, \ldots, s; \ m_0 = 0);$$

(v) *the sequence of multiplicities of the points of S_μ ($\mu = 1, \ldots, s$) is that indicated by the symbol*

$$(n_{\mu,1} \nu_{\mu+1})^{k_{\mu,1}-1} (n_{\mu,2} \nu_{\mu+1})^{k_{\mu,2}} (n_{\mu,3} \nu_{\mu+1})^{k_{\mu,3}} \ldots (\nu_{\mu+1})^{k_{\mu,\omega_\mu}},$$

where the $k_{\mu,j}$ ($j = 1, \ldots, \omega_\mu$) are the denominators in the continued fraction

$$\frac{n_{\mu,1}}{n_\mu} = \frac{1}{k_{\mu,1}+} \ \frac{1}{k_{\mu,2}+} \ldots \frac{1}{k_{\mu,\omega_\mu}} \quad (k_{\mu,\omega_\mu} \geqslant 2)$$

and the $n_{\mu,j}$ ($j = 2, \ldots, \omega_\mu$) are the partial remainders which occur in the corresponding set of equations

$$\left. \begin{aligned} n_\mu &= k_{\mu,1} n_{\mu,1} + n_{\mu,2} \\ n_{\mu,1} &= k_{\mu,2} n_{\mu,2} + n_{\mu,3} \\ \cdot \quad &\cdot \quad \cdot \quad \cdot \quad \cdot \quad \cdot \\ n_{\mu,\omega_\mu-2} &= k_{\mu,\omega_\mu-1} n_{\mu,\omega_\mu-1} + 1 \quad (\textit{i.e. } n_{\mu,\omega_\mu} = 1) \\ n_{\mu,\omega_\mu-1} &= k_{\mu,\omega_\mu} \end{aligned} \right\}; \qquad (6)$$

(vi) *the multiplicity on* α *of each point of the sequence is equal to the sum of the multiplicities of those points of the sequence that are proximate to it*;

(vii) *the multiplicity sequence given in full by* (iii), (iv), *and* (v) *uniquely determines* (*by use of* (vi)) *the complete proximity structure of the sequence of points* O, O_1,... *on* α.

With regard to this comprehensive result, we make the following remarks. First, the key *multiplicity law* (vi), which leads to (vii), comes by observing the association of each set of equations such as (6) with the alternate sets of T_1-transformations and T_2-transformations used in resolving a satellite cluster (as, for example, when we pass from equations (4) on p. 306 to equations (5)), and by using here also the results of § 4.1. Secondly, the proximity diagram of the satellite cluster S_μ ($\mu = 1,...,s$) is of the general type shown in § 4.2. In particular, the points O_{i-1} and O_i of the earlier diagram are now the two points immediately preceding S_μ, these being of multiplicities ν_μ and $n_{\mu,1}\nu_{\mu+1}$ respectively; and we now have $k_{\mu,1} - 1$ satellite points of multiplicity $n_{\mu,1}\nu_{\mu+1}$ and one such point of multiplicity $n_{\mu,2}\nu_{\mu+1}$ represented by points on the first vertical line of the diagram; and so on for the whole cluster. The reader should have no serious difficulty in verifying the details of all the results stated; and he will find it useful also to study the special branches discussed in the exercises at the end of the chapter.

7. Partially determined branch equations

The main results that emerge from Theorems 2 and 3 may now be summarized as follows.

(i) Every branch α of order ν is of a unique species $\Omega^{(\nu)}$, independent of its representation in any particular coordinate system.

(ii) The proximity structure and multiplicity sequence of the succession of points O, O_1,... on α (defined by a proper resolution) is uniquely determined by, and uniquely determines, the species $\Omega^{(\nu)}$ of α.

From (ii), in particular, we infer that no permissible variation in the resolution process (e.g. the use of one or other of T_1, T_2 when either is permissible) will affect the result.

Over and above this, however, we learn from the second part of Theorem 2 that if a branch α of a given species is determined step by step, by fixing successively the values of the coefficients in its fractional equation (in basic form), then the successive steps are effectively independent of the coordinate system employed.

On the basis of these remarks, we now propose, as was fore-shadowed in § 3, to replace the earlier geometric definition of a branch element $\mathscr{E}_r$ by a compact analytic definition, leaving it to the reader to satisfy himself, with the help of the analysis in the last section, that the two definitions are in fact equivalent. According to the new definition, a branch α will contain a given $\mathscr{E}_r$ if and only if its fractional equation, written in basic form, has an initial group of wholly or partially assigned terms; or, in other words, *an $\mathscr{E}_r$ is to be defined by a partially determined branch equation.*

The partial determination of a branch equation $Y = S(X)$ that will define an $\mathscr{E}_r$ is of one or other of two kinds, the first corresponding to an $\mathscr{E}_r$ of which the last component point O_r is free, and the second to an $\mathscr{E}_r$ for which O_r is a satellite point.

If O_r is a free point, the partial determination consists simply of the fixation (indices and coefficients) of all the terms of an initial block in the basic fractional power series $S(X)$. Thus *an $\mathscr{E}_r$ ending with a free point is defined by a fixed initial† block of terms in $S(X)$, where $Y = S(X)$ is the fractional equation of any branch containing the $\mathscr{E}_r$.* The number of terms in the initial block will be equal to the number $r' \leqslant r$ of free points (excluding O) in the composition of the $\mathscr{E}_r$.

If O_r is a satellite point, the appropriate partial determination of $S(X)$ is not so simple. It consists of two requirements: (i) the complete fixation of an initial block of terms in $S(X)$ up to but not including a particular characteristic term $a_{\lambda+1,0} X^{m_\lambda/(n_1 n_2 \ldots n_\lambda)}$ and (ii) partial information about the two integers m_λ and n_λ ($\geqslant 2$) which are to determine the exponent of X in this term.

The partial information in question takes the form of a partial specification of the continued fraction for $n_{\lambda,1}/n_\lambda$, where

$$n_{\lambda,1} = m_\lambda - (m_{\lambda-1} + k_\lambda) n_\lambda.$$

More precisely, if we write

$$\frac{n_{\lambda,1}}{n_\lambda} = \frac{1}{k_{\lambda,1}+} \frac{1}{k_{\lambda,2}+} \cdots \frac{1}{k_{\lambda,\omega_\lambda}} \quad (k_{\lambda,\omega_\lambda} \geqslant 2),$$

† It must always be remembered, in speaking of the fractional equation of a branch, that if this equation is of index ν, then the branch is equally representable by each of its ν conjugate equations. In the present case, therefore, a branch α will contain the $\mathscr{E}_r$ if *some one* of its conjugate equations has the required block of initial terms; and similar remarks apply in the sequel.

the conditions to be imposed are that, for some fixed integers $p \geqslant 0$ and $q \geqslant 1$, we must have

(a) $\omega_\lambda \geqslant p+1$,

(b) the first p denominators $k_{\lambda,1}, ..., k_{\lambda,p}$ have assigned (positive) values,

(c) $k_{\lambda,p+1} \geqslant q$ if $\omega_\lambda > p+1$, and $k_{\lambda,p+1} \geqslant q+1$ if $\omega_\lambda = p+1$.

Any $\mathscr{E}_r$ ending with a satellite point O_r is defined by this kind of partial determination of the fractional equation of an arbitrary branch containing it.

The fact that this new characterization of branch elements $\mathscr{E}_r$ is derived directly from the old makes it clear that all the arbitrary elements in the old definition—choice of coordinate systems in π, $\pi_1, ..., \pi_r$, and permissible variations in the choice of T_1 or T_2—have no essential significance. The deductions from the earlier definition, in particular the analysis of $\mathscr{E}_r$-structure, are therefore also independent of the arbitrary elements in question. Further, we can now define the composition of any $\mathscr{E}_r$—as a sequence of points $O, O_1, ..., O_r$—in the straightforward way we adopted when dealing with linear branch elements in § 2. That is to say, we can define each O_i in turn $(1 \leqslant i \leqslant r)$ as the condition on a branch α, which already contains a given $\mathscr{E}_{i-1}$, that it should contain a given $\mathscr{E}_i$ consecutive to that $\mathscr{E}_{i-1}$.

We may now assert the following extension of Theorem 2:

THEOREM 4. *Any $\mathscr{E}_r$ which is defined (as above) in relation to a given affine coordinate system in S_2 with O as origin is also defined in the same way as an $\mathscr{E}_r$, with the same proximity structure, in relation to any other affine coordinate system with the same origin.*

In stating the above theorem without qualification, we imply that branches or branch elements with tangents along OY are to be dealt with always by interchanging the roles of X and Y.

8. Multiplicity of intersection

We are now in a position to give an interpretation of the multiplicity of intersection $I_{\alpha,\alpha'}$ of two branches α, α' at O in terms of the multiplicities of the branches at O and at any consecutive fictitious points which they may have in common.

Let α and α' be of orders ν and ν', these numbers being also, by definition, the multiplicities of α and α' at O. By the definition and analysis of Chapter V, §§ 7–7.2, we know that

$$I_{\alpha,\alpha'} \geqslant \nu\nu',$$

equality holding if and only if the branch tangents are distinct. We now suppose that the branch tangents coincide with each other, but not with OY; and we apply a transformation T_1 to carry the branches into first resolutes α_1, α_1', with a common centre O_1, in a plane π_1, the object being to compare $I_{\alpha,\alpha'}$ with $I_{\alpha_1,\alpha_1'}$.

We are clearly at liberty to suppose that the common branch tangent at O is OX, so that the fractional equations of α, α', of indices ν, ν' respectively, are of the forms

$$Y = XP(X^{1/\nu}) \quad \text{and} \quad Y = XQ(X^{1/\nu'}),$$

where $P(z)$ and $Q(z)$ are elements of $K\{z\}$ of positive order. Further, the equations of α_1, α_1', also of indices ν, ν', are seen to be

$$Y = P(X^{1/\nu}) \quad \text{and} \quad Y = Q(X^{1/\nu'}).$$

By definition, then,

$$I_{\alpha,\alpha'} = O_X \prod_{i=0}^{\nu-1} \prod_{j=0}^{\nu'-1} (XP(\zeta^i X^{1/\nu}) - XQ(\zeta'^j X^{1/\nu'})),$$

where ζ, ζ' are primitive νth and ν'th roots of unity; and similarly,

$$I_{\alpha_1,\alpha_1'} = O_X \prod_{i=0}^{\nu-1} \prod_{j=0}^{\nu'-1} (P(\zeta^i X^{1/\nu}) - Q(\zeta'^j X^{1/\nu'})).$$

We see at once that

$$I_{\alpha_1,\alpha_1'} = I_{\alpha,\alpha'} - \nu\nu',$$

and so we have our first result:

LEMMA. *A transformation T_1 or T_2, if properly applied to two branches with the same centre O, reduces the multiplicity of intersection of the branches by an amount equal to the product of their orders.*

The implications of this result are far-reaching. We may say that α and α' have precisely their first $r+1$ consecutive points $O, O_1, ..., O_r$ in common if the unique branch elements of rank r which they contain are identical, but not those of rank $r+1$. In such circumstances there exists, as we have seen, a chain of transformations, each of them either a T_1 or a T_2, which carry the pair (α, α') into r consecutive pairs (α_i, α_i') $(i = 1, ..., r)$, the members of each pair having a common centre, and those of the last pair only having distinct branch tangents. By repeated application of the lemma, we see at once that if the sets of multiplicities of $O, O_1,..., O_r$ for α and for α' are

$$\mu(= \nu), \mu_1, \mu_2,..., \mu_r \quad \text{and} \quad \mu'(= \nu'), \mu'_1, \mu'_2,..., \mu'_r$$

respectively, then the total multiplicity of intersection of the branches is given by the formula

$$I_{\alpha,\alpha'} = \mu\mu' + \mu_1\mu'_1 + ... + \mu_r\mu'_r.$$

We have thus arrived at the following simple statement as the conclusion of our long and sometimes complicated argument.

THEOREM 5. *The multiplicity of intersection $I_{\alpha,\alpha'}$ of two concentric branches α and α' in S_2 is the sum of the products of the multiplicities of the branches at their common centre and at any consecutive fictitious points that they may have in common.*

This notable interpretation of the multiplicity of intersection of branches brings to a fitting climax the main development of ideas that we have tried to outline in the present chapter. We shall, nevertheless, proceed some little distance farther in order to draw attention to certain other lines of development and to important alternative approaches to the theory of infinitely near points and of the structure of branches in general.

9. The neighbourhoods of O

In looking back over this chapter, we may observe in the first place that the basis of the entire theory is the concept of a branch element $\mathscr{E}_r$ of arbitrary rank r. Already, however, we have gone some way in elaborating this notion—first, by introducing the concept of consecutive branch elements $\mathscr{E}_i, \mathscr{E}_{i+1}$, such that $\mathscr{E}_{i+1}$ is any one of the pencil of elements of rank $i+1$ that contains or follows immediately out of $\mathscr{E}_i$; then, by recognizing that any $\mathscr{E}_r$ is the last member of a unique chain of consecutive elements $\mathscr{E}_0, \mathscr{E}_1,..., \mathscr{E}_r$ leading up to it; and finally, by analysing any $\mathscr{E}_r$, as a condition on branches required to contain it, into a sequence of 'points' $O, O_1,..., O_r$, each of which after the first is to be envisaged as a differential condition requiring branches which already contain an element $\mathscr{E}_{i-1}$ of the chain to contain its successor $\mathscr{E}_i$. The introduction of such fictitious points has proved to be both suggestive and linguistically convenient; but we must always remember, nevertheless, that the points have in fact no separate existence apart from the branch elements $\mathscr{E}_r$ to which they belong or the sequences $O, O_1,...$ in which they appear. Thus, in particular, *if a branch α*

is said to contain (or pass through) a point O_r, this statement necessarily implies that α contains all the points of the unique sequence $O, O_1,..., O_r$ that leads up to O_r.

Keeping these considerations in mind, we may now look generally at the aggregate of fictitious points consecutive to O in S_2, ranging these in *neighbourhoods* (O_1), $(O_2),...$ of O according to their rank, that is to say according to the rank of the elements $\mathscr{E}_r$ of which they are the last component points.

To begin with, then, we have the *first neighbourhood* (O_1) of O, consisting of ∞^1 points (all necessarily free) associated with directions at O.

The *second neighbourhood* (O_2) of O has ∞^2 members, of which ∞^1 are consecutive to each point O_1 of the first neighbourhood. Further, corresponding to each O_1 there is a unique satellite point O_2^*, proximate to O as well as to O_1; and thus (O_2) contains in all ∞^1 such satellites O_2^* as a unique special subsystem.

Similarly, the *third neighbourhood* (O_3) of O has ∞^3 members, of which ∞^1 are consecutive to each O_2. In particular, it has three subsystems of satellite points: (i) ∞^2 satellites O_3^*, each proximate to a pair of consecutive free points O_1, O_2; (ii) ∞^1 satellites O_3^{**}, each proximate to consecutive points O_1 and O_2^*; and (iii) ∞^1 satellites O_3^{***}, each proximate to O and to a satellite O_2^*.

We see then, generally, that the *r-th neighbourhood* (O_r) of O contains ∞^r points, and that its satellite members distribute themselves into a finite number of distinct subsystems of various dimensionalities.

With regard to any particular neighbour O_r of O, a special interest naturally attaches to the branches α of lowest possible order that contain this point, these having some slight analogy, for the local geometry of S_2 at O, with the aggregate of lines through a given point in a projective space. We shall call such branches primitive branches.

DEFINITION. A branch is said to be *primitive* at a given point O_r in the rth neighbourhood of O if (i) it contains O_r, and (ii) its order has the least possible value for any branch which does so.

By being given O_r, we are given by implication all the proximity relations of the sequence of points $O, O_1,..., O_r$ leading up to O_r. We have already noted (Theorem 3 (vii)) that, by virtue of a simple law of multiplicity (Theorem 3 (vi)), the multiplicity sequence of the successive points $O, O_1,...$ on any branch α uniquely determines the proximity relations between the points; and we now observe that, conversely, these proximity relations determine likewise the multiplicity sequence. For, if α is not linear and O_{s+m} is its last satellite point, necessarily of multiplicity 1 on α, and if O_{s+m} is the last of a set of m points $O_{s+1}, ..., O_{s+m}$ which are all proximate to the same point O_s of α, then, by the law of multiplicity referred to above, these m points are all of multiplicity 1 and O_s is of multiplicity m on α. By proceeding backwards in this way, we can compute the multiplicity of every earlier point on α.

By applying the result just obtained, we deduce first of all that any point O_r must be of multiplicity 1 on any branch α that is primitive at O_r, since otherwise its order (i.e. its multiplicity at O) would not be the least possible; and further that, for the same reason, O_r cannot immediately precede a satellite point on α. The complete multiplicity sequence of the primitive branch, and in particular its order, is therefore uniquely determined by O_r. We thus have the following theorem.

THEOREM 6. *If O_r is any point in the r-th neighbourhood of O ($r \geqslant 1$), then (i) a branch α is primitive at O_r if and only if the multiplicity of O_r on α is 1 and the successor of O_r on α is a free point, and (ii) all branches that are primitive at O_r have the same fixed multiplicities at the points $O, O_1, ..., O_r$ leading up to O_r.*

We may say also, in terms of the procedure of resolution, that α is primitive at O_r if and only if (i) its rth resolute α_r is a linear branch at O_r in π_r, and (ii) the tangent to α_r is not a fundamental line in π_r. We may note, incidentally, that *the lines of π_r which pass through O_r, excepting only any which may be fundamental, correspond in particular to algebraic branches†* in π that are primitive at O_r. Further, if we take α_r to be a linear branch at O_r such that the coefficients in its equation are all indeterminates, then we may call the corresponding branch in π a *generic primitive branch at O_r*.

10. Analytic curves at O

In this section we refer briefly to a final application of our ideas to the structure of analytic curves at O (cf. Chapter V, § 7.2). This is a topic which includes, in particular, the structure of singularities of algebraic curves at O.

---

† The equations of these branches may readily be computed from the partially determined branch equation of the $\mathscr{E}_r$ associated with O_r.

Suppose C is a given analytic curve at O, compounded of s branches $\alpha^{(1)},..., \alpha^{(s)}$ with O as their common centre; and let us assume for simplicity that the $\alpha^{(i)}$ $(i = 1,...,s)$ are all distinct, since the necessary modifications for multiple components of C can safely be left to the reader. We may then define the points of C consecutive to O as all the points of the s distinct infinite sequences

$$O,\ O_1^{(i)},\ O_2^{(i)},...\quad (i = 1,...,s)$$

on the separate branches $\alpha^{(i)}$, noting that every pair of these sequences, although they may have an initial block of points in common, will ultimately separate out. The appropriate diagram for the whole set of points will accordingly be a tree-graph which forks ultimately into s infinite branches (Fig. 3).

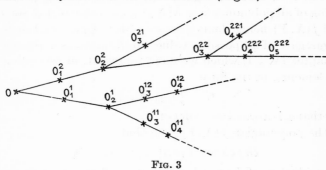

FIG. 3

We may now define the *multiplicity of O or any neighbour of O on C* as the sum of its multiplicities on those of the $\alpha^{(i)}$ which contain it. By virtue of Theorem 5, *we are then able to express the multiplicity of intersection of any two analytic (or algebraic) curves C, C' at O as the sum of the products of the multiplicities of C and C' at O and at any neighbouring points that they may have in common.*

We may refer, in conclusion, to a further question that arises in the present connexion. If $O, O_1, O_2,...$ is the sequence of points on a given branch α, we may ask under what conditions it is possible to construct an algebraic curve (not necessarily irreducible) with assigned multiplicities at $O, O_1,..., O_r$. It can in fact be shown (in particular by using sets of algebraic branches that are primitive at the points in question) that necessary and sufficient conditions for such a curve to exist are

$$m_i \geqslant m_{i+1}+...+m_{i+s}\quad (i = 0,...,r-1;\ m_0 = m),$$

where $O_{i+1},..., O_{i+s}$ are those of the points $O_{i+1},..., O_r$ that are proximate to O_i. This result is sometimes referred to as the *generalized law of proximity*.

11. Infinitely near points and polynomial ideals

In the last two sections of this chapter we shall attempt to give brief indications of two recently evolved ways of setting up invariant theories of infinitely near points and of the structure of branches generally. The first of these, now to be considered, applies to S_2 only. Originally developed by Zariski,† and further advanced by Hoskin,‡ it uses the technique and language of the theory of ideals in a way that we shall now describe.

We start with a (minimal) parametric representation $(X(u), Y(u))$ of a branch α, and we regard this as determining primarily a *valuation* of all polynomials in $K[X, Y]$, the value of any such polynomial $f(X, Y)$ being defined as its order $O[f(X(u), Y(u))]$ on α. The aggregate of all possible values so obtained is a semigroup G (cf. Chapter IV, § 4) which we now§ represent, in ascending order of its elements, in the form

$$G = \{0, g_0, g_1, ...\},$$

noting that g_0 is always the order of α.

All the polynomials $f(X, Y)$ such that

$$O[f(X(u), Y(u))] \geqslant g_i \quad (i \geqslant 0)$$

form an ideal $\mathfrak{q}_i$ of $K[X, Y]$, which we call the $(i+1)th$ *valuation ideal* of α; and we obtain in this way an infinite descending sequence

$$(\mathfrak{q}) = (\mathfrak{q}_0, \mathfrak{q}_1, ...)$$

of such valuation ideals, uniquely associated with α. The curves $f(X, Y) = 0$ for which $f(X, Y) \in \mathfrak{q}_i$ (called the *curves of the ideal* $\mathfrak{q}_i$) are all those curves for which the multiplicity of intersection $I_\alpha(f)$ is not less than g_i. If α is an algebraic branch, then the sequence $(\mathfrak{q})$ is closed by an ideal $\mathfrak{q}_\infty$ consisting of all those polynomials $f(X, Y)$ which are such that the curve $f(X, Y) = 0$ has as a component the unique irreducible curve to which the branch α belongs.

We may suppose, for convenience, that the centre of α is O and that its branch tangent is OX; and it is then easy, in any particular

† O. Zariski, 'Polynomial ideals defined by infinitely near base points', *Amer. J. Math.* **60** (1938), 151–204.

‡ M. A. Hoskin, 'Zero-dimensional valuation ideals associated with plane curve branches', *Proc. Lond. Math. Soc.* (3) **6** (1956), 70–99.

§ In present circumstances it is convenient to replace the symbols $g_1, g_2, ...$ used in Chapter IV by $g_0, g_1, ...$ respectively.

case, to find bases for at least the first few valuation ideals of α, and also to factorize these ideals into irreducible components. Thus, for example, q_0 is always the prime ideal with basis (X, Y), and q_1 is the primary ideal with basis (Y, X^2); and these are both irreducible.

The main features of the connexion between the structure of the sequence (q) of valuation ideals and the sequence of points $O, O_1, O_2,...$ on α may now be summarized as follows.

I. *If we pick out from the sequence* (q) *those of its members, to be called* simple ideals, *which cannot be expressed as products of preceding ideals in* (q), *then these simple ideals*

$$p_0 \; (= q_0), \; p_1 \; (= q_1), \; p_2, \; p_3,...$$

correspond in a well-defined sense to the consecutive points $O, O_1, O_2, O_3,...$ on α, and they are all irreducible ideals.

The ideal p_i is, in fact, the last and therefore the least member of (q) that contains every curve with a branch that is primitive at O_i. The fact that the simple ideals p_i represent the points O_i independently of their derivation from the branch α follows from the following principle.

II. *Any simple ideal p_i uniquely determines all its predecessors in any sequence* (q) *of valuation ideals to which it belongs.*

To introduce next the equivalent in the theory of valuation ideals of the relation of proximity in the classical theory of resolutions, we first define the *dominant* of any simple ideal p_j in (q) as the ideal which immediately precedes p_j in (q), and which we shall denote by $^{(j)}q$. Then we have the result:

III. *The dominant $^{(j)}q$ of any simple ideal p_j of* (q) *is either* (i) *the preceding simple ideal p_{j-1} if O_j is a free point, or* (ii) *a product $p_{j-1} p_{j-\alpha}$ ($\alpha > 1$) if O_j is a satellite point proximate to O_{j-1} and $O_{j-\alpha}$.*

A further identification can be formulated as follows.

IV. *If the elements q_i and q_{i-1} in a sequence* (q) *of valuation ideals are respectively a simple ideal p_j and its dominant $^{(j)}q$, then the multiplicity of O_j on α is $g_i - g_{i-1}$, where g_i and g_{i-1} are the values (elements of G) corresponding to q_i and q_{i-1}.*

It is hoped that these few remarks will be sufficient to indicate how an *a priori* invariant theory of infinitely near points can be developed in the way indicated. For details of the proofs and of many other developments of interest we must refer the reader to the original sources mentioned at the beginning of this section.

12. Rings of power series and curve branches in S_r

The methods of the preceding section, although they deal admirably with infinitely near points in the plane, would not seem to admit of any simple extension capable of representing infinitely near points in S_r ($r > 2$) by polynomial ideals. From the geometrical point of view, however, and by the use of quadratic transformations exactly analogous to T_1 and T_2 in S_2, the extension to S_r of the concept of the succession $O, O_1, O_2,...$ of points on a branch, and the proximity structure of this succession, presents no particular theoretical difficulty. There is, however, the serious practical problem of having to handle simultaneously a whole set of power series, instead of just one such series, which we could arrange in a standard basic form. The object of the present section is to give some general indication of a newer and much broader approach to the structural analysis of branches in spaces of arbitrary dimensionality. This approach, which is based on the rings of power series generated by the branches, was largely initiated by Cahit Arf† and has been developed and extended by Kirby.‡ We now attempt to summarize the basic ideas.

A branch α of S_r, with centre at the origin O, and with minimal representation

$$X_i = X_i(u) \quad (i = 1,...,r), \quad (X_i(0) = 0),$$

generates a (minimal) ring of power series

$$H(u) \equiv K\{X_1(u),..., X_r(u)\} \subset K\{u\},$$

the elements of which are those power series $h(u) = f(\mathbf{X}(u))$ that can be obtained by substituting $X_i(u)$ for X_i ($i = 1,...,r$) in the elements $f(\mathbf{X})$ of the ring of formal power series $K\{X_1,..., X_r\}$. It can be shown, then, that every such ring is *complete* in the sense that it contains the sum of every sequence of elements of itself which is such that the orders of these elements tend to infinity (so that the

† Cahit Arf, 'Une interprétation algébrique de la suite des ordres de multiplicité d'une branche algébrique', *Proc. Lond. Math. Soc.* (2) **50** (1948), 256–87. See also P. du Val, 'Note on Cahit Arf's "Une interprétation . . ."', ibid., 288–94.

‡ D. Kirby, 'Intorno alla classificazione dei rami e dei loro centri associati di proiezione, I, II, III', *R. C. Accad. Lincei*, (8) **20** (1956), 179–84, 325–8, 446–51. These papers are an abridged version of the first part of a thesis, entitled 'The Application of Formal Power Series to the Study of Singularities', approved in June 1955 by the University of London for the degree of Doctor of Philosophy.

sequence has a formal sum); and conversely, it can be shown also that every complete subring of $K\{u\}$ is *finitely generated* after the manner of $H(u)$.

The first fundamental result, which is also the basis of the subsequent development, may now be stated as follows.

I. *Every (minimal) finitely generated ring $H(u)$, defined to within regular substitution for the parameter, characterizes a complete class of analytically equivalent branches, in spaces of various dimensionalities, such that every branch of the class generates $H(u)$.*

When we say, in relation to this statement, that a branch $(\mathbf{X}(u))$ *generates* $H(u)$ we mean, as above, that

$$H(u) = K\{X_1(u),...,X_r(u)\};$$

and also, when we say that two branches α, α', with centres O, O', n spaces S_r, $S_{r'}$, are *analytically equivalent*, we imply (i) if $r = r'$, that α' is the transform of α by a regular analytic transformation of the neighbourhood of O in S_r into the neighbourhood of O' in $S_{r'}$, and (ii) if $r > r'$, that (i) is true when $S_{r'}$ is replaced by any space S_r'' in which it is contained.

The import of I is that the properties of a branch α that are analytically invariant correspond precisely to those properties of the corresponding ring $H(u)$ that are invariant over regular transformation of the parameter u; and the subsequent development of the theory consists accordingly in exhibiting the proximity structure of the sequence of points $O, O_1,...$ on α, the multiplicity sequence of these points, and other like properties of α, as invariant structural properties of $H(u)$.

Thus, in particular, if α_1 is any *first resolute* of α, derived from α by a quadratic transformation such as

$$X_1' = X_1, \qquad X_i' = X_i/X_1 \quad (i = 2,...,r),$$

then the ring generated by α_1 is the *first extension $H^{(1)}(u)$* of $H(u)$, a ring that is uniquely derived from $H(u)$ in a way that does not depend† on α. The complete reduction of the branch (to a linear branch) is thus reduced to the formation of successive extensions $H^{(1)}(u), H^{(2)}(u),...$ of $H(u)$, until an extension $H^{(r)}(u)$ is obtained which is $K\{u\}$ itself.

---

† In fact $H^{(1)}(u)$ can be derived from $H(u)$ by first forming the set $I_1(u)$ of all quotients of elements of $H(u)$ by some fixed element of $H(u)$ of least positive order, and then completing $I_1(u)$ to a ring $H^{(1)}(u)$ if it is not a ring already. The choice of the divisor element, as may then be shown, does not affect the result.

Further analysis requires the construction from any ring such as $H(u)$ of a unique associated ring called the *canonical closure* $H^*(u)$ of $H(u)$—but this is something that we shall not attempt to define here. We may say, however, that one basic property of $H^*(u)$ runs as follows.

II. *If $H^*(u)$ is the canonical closure of the ring $H(u)$ generated by a branch α, and if the semigroup of orders of elements of $H^*(u)$ is written in the form*

$$\{0, w_0, w_0+w_1, w_0+w_1+w_2,...\},$$

then $w_0, w_1, w_2,...$ is the sequence of multiplicities of the successive points $O, O_1, O_2,...$ on α, as defined, for example, by a suitable sequence of quadratic transformations.

The above remarks may give some indication of the general lines of the treatment of the structure of branches by means of rings of power series; but here, once again, we must refer the reader to the original memoirs for details and further developments.

NOTES AND EXERCISES ON CHAPTER XI

[In what follows we shall use the abbreviations 'p.m. diagram' for 'proximity-multiplicity diagram' and 'p.d.b. equation' for 'partially determined branch equation'.]

1. If α is the branch of which the first eight resolutes $\alpha_1,..., \alpha_8$ are given in the table on p. 304, show that the circumstances in which these successive resolutes appear are as shown in Fig. 4.

Show further that the p.m. diagram of the successive points on α is as shown in Fig. 5.

2. Show that the branch α with fractional equation

$$Y = X+X^2+X^3+X^{26/7}+X^{27/7}+X^{28/7}+X^{86/21}+X^{88/21}$$

has O_{12} (the twelfth point after O) as its last satellite point, and construct twelve diagrams, analogous to those in the preceding example, showing the construction of a proper sequence of resolutes $\alpha_1,..., \alpha_{12}$.

Show that the p.m. diagram of points on α is as shown in Fig. 6, and that this is completely determined by the two characteristic indices $26/7$ and $86/21$.

3. *Simple branch types.* In Chapter IV, p. 77, we defined certain elementary types of branch by means of their reduced equations. In most of these cases[†] it is now possible to give an equivalent geometric definition in terms of the proximity structure of the sequence of points on the branch; or, more briefly, *to define each type of branch by the condition that it is primitive at a*

† The proposed kind of definition will not apply to non-analytically-invariant branch types, such as the linear inflexional or ramphoid cuspidal types.

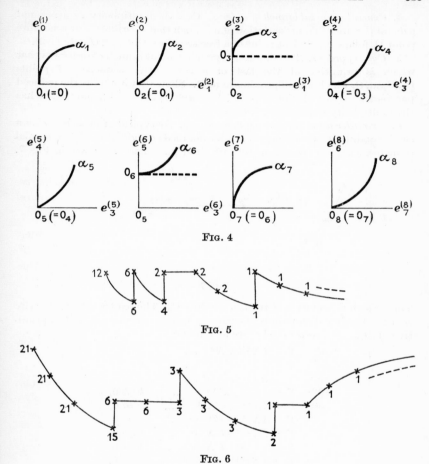

Fig. 4

Fig. 5

Fig. 6

specified type of point O_r in some neighbourhood of O. The reader should now verify the following results:

(i) A *simple cuspidal branch* is one which is primitive at a point O_2 proximate to consecutive points O, O_1.

(ii) A *double cuspidal branch* is one which is primitive at a point O_3 proximate to consecutive free points O_1, O_2 following O.

(iii) A *cubical cuspidal branch* is one which is primitive at the last of a triad of consecutive points O_1, O_2, O_3 all proximate to O.

(iv) A *cubo-quadratic cuspidal branch* is one which is primitive at a point O_3 proximate to consecutive points O_1, O_2 such that O_2 is proximate to O and O_1.

Show that the multiplicity sequences on these branches are respectively $(2, 1, 1, \ldots)$, $(2, 2, 1, 1, \ldots)$, $(3, 1, 1, \ldots)$, $(3, 2, 1, 1, \ldots)$.

4. *General cuspidal branch of order* 2. Find the multiplicity sequence and general parametric representation of a branch that is primitive at a satellite point O_r following the last point of a free sequence $O, O_1,..., O_{r-1}$ $(r \geqslant 2)$.

5. *Cusp of order* r. The simplest type of cuspidal branch of order r is that which is primitive at the last of a consecutive sequence of points $O_1, O_2,..., O_r$ which are all proximate to O. Show that it admits the reduced parametric representation $X = u^r$, $Y = au^{r+1}+...$ $(a \neq 0)$, and that it has the multiplicity sequence $(r, 1, 1,...)$.

6. *Primitive branches and p.d.b. equations.* As typical of branches with a single satellite cluster we may select for detailed consideration the monomial branch α with representation (u^{16}, u^{55}) and p.m. diagram shown in Fig. 7.

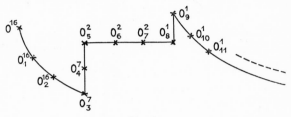

FIG. 7

This branch is primitive at the last satellite O_9. The reader may now verify that the fractional equations of arbitrary branches $\alpha^{(i)}$ $(i = 1,..., 10)$, primitive at $O_1,..., O_{10}$ respectively, are as follows:

$$\alpha^{(1)}: \quad Y = kX^2+k'X^3+...,$$
$$\alpha^{(2)}: \quad Y = kX^3+k'X^4+...,$$
$$\alpha^{(3)}: \quad Y = kX^4+k'X^5+...,$$
$$\alpha^{(4)}: \quad Y = kX^{7/2}+k'X^{8/2}+..., \quad\quad k \neq 0,$$
$$\alpha^{(5)}: \quad Y = kX^{10/3}+k'X^{11/3}+..., \quad k \neq 0,$$
$$\alpha^{(6)}: \quad Y = kX^{17/5}+k'X^{18/5}+..., \quad k \neq 0,$$
$$\alpha^{(7)}: \quad Y = kX^{24/7}+k'X^{25/7}+..., \quad k \neq 0,$$
$$\alpha^{(8)}: \quad Y = kX^{31/9}+k'X^{32/9}+..., \quad k \neq 0,$$
$$\alpha^{(9)}: \quad Y = kX^{55/16}+k'X^{56/16}+..., \quad k \neq 0,$$
$$\alpha^{(10)}: \quad Y = X^{55/16}+k'X^{56/16}+....$$

In the case of α the continued fraction which determines the composition of the satellite cluster is

$$\frac{55-3.16}{16} = \frac{7}{16} = \frac{1}{2+} \frac{1}{3+} \frac{1}{2},$$

the same being true of any branch $\alpha^{(9)}$. The corresponding fractions for branches $\alpha^{(8)}$ and $\alpha^{(7)}$, for example, are

$$\frac{1}{2+} \frac{1}{4} \quad \text{and} \quad \frac{1}{2+} \frac{1}{3},$$

and the reader should continue this sequence backward.

The *free* point O_{10} is defined by the p.d.b. equation

$$Y = X^{55/16}+....$$

The p.d.b. equation defining the satellite point O_9, however, is

$$Y = kX^{m/n} + ...,$$

where k is an arbitrary non-zero constant, and m, n are subject to the conditions:

$$\left. \begin{array}{ll} \text{either} & \dfrac{m}{n} = 3 + \dfrac{1}{2+} \dfrac{1}{3+} \dfrac{1}{p+1} \\[2mm] \text{or} & \dfrac{m}{n} = 3 + \dfrac{1}{2+} \dfrac{1}{3+} \dfrac{1}{p+} \cdots \dfrac{1}{s} \end{array} \right\} \quad p \geqslant 1, s \geqslant 2.$$

Define in the same way the p.d.b. equation which represents the point O_8.

7. Show how to characterize by p.d.b. equations the point O_8 on the branch considered in Exercise 1 and the point O_{12} on that considered in Exercise 2.

8. Show that the six branches α, β, γ, δ, ϵ, η with representations

$$(u^4, u^6 + u^8 + u^{10} + u^{11}), \quad (u^4, u^6 + u^8 + u^{11}), \quad (u^4, u^6 + u^{10} + u^{11}),$$

$$(u^4, u^6 + u^{11}), \quad (u^4, u^6 + u^{11} + u^{12}), \quad (u^4, u^6 + 2u^{11})$$

all have the same multiplicity sequence.

Verify the multiplicities of intersection

$$\alpha.\beta = \gamma.\delta = 32, \qquad \alpha.\gamma = \alpha.\delta = \beta.\gamma = \beta.\delta = 28,$$

$$\delta.\epsilon = 35, \qquad\qquad\qquad \delta.\eta = 34.$$

9. Show that the branches $(u^6, u^8 + u^{11})$ and $(u^{18}, u^{24} + 2u^{33} + u^{38})$ have seven consecutive points in common (including the origin) and that their multiplicity of intersection is 162.

10. *Quartic with three consecutive double points.* Show that any irreducible quartic curve C with double points at three successive points O, O_1, O_2 on the curve $Y = X^2$ has an equation of the form

$$(Y - X^2 - aXY)^2 = Y^2(bY + cX^2 + dXY + eY^2),$$

where a, b, c, d, e are constants.

Show that C has in general two linear branches at O, both having 3-point contact with $Y = X^2$; but that, if $b + c = 0$, C has only one branch of order 2 at O.

11. *Singularities of first polars.* It has been pointed out by B. Segre† (in contradiction of certain errors) that whereas the first polar $C^{(1)}(P)$ of a generic point P of the plane with respect to a curve C has certainly an $(s-1)$-fold point at any actual (proper) s-fold point of C, the same is not necessarily true for a fictitious (infinitely near) s-fold point of C. The example he gave was as follows.

Let C be the curve $Y^{12} - X^{113} = 0$, with the single (monomial) branch (u^{12}, u^{113}) at O. Of the succession of points on this branch, we find easily that those with multiplicities greater than unity are O, O_1,..., O_{12}, and that these have the multiplicities indicated by the symbol

$$C[O^{12}, O_1^{12}, ..., O_8^{12}, O_9^5, O_{10}^5, O_{11}^2, O_{12}^2].$$

† B. Segre, 'Sullo scioglimento delle singolarità delle varietà algebriche', *Ann. Mat. pura appl.* iv. **33** (1952), 5–48, cf. p. 29.

The first polars $C^{(1)}(P)$ of all points P of S_2 with respect to C form the linear net with equation $\qquad \lambda Y^{11} + \mu Y^{12} + \nu X^{112} = 0.$

Provided only that $\lambda \neq 0$, the multiplicities of $C^{(1)}(P)$ at O, $O_1,..., O_{12}$ are those indicated by the symbol

$$C^{(1)}(P)[O^{11}, O_1^{11},..., O_8^{11}, O_9^{11}, O_{10}^0, O_{11}^0, O_{12}^0].$$

Furthermore, it may easily be verified, as Segre showed, that *no* curve of the net in question (i.e. no first polar of any point P of the plane) contains the last double point O_{12} on C.

It may be added that the precise determination, for any given curve C, of the behaviour of the generic first polar $C^{(1)}(P)$ at singular points of C is still an unsolved problem.

12. *Base points of first polars.* Another interesting remark concerning the behaviour of the polars $C^{(1)}(P)$ at a singular point O of C has been made by D. B. Scott.[†] If Π is the net of all $C^{(1)}(P)$ for a given curve C, then any actual base point of Π is certainly a multiple point of C; but here again the result is not always true for a fictitious base point of Π. Thus Scott remarks that if C is the curve with equation

$$Y(Y^2 - X^3) + X^5 = 0,$$

then the third neighbour of the origin O on the branch $Y = X^{3/2}$ lies on C; but the third neighbour of O on the branch $Y = 3^{-1/2}X^{3/2}$—a point which does not lie on C—lies on the *generic* first polar curve of C.

13. *Analytic equivalence; critical points.* The species of a branch α, as we have noted on p. 303, is certainly invariant over analytic transformation of α, but the converse is not true in general. In certain simple cases the converse is true; for example, all linear branches are analytically equivalent to the line-branch $(u, 0)$, and all branches of order 2 of the same species are analytically equivalent to the appropriate monomial branch (u^2, u^{2p+1}) $(p \geqslant 1)$. A simple type of branch that is not uniquely determined to within analytic transformation by its species is that with multiplicity sequence $(3, 3, 1, 1,...)$, and we now consider this in detail.

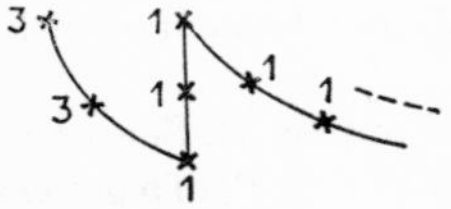

The sequence of points on a branch of the kind in question is indicated by the symbol

$$[O^3, O_1^3, O_2^1, O_3^1, O_4^1, O_5^1,...],$$

the two points O_3, O_4 being satellites remotely proximate to O_1, and it has the p.m. diagram shown in Fig. 8.

FIG. 8

Any such branch is easily seen[‡] to be analytically equivalent to a branch α with representation of the form

$$\alpha: \quad X = u^3, \quad Y = u^7(1 + au + bu^4),$$

[†] D. B. Scott, 'On base points of polar curves', *Ann. Mat. pura appl.* iv. **36** (1955) 73–75.

[‡] If $X = u^3$ and $Y = a_{11}u^3 + a_{12}u^6 + a_{20}u^7 + a_{21}u^8 + \cdots$ $(a_{20} \neq 0)$, then, by considering the semigroup of the branch, it can be seen that

$$Y = \{a_{20}u^7 + a_{21}u^8 + a_{24}u^{11}\} + \{a_{11}X + P(X, Y)\},$$

where $P(X, Y)$ belongs to $K\{X, Y\}$ and contains only terms of degree $\geqslant 2$ in X and Y.

and the question arises as to when α can be further transformed analytically into the monomial branch

$$\bar{\alpha}: \quad X = u^3, \quad Y = u^7.$$

The reader should now verify the following results:

(i) For all values of the coefficients a, b, the branches α and $\bar{\alpha}$ have their first six points $O, O_1,..., O_5$ in common, the last of these being a free point.

(ii) α passes through the next point $\bar{O}_6$ on $\bar{\alpha}$ if and only if $a = 0$.

(iii) α is analytically equivalent to $\bar{\alpha}$ if and only if $a = 0$.

(iv) If $a \neq 0$, then α is analytically equivalent to the branch $\bar{\alpha}_1$ with representation $(u^3, u^7 + u^8)$.

By a slight generalization of the above we obtain the result: *If $O, O_1, O_2,...$ is any simplicial sequence of the proximity type above defined, then there exists in the first neighbourhood of O_5 a unique critical point O_6—one of the free successors of O_5—such that any branch that is primitive at O_6 is analytically equivalent to the monomial branch (u^3, u^7), while any branch that is primitive at any other free successor O_6 of O_5 is analytically equivalent to the branch $(u^3, u^7 + u^8)$.*

Little appears to be known about the general role of such critical points as O_6 in the separation of the branches of a given species into classes of analytically equivalent branches.

14. Show that any branch with multiplicity sequence $(4, 1, 1,...)$ is analytically equivalent to a branch α of the form $(u^4, u^5 + au^6 + bu^7 + cu^{11})$.

Show that a necessary condition for α to be analytically equivalent to the monomial branch $\bar{\alpha}$ with representation (u^4, u^5) is $10b = 11a^2$.

Show similarly that if β is the branch $(v^4, v^5 + Av^6 + Bv^7 + Cv^{11})$, then a necessary condition for the analytic equivalence of α and β is

$$10(B-b) = 11(A^2 - a^2).$$

15. *Proximity and multiplicity matrices.* The proximity character of the sequence of $r+1$ points $O, O_1,..., O_r$ composing an $\mathscr{E}_r$ can conveniently be represented by its *proximity matrix* $\mathbf{m}$. This is the $(r+1) \times (r+1)$ matrix with elements m_{ij} $(i, j = 0,..., r)$ such that

(i) $m_{ii} = 1$ $(i = 0,..., r)$,

(ii) if $i \neq j$, then $m_{ij} = \begin{cases} -1 \text{ if } O_j \text{ is proximate to } O_i, \\ 0 \text{ if } O_j \text{ is not proximate to } O_i. \end{cases}$

It follows that $m_{ij} = 0$ if $j < i$, so that $\mathbf{m}$ is triangular; and we note also that there are either one or two elements equal to -1 in each column after the first above the leading diagonal.

The inverse $\mathbf{n} = \mathbf{m}^{-1}$ of the proximity matrix is another triangular matrix such that $n_{ii} = 1$ $(i = 0,..., r)$, $n_{ij} = 0$ if $j < i$ and $n_{ij} > 0$ if $j > i$. This matrix $\mathbf{n}$ is called the *multiplicity matrix* of the $\mathscr{E}_r$. The reader should now prove the result:

The integer n_{ij} $(j > i)$ is equal to the multiplicity of O_i on any branch which is primitive at O_j.

Thus, in particular, the elements of the last column of $\mathbf{n}$ are the multiplicities of $O, O_1,..., O_r$ on a branch that is primitive at O_r.

16. Construct the proximity and multiplicity matrices of the sequences of points that are terminated by the last satellite points on the simple branch types considered in Exercise 3.

17. *A sequence of v-ideals.* To illustrate the ideas mentioned in § 11, we apply them to the branch α with representation $(u^4, u^6+u^7+...)$. The semi-group of all possible non-zero orders of elements of $K[X, Y]$ on α is

$$(4, 6, 8, 10, 12, 13, 14,...);$$

and the successive v-ideals for α in $K[X, Y]$, each defined by one of the above orders, can be represented in the form:

$$
\begin{aligned}
\mathfrak{q}_0 &= (X, Y) & &= \mathfrak{p}_0 \\
\mathfrak{q}_1 &= (X^2, Y) & &= \mathfrak{p}_1 \\
\mathfrak{q}_2 &= (X^2, XY, Y^2) & &= \mathfrak{p}_0^2 \\
\mathfrak{q}_3 &= (XY, Y^2, X^3) & &= \mathfrak{p}_0\,\mathfrak{p}_1 \\
\mathfrak{q}_4 &= (Y^2, X^3, X^2Y) & &= \mathfrak{p}_2 \\
\mathfrak{q}_5 &= (Y^2 - X^3, X^2Y, X^4) & &= \mathfrak{p}_3 \\
\mathfrak{q}_6 &= (X^2Y, Y^3, XY^2, X^4) & &= \mathfrak{p}_0^2\,\mathfrak{p}_1.
\end{aligned}
$$

The simple ideals $\mathfrak{p}_0, \mathfrak{p}_1, \mathfrak{p}_2, \mathfrak{p}_3,...$ correspond to the successive points $O, O_1, O_2, O_3,...$ on α, the p.m. diagram of these points being as shown in Fig. 9. We note (cf. III on p. 317) that the dominant of $\mathfrak{p}_3$ is $\mathfrak{p}_2$, in agreement

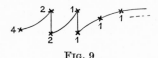

FIG. 9

with the fact that O_3 is free (proximate only to O_2); and on the other hand the dominant of $\mathfrak{p}_2$ is $\mathfrak{p}_0\,\mathfrak{p}_1$, in agreement with the fact that O_2 is a satellite proximate to O and O_1.

18. *Branches in S_3.* By use of the three special quadratic transformations such as $X' = X$, $Y' = Y/X$, $Z' = Z/X$, develop the geometrical theory of branch elements $\mathscr{E}_r = (OO_1...O_r)$ in S_3 so far as to show that a point O_i ($i \geqslant 1$) of such a sequence can be proximate *either* (i) only to its immediate ancestor O_{i-1}, *or* (ii) to O_{i-1} and to one remote ancestor $O_{i-\alpha}$ ($\alpha > 1$), in which case it is called a *semi-satellite*, *or* (iii) to O_{i-1} and to two remote ancestors $O_{i-\alpha}$ and $O_{i-\alpha-\beta}$ ($\alpha > 1, \beta \geqslant 1$), in which case it is called a *satellite*.

Discuss the types of semi-satellites or satellites that can follow a point O_i of any one of the three kinds described above.

19. If $a_2 b_3 - a_3 b_2 \neq 0$, show that the multiplicity sequence of the points $O, O_1,...$ on the space branch α with equations

$$X = u^4, \quad Y = a_1 u^4 + a_2 u^6 + \sum_1^\infty a_{2+i} u^{6+i}, \quad Z = b_1 u^4 + b_2 u^6 + \sum_1^\infty b_{2+i} u^{6+i}$$

is $4, 2, 1, 1,...$. Show also that O_2 is a semi-satellite proximate to O and O_1, and that O_3 is a satellite proximate to O, O_1, and O_2.

20. *Projection of a space branch.* If α is the space branch (u^4, u^6, u^7), with multiplicity sequence 4, 2, 1, 1,..., and α' is the projection of α from the point (a, b, c) of S_3 on to the (X, Y)-plane, show that the multiplicity sequence of α' for general values of a, b, c is 4, 2, 2, 1, 1,... and therefore different from that of α.

Investigate the positions of the point (a, b, c) which give rise to projected branches α' with a multiplicity sequence other than 4, 2, 2, 1, 1,....

21. If α is the space branch (u^4, u^6, u^7) and $P_1(u)$, $P_2(u)$, $P_3(u)$ are any three power series which generate the ring $K\{u^4, u^6, u^7\}$, show that the branch α' with representation $(P_1(u), P_2(u), P_3(u))$ is analytically equivalent to α. Show also, assuming that the results obtained by use of quadratic transformations are invariant, that α and α' have the same proximity character and multiplicity sequence.

APPENDIX

A. THE ALGEBRAIC BACKGROUND

IN this appendix we shall summarize briefly the algebra that we have taken as known in our treatment of the theory of algebraic curves. We shall not include algebraic theories that are now assumed to be part of every mathematician's normal equipment (e.g. the theory of vector spaces) nor do we propose to deal here with algebraic topics that are developed from first principles in the text. Our aim will be to give precise definitions of algebraic concepts and precise statements of algebraic theorems, sufficient to indicate to the reader the nature and extent of our reliance upon the standard literature of algebra. Full proofs of nearly all the results quoted are to be found in van der Waerden's *Modern Algebra*, to which general reference may be made. Specific references to this book, designated here by *M.A.*, are to the section numbers in the second German edition, of which the English edition is a translation. General reference may also be made to Book I of Hodge and Pedoe's *Methods*, on algebraic preliminaries, to Gröbner's *Moderne algebraische Geometrie*, and especially to Zariski and Samuel's *Commutative Algebra*, I (Princeton, 1958), which appeared just as the present book was going to press.

1. Algebraic structures

Algebra consists of the study of various *algebraic structures*. Each algebraic theory is constructed by taking a set $\mathscr{E}$ with a structure that arises from certain internal rules of composition (e.g. addition, multiplication), external rules of composition (e.g. application of the scalar operators to the elements of a vector space), and internal relations (e.g. an ordering relation), all of which are required to satisfy suitable axioms which define the structure in question.

If $\mathscr{E}$ is a set with a certain structure, and $\mathscr{E}'$ is a subset of $\mathscr{E}$ which is closed with respect to all the rules of composition that are involved, it may be that $\mathscr{E}'$ satisfies the same axioms as $\mathscr{E}$. We then have a substructure of the given structure—a subgroup of a given group, a subfield of a given field, and so forth.

We take as already familiar the structures of groups, rings, fields, and vector spaces. In the present book, moreover, we are concerned exclusively with *commutative* rings and fields, and in these notes we shall accordingly use the terms 'ring' and 'field' with the understanding that multiplication is taken to be commutative.

Another specific structure to which occasional reference is made in the text is that of a *semigroup*. A semigroup is simply a set with an associative (internal) rule of composition, with respect to which it is closed. The semigroups that we have occasion to mention are additive semigroups of integers.

2. Adjunction to rings and fields

If $\mathscr{R}$ and $\mathscr{R}'$ are rings, $\mathscr{R}$ being a subring of $\mathscr{R}'$, and if $\mathscr{S}$ is any set of elements of $\mathscr{R}'$, then there exists a smallest subring of $\mathscr{R}'$ which contains the union $\mathscr{R} \cup \mathscr{S}$, and we denote this subring by $\mathscr{R}[\mathscr{S}]$. $\mathscr{R}[\mathscr{S}]$ is said to be obtained from $\mathscr{R}$ by *ring-adjunction* of the set $\mathscr{S}$.

In the same way, if $\mathscr{K}$ and $\mathscr{K}'$ are fields, $\mathscr{K}$ being a subfield of $\mathscr{K}'$, and $\mathscr{S}$ is any subset of $\mathscr{K}'$, we denote by $\mathscr{K}(\mathscr{S})$ the smallest subfield of $\mathscr{K}'$ which contains the union $\mathscr{K} \cup \mathscr{S}$; and we say that $\mathscr{K}(\mathscr{S})$ is obtained from $\mathscr{K}$ by *field-adjunction* of the set $\mathscr{S}$.

When a field $\mathscr{K}$ is a proper subfield of another field $\mathscr{K}'$ we often say that $\mathscr{K}'$ is an *extension field* (or *extension*) of $\mathscr{K}$. We also refer sometimes, though less frequently, to an extension ring of a ring.

3. Isomorphism

By an *isomorphism* between two structured sets $\mathscr{E}_1$ and $\mathscr{E}_2$ of the same kind we understand a one-one correspondence between them which is such that elements of either set which stand in any structural relation correspond to elements of the other set which stand in the corresponding relation. When there is such an isomorphism between $\mathscr{E}_1$ and $\mathscr{E}_2$ we write $\mathscr{E}_1 \cong \mathscr{E}_2$. In particular, a one-one correspondence between two fields $\mathscr{K}_1$ and $\mathscr{K}_2$ is an isomorphism if sums correspond always to sums and products to products.

An isomorphism of a structured set $\mathscr{E}$ with itself is called an *automorphism* of $\mathscr{E}$. A many-one mapping of $\mathscr{E}_1$ on to $\mathscr{E}_2$ which preserves all structural relations is said to be a *homomorphism* of $\mathscr{E}_1$ on $\mathscr{E}_2$.

If two fields $\mathscr{K}_1$ and $\mathscr{K}_2$ are both extensions of the same field $\mathscr{K}$, an *isomorphism over $\mathscr{K}$* or *$\mathscr{K}$-isomorphism* between $\mathscr{K}_1$ and $\mathscr{K}_2$ is an isomorphism between these fields in which every element of $\mathscr{K}$ is self-corresponding. The concepts of $\mathscr{K}$-automorphism and $\mathscr{K}$-homomorphism are defined similarly.

4. Equivalence relations

A relation xRy, defined in a set $\mathcal{E}$, is said to be an *equivalence relation* if (i) it is reflexive (xRx for every x in $\mathcal{E}$), (ii) it is symmetrical (if xRy, then yRx), and (iii) it is transitive (if xRy and yRz, then xRz). Such a relation separates $\mathcal{E}$ into a set of disjoint subsets, called *equivalence classes*, each of which is a complete set of mutually related elements of $\mathcal{E}$. [*M.A.*, § 5.]

5. Integral domains

An *integral domain* is a commutative ring without divisors of zero, i.e. a ring $\mathcal{D}$ such that (i) $xy = yx$ for all x, y in $\mathcal{D}$, and (ii) if $x \neq 0$ and $y \neq 0$, then $xy \neq 0$. [*M.A.*, § 11.]

By an *identity element* of $\mathcal{D}$ we understand an element e of $\mathcal{D}$ which is such that $ex = x$ for every x in $\mathcal{D}$. An integral domain, as we have defined it, need not possess any such element at all; but if it does, then this element is unique. All the integral domains with which we are concerned in this book are domains with an identity element; and in this appendix, for the sake of brevity, we shall indicate that an integral domain $\mathcal{D}$ has an identity element by denoting it by $\mathcal{D}_e$. It should be noted that some authors proceed differently, using the term 'integral domain' always to mean integral domain with an identity element.

An element a of a domain $\mathcal{D}_e$ is said to be a *unit* of $\mathcal{D}_e$ if and only if it possesses a multiplicative inverse in $\mathcal{D}_e$, i.e. if there is an element a^{-1} such that $a^{-1}a = e$. An element of $\mathcal{D}_e$ is said to be *prime* or *irreducible* if it cannot be written as a product of two elements of $\mathcal{D}_e$, neither of which is a unit of $\mathcal{D}_e$. Two elements of $\mathcal{D}_e$, such that one can be obtained from the other by multiplication by a unit of $\mathcal{D}_e$ are said to be *associated*.

A *domain with unique factorization* is an integral domain $\mathcal{D}_e$ which is such that each of its non-units is expressible as a finite product of irreducible non-units, and this expression is unique to within rearrangement of the factors and replacement of factors by associated elements of $\mathcal{D}_e$.

A field is simply a domain $\mathcal{D}_e$ which has no non-unit except 0.

6. Ideals

An *ideal* in a (commutative) ring $\mathcal{R}$ is a subring $\mathfrak{p}$ of $\mathcal{R}$ which is closed with respect to multiplication by elements of $\mathcal{R}$, i.e. which is such that, if $x \in \mathcal{R}$ and $y \in \mathfrak{p}$, then $xy \in \mathfrak{p}$.

An ideal $\mathfrak{p}$ of a ring $\mathscr{R}$ is said to be *generated* by a set of elements $a_1,...,a_k$ of $\mathfrak{p}$ if it is the smallest ideal of $\mathscr{R}$ which contains these elements. The ideal consists of all elements of $\mathscr{R}$ which can be expressed in the form $\sum_{i=1}^{k} n_i a_i + \sum_{i=1}^{k} r_i a_i$, where the n_i are arbitrary rational integers and the r_i are arbitrary elements of $\mathscr{R}$—or all elements of the form $\sum_{i=1}^{k} r_i a_i \; (r_i \in \mathscr{R})$ if $\mathscr{R}$ has an identity element— and it is usually denoted by the symbol $(a_1,...,a_k)$. If $k = 1$, $\mathfrak{p}$ has a single generator a, and we refer to it as the *principal ideal* (a). A ring $\mathscr{R}$ with the property that all its ideals are principal ideals is said to be a *principal ideal ring*.

THEOREM. *Every integral domain which is also a principal ideal ring is a domain with unique factorization.* [*M.A.*, §§ 16, 18, 19.]

7. Euclidean rings

A *euclidean ring* is an integral domain $\mathscr{D}$ which has the property that it is possible to associate with each non-zero element a of $\mathscr{D}$ a real number $g(a)$ in such a way that (i) if $a \neq 0$ and $b \neq 0$, then $g(ab) \geqslant g(a)$, and (ii) if a and b are any two elements of $\mathscr{D}$, and $a \neq 0$, then b can be expressed in the form $qa+r$, with either $r = 0$ or $g(r) < g(a)$. The most familiar examples of euclidean rings are the ring of all rational integers (with $g(a) = |a|$) and the ring $\mathscr{K}[x]$ of all polynomials in x with coefficients in a given field $\mathscr{K}$ (with $g(a)$ equal to the degree of the polynomial a).

THEOREM. *Every euclidean ring is a principal ideal ring, and it is both a domain $\mathscr{D}_e$ and a domain with unique factorization.*

THEOREM. *In a euclidean ring $\mathscr{R}$, any two non-zero elements a, b have a highest common factor $d = (a,b)$, unique to within multiplication by a unit of $\mathscr{R}$, with the property that $d = ra+sb$, $a = gd$, $b = hd$ $(r,s,g,h \in \mathscr{R})$.*

The highest common factor d of a and b may be determined, and also expressed in the form $ra+sb$, by means of *Euclid's algorithm*. [*M.A.*, § 18.]

8. Congruence

If $\mathscr{R}$ is a commutative ring and $\mathfrak{p}$ is an ideal of $\mathscr{R}$, two elements x and y of $\mathscr{R}$ are said to be *congruent modulo* $\mathfrak{p}$—a relation that is written $x \equiv y(\mathfrak{p})$—if and only if $x-y \in \mathfrak{p}$. In a principal ideal ring, where $\mathfrak{p} = (p)$, it is customary to write $x \equiv y(p)$ instead of $x \equiv y((p))$; and we speak in this case of *congruence modulo p*. If $\mathscr{R}$ is the ring of all rational integers we have congruence in the familiar arithmetical sense.

Congruence modulo $\mathfrak{p}$ is an equivalence relation in $\mathscr{R}$, and the equivalence classes defined by this relation are referred to as *residue classes modulo* $\mathfrak{p}$ (or modulo p if $\mathfrak{p} = (p)$). [*M.A.*, § 16.]

9. Fields of quotients

It can be proved that a ring can be embedded in a field if and only if it is an integral domain (with or without an identity element). The smallest field in which a given integral domain $\mathscr{D}$ can be embedded is called the *field of quotients* of $\mathscr{D}$. It is unique to within isomorphism over $\mathscr{D}$. [*M.A.*, § 13.]

10. The characteristic of a field

It can be proved that, if e denotes the multiplicative identity element of a field $\mathscr{K}$, and ne denotes the sum of n elements all equal to e, then either (i) ne is different from 0 for every natural number n, or (ii) $ne = 0$ if and only if n is a multiple of a certain prime number p. In case (ii), $\mathscr{K}$ is said to have *characteristic p*, while in case (i) it is said conventionally to have *characteristic zero*. All the fields that occur in this book are of characteristic zero. [*M.A.*, § 30.]

11. Algebraic and transcendental elements

Let $\mathscr{K}$ be a given field, and let $\mathscr{K}'$ be an extension field of $\mathscr{K}$. An element of $\mathscr{K}'$ is said to be *algebraic over $\mathscr{K}$* if it satisfies at least one algebraic equation

$$\sum_{k=0}^{n} a_k x^{n-k} = 0 \quad (n \geqslant 1; \, a_k \in \mathscr{K}, \, k = 0,...,n; \, a_0 \neq 0).$$

An element of $\mathscr{K}'$ which is not algebraic over $\mathscr{K}$ is said to be *transcendental over $\mathscr{K}$*.

THEOREM. *For any element a of $\mathscr{K}'$, the set of all polynomials $f(x)$ in the polynomial ring $\mathscr{K}[x]$ which are such that $f(a) = 0$ in $\mathscr{K}'$ is an ideal $\mathfrak{p}$ in $\mathscr{K}[x]$.*

The ring $\mathscr{K}[x]$ being euclidean, $\mathfrak{p}$ is a principal ideal $(m(x))$. The generating element $m(x)$ of $\mathfrak{p}$, which is unique to within a factor in $\mathscr{K}$, is irreducible over $\mathscr{K}$, and it is a polynomial $f(x)$ of lowest degree such that $f(a) = 0$. It is known as the *minimum polynomial* of the element a over $\mathscr{K}$.

If $a, a_1, ..., a_h$ are elements of $\mathscr{K}'$, a is said to be *algebraically dependent* on $a_1, ..., a_h$ with respect to $\mathscr{K}$ if and only if it satisfies an algebraic equation with coefficients in the ring $\mathscr{K}[a_1, ..., a_h]$. The formal properties of algebraic dependence over $\mathscr{K}$ are strictly analogous to those of linear dependence of elements of a vector space over a given field.

If there exists a finite set of elements $a_1, ..., a_h$ of $\mathscr{K}'$ such that every element of $\mathscr{K}'$ is algebraically dependent on these elements with respect to $\mathscr{K}$, then there is a finite maximum to the number of algebraically independent elements that can be selected from $\mathscr{K}'$, and this number is called the *degree of transcendence* of $\mathscr{K}'$ over $\mathscr{K}$. [*M.A.*, §§ 32, 64.]

12. Indeterminates

Letters $a, b, ..., x, y, ...$ are used to denote elements, sometimes specified and sometimes unspecified, of algebraic systems that are under discussion, and relations between the elements denoted are then written as equations, etc., involving the letters which denote them. Indeterminates, on the contrary, are letters which function solely as constituents in formal expressions, without denoting anything; and there is no relationship between an indeterminate and any other symbol. In particular, an indeterminate cannot satisfy non-trivially any algebraic equation; and when an indeterminate is adjoined to a field it is necessarily transcendental over the field.

13. Algebraically closed fields

If $\mathscr{K}$ is any given field, and $f(x) = 0$ is an equation with co-efficients in $\mathscr{K}$, an extension of $\mathscr{K}$ can be constructed in which the equation has a root. Extending $\mathscr{K}$ a finite number of times, we can construct an extension which contains all the roots of the equation (i.e. a field over which the polynomial $f(x)$ is resolvable completely into linear factors). There exists a smallest extension of $\mathscr{K}$ with this property, and it is called the *splitting field* of the polynomial $f(x)$.

If $\mathscr{K}$ is such that it is itself the splitting field of every $\mathscr{K}$-polynomial (i.e. it is such that every equation with coefficients in $\mathscr{K}$ has all its roots in $\mathscr{K}$) then $\mathscr{K}$ is said to be *algebraically closed*.

The so-called Fundamental Theorem of Algebra asserts that the field K of all complex numbers has this property; and Puiseux's Theorem (p. 83) asserts that the field $K^*|u|$ of all extended fractional power series in an indeterminate u with complex coefficients also has it. [*M.A.*, §§ 32, 35, 62.]

14. Polynomials and polynomial rings

If $\mathscr{R}$ is a given commutative ring with identity element, we understand by a *polynomial over $\mathscr{R}$ in an indeterminate x*, or an *$\mathscr{R}$-polynomial* in x, a formal expression

$$a_0 x^n + a_1 x^{n-1} + \ldots + a_n \quad (a_i \in \mathscr{R}, \; i = 0, \ldots, n; \; a_0 \neq 0).$$

The integer n is called the *degree* of the polynomial.

The set of all $\mathscr{R}$-polynomials in x, with the natural definitions of addition and multiplication, is a ring $\mathscr{R}[x]$.

The ring $\mathscr{R}[x_1, \ldots, x_r]$ of all $\mathscr{R}$-polynomials in the r indeterminates $x_1, \ldots, x_r$ is defined recursively. $\mathscr{R}[x_1]$ is defined as above, and we define $\mathscr{R}[x_1, \ldots, x_r]$ as $(\mathscr{R}[x_1, \ldots, x_{r-1}])[x_r]$.

Hilbert's Basis Theorem asserts that, if $\mathscr{R}$ is a ring with an identity element and $\mathscr{R}$ is such that every ideal in it has a finite basis, then every ideal in the polynomial ring $\mathscr{R}[x]$ also has a finite basis. [*M.A.*, § 84.]

15. Forms

An *$\mathscr{R}$-form* of degree n in $x_1, \ldots, x_r$ is a homogeneous polynomial of the nth degree in $x_1, \ldots, x_r$, i.e. a formal expression

$$\sum a_{\lambda_1 \ldots \lambda_r} x_1^{\lambda_1} \ldots x_r^{\lambda_r} \quad (a_{\lambda_1 \ldots \lambda_r} \in \mathscr{R}),$$

in which the summation extends over all ordered sets of r non-negative integers $(\lambda_1, \ldots, \lambda_r)$ for which $\sum \lambda_i = n$. The number of such sets (sometimes referred to as $^n H_r$, the number of homogeneous products of the nth degree that can be formed from r letters) is $\binom{n+r-1}{r-1}$. [See, for example, C. Smith, *A Treatise on Algebra*.]

The set of all $\mathscr{R}$-forms in $x_1, \ldots, x_r$ is not a ring, and it has no simple structure.

By a *homogeneous ideal* in the ring $\mathscr{R}[x_1, \ldots, x_r]$ of all $\mathscr{R}$-polynomials in $x_1, \ldots, x_r$ is meant an ideal with the property that, if any element of it is written as a sum of homogeneous parts of different degrees, each of these constituents is separately an element of the ideal.

16. Factorization of polynomials

THEOREM. *If $\mathscr{D}_e$ is an integral domain with an identity element, then so also is $\mathscr{D}_e[x_1, \ldots, x_r]$. If, in addition, $\mathscr{D}_e$ is a domain with unique factorization, then so also is $\mathscr{D}_e[x_1, \ldots, x_r]$.*

If $\mathscr{D}_e$ is a domain with unique factorization, an element of $\mathscr{D}_e[x]$ is said to be a *primitive polynomial* (with respect to $\mathscr{D}_e$) if the highest common factor of its coefficients, as elements of $\mathscr{D}_e$, is 1.

THEOREM (Gauss's lemma). *If $\mathscr{D}_e$ is a domain with unique factorization, and $\mathscr{K}$ is the field of quotients of $\mathscr{D}_e$, then any element of $\mathscr{D}_e[x]$ that is irreducible over $\mathscr{D}_e$ is also irreducible over $\mathscr{K}$. [M.A., § 23.]*

17. Zeros

Let $\mathscr{D}_e$ be an integral domain with an identity element, and let $f(x)$ be an element of $\mathscr{D}_e[x]$. An element α of $\mathscr{D}_e$, or of any ring $\mathscr{R}$ which is an extension of $\mathscr{D}_e$, is said to be a *zero* of the polynomial $f(x)$ if and only if $f(\alpha) = 0$. [M.A., § 21.]

THEOREM. *A necessary and sufficient condition for α to be a zero of $f(x)$ is that $f(x)$ is divisible by $x-\alpha$ in $\mathscr{R}[x]$.*

We say that α is a *k-fold zero* of $f(x)$ if $f(x)$ is divisible by $(x-\alpha)^k$ but not by $(x-\alpha)^{k+1}$.

THEOREM. *If α is a k-fold zero of $f(x)$, then it is a $(k-1)$-fold zero of the derivative $f'(x)$ of $f(x)$ (cf. § 23, p. 340).*

THEOREM. *A zero of $f(x)$ is multiple (i.e. k-fold for some $k \geqslant 2$) if and only if it is a common zero of $f(x)$ and $f'(x)$.*

It is convenient to use the term 'zero of a polynomial' also in relation to polynomials in more than one indeterminate. Thus we say that $(\alpha_1,..., \alpha_n)$ is a zero of $f(x_1,..., x_n)$ if and only if $f(\alpha_1,..., \alpha_n) = 0$. In stating the important results which follow, we shall confine ourselves to polynomials over the ground field K.

THEOREM (Hilbert's Zero Theorem). *A polynomial f, belonging to the ring $K[x_1,..., x_n]$, takes the value 0 at all the common zeros of a set of polynomials $f_1,...,f_r$ in the same ring if and only if, for some positive integer σ, the congruence*

$$f^\sigma \equiv 0 \quad (f_1,..., f_r)$$

holds in $K[x_1,..., x_n]$.

COROLLARY 1. *If f and g are non-zero elements of $K[x_1,...,x_n]$, such that f is irreducible and every zero of f is also a zero of g, then f is a factor of g in $K[x_1,...,x_n]$.*

COROLLARY 2. *Let f, g, h be non-zero elements of $K[x_1,...,x_n]$ such that f is irreducible and h does not have f as a factor. If all the zeros of f, with the possible exception of any that are also zeros of h, are zeros of g, then f is a factor of g in $K[x_1,...,x_n]$.*

[The second corollary follows at once from the first if g is replaced in it by gh. For Hilbert's Theorem, see $M.A.$, § 79.]

18. The resultant of two polynomials

An algebraic concept that is of particular importance in algebraic geometry is that of the resultant of two polynomials.

Let $f(x)$ and $g(x)$ be two elements of the polynomial ring $\mathscr{K}[x]$ over an arbitrary field $\mathscr{K}$:

$$f(x) \equiv a_0 x^n + a_1 x^{n-1} + \ldots + a_n,$$
$$g(x) \equiv b_0 x^m + b_1 x^{m-1} + \ldots + b_m.$$

The *resultant* $R(f,g)$ of $f(x)$ and $g(x)$, also called their *Sylvester eliminant*, is the determinant

$$R = \begin{vmatrix} a_0 & a_1 & \cdot & \cdot & \cdot & \cdot & \cdot & \cdot & a_n & 0 & \cdot & 0 \\ 0 & a_0 & \cdot & \cdot & \cdot & \cdot & \cdot & \cdot & \cdot & a_n & \cdot & 0 \\ \cdot & \cdot & \cdot & \cdot & \cdot & \cdot & \cdot & \cdot & \cdot & \cdot & \cdot & \cdot \\ 0 & \cdot & \cdot & a_0 & \cdot & \cdot & \cdot & \cdot & \cdot & \cdot & \cdot & a_n \\ b_0 & b_1 & \cdot & \cdot & b_m & 0 & \cdot & \cdot & \cdot & \cdot & \cdot & 0 \\ 0 & b_0 & \cdot & \cdot & \cdot & b_m & \cdot & \cdot & \cdot & \cdot & \cdot & 0 \\ \cdot & \cdot & \cdot & \cdot & \cdot & \cdot & \cdot & \cdot & \cdot & \cdot & \cdot & \cdot \\ 0 & \cdot & \cdot & \cdot & \cdot & \cdot & b_0 & \cdot & \cdot & \cdot & \cdot & b_m \end{vmatrix} \begin{matrix} \\ \\ \\ m \text{ rows} \\ \\ \\ \\ n \text{ rows} \end{matrix}$$

of order $m+n$; and it has the following properties:

(i) $R(f,g) = 0$ if and only if either $a_0 = b_0 = 0$ or $f(x)$ and $g(x)$ have a non-constant common factor.

(ii) Every term in the expanded form of R is of degree m in the a_i and of degree n in the b_k. The *weight* of each term (by which we understand the sum of the subscripts of the m factors a_i and the n factors b_k which occur in it) is mn.

(iii) R is expressible in the form

$$A.f(x) + B.g(x),$$

where A and B are polynomials in the a_i and b_k and in x, the degree of A in x is at most $m-1$, and the degree of B in x is at most $n-1$.

(iv) If $\xi_1,\ldots,\xi_n$ are the zeros of $f(x)$ and $\eta_1,\ldots,\eta_m$ are the zeros of $g(x)$ (in any extension of $\mathscr{K}$ which contains the splitting fields of both polynomials) then

$$R = a_0^m \prod_{\nu=1}^{n} g(\xi_\nu)$$
$$= (-1)^{mn} b_0^n \prod_{\mu=1}^{m} f(\eta_\mu)$$
$$= a_0^m b_0^n \prod_{\nu=1}^{n} \prod_{\mu=1}^{m} (\xi_\nu - \eta_\mu).$$

If $f(x)$, $g(x)$, $h(x)$ are any three polynomials, it follows at once from the formulae just given that

$$R(fg, h) = R(f, h) . R(g, h)$$

and
$$R(f, g+fh) = a_0^{m'-m} R(f, g),$$

where m' is the degree of $g+fh$.

Reverting to the general theory, if, instead of the polynomials $f(x)$ and $g(x)$ in x, we take two forms in x_0, x_1,

$$f(x_0, x_1) \equiv a_0 x_0^n + a_1 x_0^{n-1} x_1 + ... + a_n x_1^n,$$

$$g(x_0, x_1) \equiv b_0 x_0^m + b_1 x_0^{m-1} x_1 + ... + b_m x_1^m,$$

the determinant R already defined is said to be the resultant of the two forms. It is zero if and only if the forms have a non-constant common factor.

[Several excellent accounts of the theory of resultants are available. See, for instance, (i) van der Waerden's *Modern Algebra*, i, §§ 27, 28, together with the more general treatment of the theory of elimination in volume ii, chapter xi, and also his summary of the results of the theory in his *Einführung*, § 15; (ii) the admirable treatment given by Hodge and Pedoe in *Methods*, i, chapter iv; (iii) chapter ii of Gröbner's book.]

19. The general theory of elimination

Necessary and sufficient conditions for a finite set of $\mathcal{K}$-polynomials in one or more indeterminates, or a finite set of $\mathcal{K}$-forms, to have a (non-trivial) common zero can be given in terms of finite systems of resultants. Such resultant systems are the basis of the general theory of elimination, fully discussed in van der Waerden's *Modern Algebra*, chapter xi.

The theorems which follow are quoted from Hodge and Pedoe's *Methods*, i, p. 158 and p. 160.

THEOREM. *Given r polynomials $f_1(x), ..., f_r(x)$ in one indeterminate with indeterminate coefficients there exists a set $d_1, ..., d_N$ of polynomials in the coefficients with the property that for specializations of the coefficients the conditions $d_1 = 0, ..., d_N = 0$ are necessary and sufficient to ensure that* (i) *the equations $f_1(x) = 0, ..., f_r(x) = 0$ are soluble in some extension field; or* (ii) *the leading coefficients in $f_1(x), ..., f_r(x)$ all vanish. Moreover, if the equations have a solution, they have a solution in an algebraic extension of the field of coefficients.*

THEOREM. *Let*

$$f_i(x_0,...,x_n) = 0 \quad (i = 1,...,r) \tag{1}$$

be a set of homogeneous equations with indeterminate coefficients, and let

$$\bar{f}_i(x_0,...,x_n) = 0 \quad (i = 1,...,r) \tag{2}$$

be the equations obtained from (1) by a given specialization of the coefficients in (1). Then there exists a finite set of polynomials in the coefficients of (1), $d_1,...,d_k$, with the properties

(i) $$d_i x_0^m \equiv \sum_{j=1}^{r} a_{ij}(x_0,...,x_n) f_j(x_0,...,x_n)$$

for some value of m, the coefficients of $a_{ij}(x_0,...,x_n)$ being in the ring of coefficients of (1); and

(ii) *a necessary and sufficient condition that the equations (2) have a solution in an algebraic extension of the ring of coefficients is that the specializations of the polynomials d_i arising from the given specialization of the coefficients should be zero.*

20. The discriminant of a polynomial

Let $$f(x) \equiv a_0 x^n + a_1 x^{n-1} + ... + a_n$$

be a polynomial in x with coefficients in a given field $\mathscr{K}$, and let $\mathscr{K}'$ be the splitting field of $f(x)$. Then

$$f(x) = a_0 \prod_{i=1}^{n} (x - \xi_i) \quad (\xi_i \in \mathscr{K}', \ i = 1,...,n).$$

The *discriminant* $D(f)$ of $f(x)$ is then defined by the equation

$$D(f) = a_0^{2n-2} \prod_{1 \leqslant i < k \leqslant n} (\xi_i - \xi_k)^2.$$

Being a symmetric polynomial in the roots of the equation $f(x) = 0$, $D(f)$ can be expressed explicitly in terms of the ratios of the coefficients $a_0,...,a_n$; and it can be shown that

$$a_0 D(f) = (-1)^{\frac{1}{2}n(n-1)} R(f, f'),$$

where $f'(x)$ is the derivative of $f(x)$.

$D(f) = 0$ is a necessary and sufficient condition for at least two of the roots of the equation $f(x) = 0$ to be coincident—cf. § 17 above. [*M.A.*, § 26.]

21. Valuations of a field

Let $\mathscr{K}$ be a given field. By a *valuation* of $\mathscr{K}$ into the field of real numbers we understand a function $v(a)$, defined in $\mathscr{K}$, with the following properties:

(i) for any non-zero element a of $\mathscr{K}$, $v(a)$ is a real number,
(ii) $v(0) = \infty$ (conventionally),
(iii) $v(ab) = v(a)+v(b)$,
(iv) $v(a+b) \geqslant \min(v(a), v(b))$.

22. Invariants

Let $f(x_1,...,x_n)$ be a form of the rth degree in $x_1,...,x_n$ with indeterminate coefficients; and let $x_1,...,x_n$ be connected with $\bar{x}_1,...,\bar{x}_n$ by the (non-singular) linear transformation

$$x_i = \sum_{k=1}^{n} e_{ik}\bar{x}_k \quad (i = 1,...,n),$$

also with indeterminate coefficients. Then substitution for $x_1,...,x_n$ in the form $f(x_1,...,x_n)$ yields a form $\bar{f}(\bar{x}_1,...,\bar{x}_n)$ of the rth degree in $\bar{x}_1,...,\bar{x}_n$; and the set of coefficients $(\bar{a})$ in $\bar{f}$ is connected with the set of coefficients (a) in f by a non-singular linear transformation.

By an *invariant* of a set of m forms $f_j(x_1,...,x_n), j = 1,...,m$, of the rth degree in $x_1,...,x_n$, we understand a non-zero polynomial $I(a)$, with rational coefficients, in the coefficients $(a^{(j)})$ of all the forms, which has the property that

$$I(\bar{a}) = \Phi(e)I(a),$$

where $\Phi(e)$ is a polynomial, with rational coefficients, in the e_{ik} only. It can be proved that, when $I(a)$ is an invariant in this sense, $\Phi(e)$ is a positive integral power of the determinant $|e_{rs}|$.

THEOREM. *If* $f_j(x_1,...,x_n) = \sum_{h=1}^{n} a_{jh}x_h \ (j = 1,...,m)$, *where* $m \geqslant n$, *then every invariant* $I(a_{jh})$ *of the m linear forms* $f_j(x_1,...,x_n)$ *is expressible as a polynomial, with rational coefficients, in the* $\binom{m}{n}$ *n-rowed determinants that can be formed out of the m rows* $(a_{j1},..., a_{jn})$ $(j = 1,...,m)$.

For the proof of this theorem, see Weitzenböck, *Invariantentheorie*, chapter i, § 9.

23. Differentiation treated algebraically

For polynomials and rational functions (and also for algebraic functions) ordinary and partial derivatives can be defined, and their general properties established, in terms of pure algebra, without recourse to limiting considerations. If, for example, $f(x)$ is a polynomial $a_0 x^n + ... + a_n$, then $f(x+h)$ can be rearranged in the form

$$f(x) + hf_1(x) + h^2 f_2(x) + ... + h^n a_0;$$

and if we *define* the derivative $f'(x)$ of $f(x)$ as the coefficient $f_1(x)$ of h in this expression we obtain the same polynomial as that yielded by the usual definition

$$f'(x) = \lim_{h \to 0} (f(x+h) - f(x))/h.$$

In this restricted theory we are able to prove Taylor's Theorem and also *Euler's Theorem on homogeneous functions*: If $f(x_1, ..., x_r)$ is a form of the nth degree in $x_1, ..., x_r$, then

$$\left(x_1 \frac{\partial}{\partial x_1} + ... + x_r \frac{\partial}{\partial x_r} \right) f = nf.$$

[*M.A.*, §§ 20, 65; Gröbner; Hodge and Pedoe.]

24. Formal power series

On the subject of formal power series the reader may consult Bochner and Martin, *Several Complex Variables*, making due allowance for the primary concern of these authors with analysis. In particular, Theorems 2 and 3 of chapter ix, § 2, are generalized versions of Weierstrass's Preparation Theorem, in the form in which we state it on p. 98, and the theorem on uniqueness of factorization in the ring $K\{X, Y\}$.

A full discussion of the topic of substitution of one formal power series (in a single indeterminate) in another is to be found in Walker's *Algebraic Curves*, chapter iv, § 1.2.

B. CONSTRUCTIVE PROOF OF PUISEUX'S THEOREM†

Puiseux's Theorem (Theorem 1, p. 83) asserts that the field $K^*|u|$ of all extended fractional power series in a single indeterminate u, with coefficients in the ground field K, is algebraically

---

† For other proofs of Puiseux's Theorem, which do not, however, have the constructive character of the one given here, the reader is referred to van der Waerden's *Einführung*, pp. 50–54, and more particularly to the proof given on pp. 52–54 of that book and there attributed to Ostrowski.

closed. In order to prove this theorem it is clearly sufficient to establish the fact that any equation of the form

$$F(v) \equiv A_0 + A_1 v + ... + A_n v^n = 0, \tag{1}$$

where $n \geqslant 1$, $A_i \equiv A_i(u) \in K^*|u|$ $(i = 0,...,n)$, and $A_0 \neq 0$, has a root in $K^*|u|$. We shall do this by giving a process for determining such a root constructively, term by term, and proving that the process can never fail. We shall assume that K is the field of all complex numbers; but it will be seen that the same proof holds when K is any algebraically closed field. The details of the proof are based on the treatment of Walker, *Algebraic Curves*, iv, 3.2.

Some of the coefficients in equation (1), as we have written it, may be zero, and these must be disregarded. To be quite explicit, we shall now write

$$F(v) \equiv A_0 + A_\lambda v^\lambda + A_\mu v^\mu + ... + A_\chi v^\chi,$$

where, for $i = 0, \lambda, \mu, ..., \chi$,

$$A_i \equiv a_i u^{\alpha_i} + b_i u^{\beta_i} + ...,$$

$\alpha_i, \beta_i, ...$ being an increasing sequence (finite or infinite) of rational numbers with a common denominator.

In order to obtain a solution of equation (1) in the form of a fractional power series, we begin by substituting an undetermined series

$$\bar{v} \equiv c_1 u^{\nu_1} + c_2 u^{\nu_1 + \nu_2} + ...$$
$$\equiv u^{\nu_1}(c_1 + c_2 u^{\nu_2} + ...)$$

for v in the equation, and then seeing how the coefficients and exponents in this series must be assigned if the equation is to be satisfied. We have

$$F(\bar{v}) = A_0 + A_\lambda \bar{v}^\lambda + A_\mu \bar{v}^\mu + ... + A_\chi \bar{v}^\chi$$
$$= (a_0 u^{\alpha_0} + b_0 u^{\beta_0} + ...)$$
$$\quad + (a_\lambda u^{\alpha_\lambda} + b_\lambda u^{\beta_\lambda} + ...)u^{\lambda \nu_1}(c_1 + c_2 u^{\nu_2} + ...)^\lambda$$
$$\quad + (a_\mu u^{\alpha_\mu} + b_\mu u^{\beta_\mu} + ...)u^{\mu \nu_1}(c_1 + c_2 u^{\nu_2} + ...)^\mu$$
$$\quad + ...$$
$$\quad + (a_\chi u^{\alpha_\chi} + b_\chi u^{\beta_\chi} + ...)u^{\chi \nu_1}(c_1 + c_2 u^{\nu_2} + ...)^\chi.$$

If we now expand the right-hand side and rearrange it as a fractional power series in u, a necessary condition for $F(\bar{v})$ to be zero is that the terms of each separate order that is represented must cancel; and this is true, in particular, of the terms of lowest order. These latter terms are certainly to be found among the terms of lowest order from each of the separate lines, i.e. among the terms

$$a_0\, u^{\alpha_0}, \quad a_\lambda\, c_1^\lambda\, u^{\alpha_\lambda + \lambda \nu_1}, \quad a_\mu\, c_1^\mu\, u^{\alpha_\mu + \mu \nu_1}, \quad ..., \quad a_\chi\, c_1^\chi\, u^{\alpha_\chi + \chi \nu_1},$$

although they need not comprise all these terms. What is therefore necessary is that, of the terms just written, there must be more than one with the lowest occurring exponent, and the sum of the co-efficients of all the terms with this exponent must be zero. To find out how this condition can be satisfied, i.e. to determine two, at least, of the numbers

$$\alpha_0, \quad \alpha_\lambda + \lambda \nu_1, \quad \alpha_\mu + \mu \nu_1, \quad ..., \quad \alpha_\chi + \chi \nu_1$$

(ν_1 still being at our disposal) which are equal and less than all the rest, we draw a *Newton diagram*. Taking rectangular axes in the plane, we plot a point P_i with coordinates (i, α_i) for each of the series A_i ($i = 0, \lambda, \mu, ..., \chi$), and we then draw a broken line, starting from P_0, round the lower boundary of the set of points. In this way we obtain some such diagram as the following:

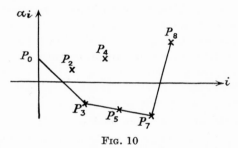

Fig. 10

The condition that we have to satisfy, namely

$$\alpha_\rho + \rho \nu_1 = \alpha_\sigma + \sigma \nu_1 \leqslant \alpha_i + i \nu_1 \quad (i = 0, \lambda, \mu, ..., \chi),$$

means that the line joining P_ρ and P_σ is one of the segments of the boundary, and it follows from this that the possible values for the exponent ν_1 are the negatives of the gradients of the bounding segments. When any one of these possible values of ν_1 has been selected, there are only finitely many possible values for c_1, namely those given by the equation

$$\sum_{(\tau)} a_\tau c_1^\tau = 0, \tag{2}$$

the summation extending over all those integers τ for which there is a point P_τ on the boundary segment in question.

We now have a finite number of possible pairs of values of the first coefficient c_1 and the first exponent ν_1 in the fractional power series that we are seeking to determine. Having selected any one of these possible pairs, we can next go on to determine the possible values of c_2 and ν_2 by a repetition of the same argument—now with the limitation, however, that only positive values of ν_2 are admissible. Let us put

$$\bar{v} = u^{\nu_1}(c_1 + \bar{v}_1),$$

writing $\bar{v}_1$ for the series $c_2 u^{\nu_2} + c_3 u^{\nu_2 + \nu_3} + \dots$. Then $\bar{v}_1$ has to satisfy the equation

$$F_1(\bar{v}_1) \equiv u^{-\beta_1} F(u^{\nu_1}(c_1 + \bar{v}_1)) = 0; \qquad (3)$$

where β_1 is the common value of $\alpha_\tau + \tau\nu_1$ for the points P_τ on the bounding segment $P_\rho P_\sigma$ of gradient $-\nu_1$ in the Newton diagram previously considered, and the factor $u^{-\beta_1}$ is inserted in equation (3) merely in order to simplify the subsequent computation. We can now draw a second Newton diagram and use it to determine the possible values of c_2 and ν_2 if $\bar{v}_1$ is to satisfy equation (3); the only difference between this case and the one already dealt with being that we may now use only those sides of the Newton polygon which have a negative gradient (thus making ν_2 positive).

The following three conditions can now be seen to be both necessary and sufficient for it to be possible to continue indefinitely in this way and to determine, step by step, a series $\bar{v}(u) \in K^*|u|$ which satisfies the original equation $F(v) = 0$:

(i) at each stage, the equation analogous to (2), which gives the possible values of the appropriate coefficient c_h, must have at least one non-zero root;

(ii) at each stage after the first, the Newton polygon must have at least one side of negative gradient;

(iii) the denominators of the successive rational numbers $\nu_1, \nu_2, \dots$, expressed as fractions in their lowest terms, must not increase indefinitely.

We shall consider the three conditions in turn.

Condition (i)

The equation analogous to (2) always has at least two terms, from its mode of definition; and, the field K being algebraically closed, such an equation necessarily has a non-zero root.

Condition (ii)

To show that condition (ii) is always satisfied, we must examine the Newton polygons more closely.

Let m be the least positive integer such that $A_0, A_\lambda, ..., A_\chi$ can all be written as integral power series in $u^{1/m}$ (each with at most a finite number of terms with negative exponents); and let us write

$$\alpha_i = m_i/m \quad (i = 0, \lambda, ..., \chi).$$

If the chosen side of the first Newton polygon has left-hand and right-hand terminal points P_ρ and P_σ, and if P_τ is any point on this side, then we have

$$\alpha_\rho + \rho\nu_1 = \alpha_\sigma + \sigma\nu_1 = \alpha_\tau + \tau\nu_1 = \beta_1, \tag{4}$$

and hence
$$\nu_1 = -\frac{m_\sigma - m_\rho}{m(\sigma - \rho)} = -\frac{m_\tau - m_\rho}{m(\tau - \rho)} = \frac{p}{mq}, \tag{5}$$

where p and q are coprime integers and $q > 0$. Thus, if P_τ is any point on $P_\rho P_\sigma$, then τ satisfies the equation

$$q(m_\tau - m_\rho) = -p(\tau - \rho);$$

and it follows that, if $\tau \neq \rho$, then q is a factor of $\tau - \rho$. We may now write, for each point P_τ on $P_\rho P_\sigma$,

$$\tau = \rho + s_\tau q \quad (s_\tau \geqslant 0),$$

and equation (2) accordingly takes the form

$$\sum_{(\tau)} a_\tau c_1^{\rho + s_\tau q} = 0,$$

i.e. $$c_1^\rho \phi(c_1^q) = 0,$$

where $\phi(z)$ is a certain polynomial, of degree $(\sigma - \rho)/q \geqslant 1$, such that $\phi(0) = a_\rho \neq 0$. If $\bar{c}_1$ is a root of this equation, of multiplicity $r \geqslant 1$, then
$$\phi(z^q) = (z - \bar{c}_1)^r \psi(z),$$

where $\psi(\bar{c}_1) \neq 0$.

Now, by (3), we have

$$\begin{aligned}
F_1(\bar{v}_1) &= u^{-\beta_1} F(u^{\nu_1}(c_1 + \bar{v}_1)) \\
&= u^{-\beta_1}(A_0 + A_\lambda u^{\lambda\nu_1}(c_1 + \bar{v}_1)^\lambda + ... + A_\chi u^{\chi\nu_1}(c_1 + \bar{v}_1)^\chi) \\
&= u^{-\beta_1} \sum_{(\tau)} A_\tau u^{\tau\nu_1}(c_1 + \bar{v}_1)^\tau + u^{-\beta_1} \sum_{(\pi)} A_\pi u^{\pi\nu_1}(c_1 + \bar{v}_1)^\pi,
\end{aligned}$$

where the summation with respect to τ extends over the suffixes of the points P_τ on the segment $P_\rho P_\sigma$ and the summation with respect to π extends over the suffixes of the remaining points of the Newton diagram. We may write the same expression in the form

$$F_1(\bar{v}_1) = u^{-\beta_1} \sum_{(\tau)} a_\tau u^{\tau\nu_1+\alpha_\tau}(c_1+\bar{v}_1)^\tau$$

$$+u^{-\beta_1} \sum_{(\tau)} (A_\tau - a_\tau u^{\alpha_\tau})u^{\tau\nu_1}(c_1+\bar{v}_1)^\tau + u^{-\beta_1} \sum_{(\pi)} A_\pi u^{\pi\nu_1}(c_1+\bar{v}_1)^\pi.$$

The first term on the right-hand side reduces, by (4), to

$$u^{-\beta_1} \sum_{(\tau)} a_\tau u^{\beta_1}(c_1+\bar{v}_1)^\tau = (c_1+\bar{v}_1)^\rho \phi((c_1+\bar{v}_1)^q)$$

$$= (c_1+\bar{v}_1)^\rho \bar{v}_1^r \psi(c_1+\bar{v}_1) = b_r \bar{v}_1^r + b_{r+1} \bar{v}_1^{r+1} + ... + b_\sigma \bar{v}_1^\sigma,$$

where $b_r,..., b_\sigma$ are in K, and $b_r = c_1^\rho \psi(c_1) \neq 0$.

If we now write

$$G(\bar{v}_1) = u^{-\beta_1}\left(\sum_{(\tau)} (A_\tau - a_\tau u^{\alpha_\tau})u^{\tau\nu_1}(c_1+\bar{v}_1)^\tau + \sum_{(\pi)} A_\pi u^{\pi\nu_1}(c_1+\bar{v}_1)^\pi \right),$$

then $G(\bar{v}_1)$ is expressible as a polynomial in $\bar{v}_1$, of degree χ, with coefficients that are all power series in u of positive order. We have, in fact,

$$O(A_\tau - a_\tau u^{\alpha_\tau}) > \alpha_\tau,$$

and hence

$$O((A_\tau - a_\tau u^{\alpha_\tau})u^{\tau\nu_1}) > \alpha_\tau + \tau\nu_1 = \beta_1,$$

and also

$$O(A_\pi u^{\pi\nu_1}) = \alpha_\pi + \pi\nu_1 > \beta_1.$$

We can thus write $F_1(\bar{v}_1)$ in the form

$$F_1(\bar{v}_1) \equiv B_0 + B_1 \bar{v}_1 + ... + B_\chi \bar{v}_1^\chi,$$

where

$$B_i \in K^*\{u\}\ (i = 0,...,\chi);\ O(B_i) > 0\ (i = 0,...,r-1);\ O(B_r) = 0.$$

In the Newton polygon drawn at the second stage, therefore (i.e. the polygon drawn for the solution of the equation $F_1(v_1) = 0$), all the points from P_0 to P_{r-1} are above the horizontal axis, while P_r is on this axis; and it follows from this that there is at least one side of negative gradient, as required. The only possible exception is the case in which $B_0,..., B_{r-1}$ are all zero and so have no order. In this case, however, $v_1 = 0$ is a solution of the equation $F_1(v_1) = 0$, and the series that we are seeking terminates with its first term $c_1 u^{\nu_1}$. The Puiseux process thus leads in every case to a determination of the first two terms of a series $v(u)$ which satisfies the given equation $F(v) = 0$; and the argument just applied to the determination of the second term applies equally to the determination of all the succeeding terms.

Condition (iii)

It only remains now for us to show that the process under discussion leads to a fractional power series in the specific sense in which we are using this term, that is to say an integral power series in some fractional power $u^{1/n}$ of u.

The least integer m such that $A_0, A_\lambda, ..., A_\chi$ can be expressed simultaneously as integral power series in $u^{1/m}$ will be referred to (momentarily) as the *rank* of the set of fractional power series in question. As we pass from $F(v) \equiv \sum A_i v^i$ to $F_1(v_1) \equiv \sum B_i v_1^i$, the rank of the set of coefficients is raised from m for the A_i to mq for the B_i, as we see from (5); and similarly, when we pass on to $F_2(v_2)$ the new rank will be mqq_1, and so on indefinitely. What we wish to show is that, after a certain stage, the multiplier q_h is always 1.

At any particular stage, we have a c-equation of the form (2), corresponding to a side $P_\rho P_\sigma$ of the relevant Newton polygon, and we select a non-zero root of this equation whose multiplicity r is at most $\sigma - \rho$, which is the horizontal length of $P_\rho P_\sigma$. In fact, we can only have $r = \sigma - \rho$ if $q = 1$. At the next stage, the whole downward path from P'_0 to P'_r is of total horizontal length r, so that the chosen side $P'_{\rho'} P'_{\sigma'}$ of the new Newton polygon must be such that $\sigma' - \rho'$ is at most r; and consequently $r' \leqslant r$. Thus the integer r is non-increasing from stage to stage, and it must therefore reach a constant value r_0 after a finite number of steps. Thereafter the passage from each Newton polygon to its successor is of the type that may be indicated diagrammatically as follows:

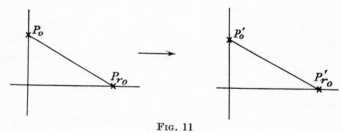

Fig. 11

This implies, however, that the c-equation (2) reduces, at each such stage, to the form

$$\phi(z^q) \equiv k(z-c)^{r_0} = 0,$$

which is only possible if $q = 1$. Thus, after a certain stage, the common denominator of $v_1, v_2, ..., v_t$ does not increase any further as t increases; and this is what we set out to prove. The proof of Puiseux's Theorem is now complete.

C. HISTORICAL NOTE

For detailed references to the historical development of the theory of algebraic curves, the reader may conveniently refer to the substantial notes in Enriques–Chisini (*Teoria geometrica delle equazioni e delle funzioni algebriche*). The note on pp. 221–4 of volume i of that work summarizes very early investigations, particularly the approach to a proper account of Bézout's Theorem; and chapter iii of the same volume, from p. 333 on, covers the origin and development of the theory of algebraic functions. In volume ii, the first chapter, on polarity and covariant curves, begins on pp. 3–9 with an historical survey of that topic; and on pp. 535–44 there is an excellent account of the historical development of the theory of branches and the analysis of singularities. Finally, in volume iii, the long note on pp. 145–56 deals fully with the historical development of geometry on a curve. The brief remarks that we make below can only serve as the slightest possible indication of the order of development of ideas.

Of the earliest books on the subject, other than works by Descartes (1637) and Newton (posthumous, 1779), particular mention may perhaps be made of Maclaurin's *Geometria organica sive descriptio linearum curvarum universalis* (London, 1720) in which the opinion is first expressed (p. 136) that the number of intersections of two plane curves is equal to the product of their orders. Bézout's proof of this theorem (1779) was an amplification of earlier proofs by Euler and Cramer, based on the theory of elimination, and it was further improved upon by Lagrange and Gauss in turn. An alternative proof by correspondences, first proposed by Chasles (1872) and later made rigorous by Zeuthen, is essentially equivalent—in accordance with a very modern technique—to reducing the general case to that of the intersections of a curve with a line. An account of this proof is given in Enriques–Chisini, i, 224–30. The proof that we have given in Chapter II, essentially a version of the proof by elimination, closely follows that given by van der Waerden in his *Einführung* (1939).

Investigation of branches of a curve, in the primitive sense of constructing a succession of curves approximating more and more closely to a branch, was initiated by Newton and Cramer, but it was in effect Puiseux (1850) who first carried this constructive process through to the point of showing that every branch can be precisely represented by a convergent fractional power series. The properties of the power series that arise in this way were investigated by Cayley (1865), Halphen (1874), and Smith (1873), the name 'branch' being used by Cayley as against 'cycle' by Halphen. The special significance of the characteristic indices was observed by these writers, and the multiplicity of intersection of a pair of branches was investigated by Smith (*Proc. London Math. Soc.* **6** (1876)) and concurrently by Halphen. At this stage a major revolution in current ideas about the subject resulted from Noether's introduction in 1871 of his method of quadratic transformations. Noether's ample account of this method in his fundamental memoir of 1875 (*Math. Ann.* **9** (1875), 166–82) threw a flood of light on the whole question of singularities of algebraic curves. A systematic account of the subject, embodying many developments due to Enriques himself, is given in chapter iii and chapter iv of Enriques–Chisini, ii, and it fully confirms the great value and fertility of Noether's ideas. The outstanding problem of establishing rigorously the invariance of Noether's analysis of singularities has been dealt with by van der Waerden in chapter ix of his *Einführung*, and also—as we have indicated in Chapter XI of this book—by other writers who have employed methods of a radically different kind.

As regards the birational geometry of curves, the basic results were first established by investigations, in the domain of complex variable theory, of the properties of algebraic functions $y(x)$, of a complex variable x, defined by algebraic equations $f(x,y) = 0$. Important results about integrals of the form $\int_0^x F(x,y)\,dx$, where y is such an algebraic function of x—termed *Abelian integrals*—had been obtained by Abel (1829), in extension of Jacobi's earlier work on elliptic integrals; but above all it was Riemann, with the help of his concept of the Riemann surface of an algebraic function (or curve), who laid the main foundations for the classical transcendental theory. This he did in his celebrated dissertation of 1851, *Grundlagen für eine allgemeine Theorie der Functionen einer veränderlichen complexen Größe*, and in his extended memoir, *Theorie der Abel'schen Functionen*, published in 1857. There emerged from his work in particular the invariance (over birational transformation) of the genus p of an algebraic curve, the associated Riemann surface having connectivity $2p+1$; and his main result, completed by

Roch in 1864, was the fundamental Riemann–Roch Theorem for curves.

After Riemann's great advances, centred on algebraic functions themselves, a new phase began in which the chief interest was centred on the algebraic curves giving rise to the functions in question. Also it was now the aim to establish and extend Riemann's discoveries by purely algebraic methods, dispensing with Riemann's transcendental and topological tools. Thus attention was focused on birational transformations and birational invariants of curves. Already, in 1865–8, Cayley had investigated these matters and had proposed the reduction of all curves of a given birational equivalence class to a 'normal' curve of a least order, and this in contrast to Riemann's rational reduction of equations $f(x, y) = 0$ to equations of the least order in one of the variables. Noether's discovery of his celebrated $Af + B\phi$ theorem (which we have discussed in Chapter X, § 5) made possible the first comprehensive algebro-geometric exposition of the theory of linear series on a curve, given by Brill and Noether (*Math. Ann.* **7** (1871), 206). On this foundation a succession of brilliant mathematicians— particularly those of the Italian school—built up the great and elegant body of knowledge of algebraic curves that we now possess. Particular reference should be made to the contributions of Corrado Segre (sometimes referred to as the father of Italian algebraic geometry) as well as to those of Castelnuovo and Enriques, more especially in the introduction and systematic use of spaces of arbitrary dimensionality (for the construction, in particular, of projective models of linear series), the completion of the algebro-geometric proof of the Riemann–Roch Theorem (Castelnuovo, 1889), and the introduction of methods from the domain of enumerative geometry.

More recently, in a comprehensive movement initiated largely by van der Waerden with his long series of papers *Zur algebraischen Geometrie*, published from 1933 onwards in *Mathematische Annalen*, the whole of the foundations of algebraic geometry in general have been subjected to radical re-examination and reconstruction, with the twofold aim of making them conform to modern standards of rigour and bringing to bear on algebraic geometry the full resources of modern algebra. Besides van der Waerden's own work, embodied largely in his *Einführung*, the main advances have been due to the basic work of Oscar Zariski, later incorporated in part in

Hodge and Pedoe's *Methods*, and to that of André Weil, as given in his book *Foundations of Algebraic Geometry* (New York, 1946). It has been our modest aim in the present work to give the beginner an entry into the subject that conforms at the appropriate level with the general spirit of the movement to which we have just referred.

Note on Noether's Theorem

Noether's first statement of his theorem (cf. Theorem 11, p. 249), in *Math. Ann.* **2** (1869), 314, applied only to the case in which the intersections of the curves $F = 0$ and $G = 0$ are all simple. The general result was given by him in a subsequent paper, ibid. **6** (1872), 351, later simplified in ibid. **40** (1891), 140. A considerable record of contemporary and subsequent investigations connected with Noether's result is given by Berzolari in *Enzyk. der Math. Wiss.* III. C. 4 (1906), 405. The systematic account given by van der Waerden in chapter viii of his *Einführung* (this also dealing with the corresponding problem for a pair of surfaces in S_3) was largely based on the following papers by P. Dubreil: (i) 'Quelques compléments au Théorème de Noether, I, II', *Comptes Rendus Ac. Sc.* **188** (1929), 1362, and **189** (1929), 784; (ii) 'Recherches sur la valeur des exposants des composants primaires des idéaux de polynomes', Thèse, Paris 1920 (*J. de Math.* **9** (1930), 231–309); and (iii) 'Remarques sur la Théorème de Noether', *Bull. Soc. Math.* **64** (1936), 99–118. An introduction to subsequent work by Dubreil, in which the general problems involved are interpreted in terms of *improper components of ideals*, was given by him in his tract *Quelques propriétés des variétés algébriques se rattachant aux théories d'algèbre moderne* (Actualités scientifiques et industrielles, no. 162, Paris 1935).

D. BIBLIOGRAPHY

BAKER, H. F. *Principles of Geometry* (6 vols., Cambridge, 1922–33.)

BERTINI, E. *Introduzione alla geometria proiettiva degli iperspazi* (2nd edition, Messina, 1923).

BOCHNER, S., and MARTIN, W. T. *Several Complex Variables* (Princeton, 1948).

CHEVALLEY, C. *Introduction to the Theory of Algebraic Functions of One Variable* (New York, 1951).

ENRIQUES, F. *Lezioni sulla teoria geometrica delle equazioni e delle funzioni algebriche, pubblicate per cura del Dott. Oscar Chisini* (Bologna, 1915).

GRÖBNER, W. *Moderne algebraische Geometrie: die idealtheoretischen Grundlagen* (Vienna and Innsbruck, 1949).

HENSEL, K., and LANDSBERG, G. *Theorie der algebraischen Funktionen einer Variabeln* (Leipzig, 1902).

HODGE, W. V. D., and PEDOE, D. *Methods of Algebraic Geometry* (3 vols., Cambridge, 1947–54).

LEFSCHETZ, S. *Algebraic Geometry* (Princeton, 1953).

SEMPLE, J. G., and KNEEBONE, G. T. *Algebraic Projective Geometry* (Oxford, 1952).

—— and ROTH, L. *Introduction to Algebraic Geometry* (Oxford, 1949).

SEVERI, F. *Vorlesungen über algebraische Geometrie: Geometrie auf einer Kurve, Riemannsche Flächen, Abelsche Integrale* (translated from the Italian by E. Löffler, Leipzig and Berlin, 1921).

VAN DER WAERDEN, B. L. *Einführung in die algebraische Geometrie* (Berlin, 1939).

—— *Moderne Algebra* (2 vols., 2nd edition, 1937–40; English translation *Modern Algebra* from the second edition, New York, 1949–50).

WALKER, R. J. *Algebraic Curves* (Princeton, 1950).

WEIL, A. *Foundations of Algebraic Geometry* (New York, 1946).

ZARISKI, O., and SAMUEL, P. *Commutative Algebra* (volume I, Princeton, 1958).

ZEUTHEN, H. G. *Lehrbuch der abzählenden Methoden der Geometrie* (Leipzig and Berlin, 1914).

INDEX OF SYMBOLS

(in order of first occurrence)

Note: The use of bold-face type is explained on p. 3

GENERAL INDEX

Abel, N. H., 348.
Abelian integral, 348.
Adjoint curve, 254, 269.
Adjunction, ring- and field-, 143, 329.
　local set of, 253.
　set of, 254.
Algebraic correspondence, 165.
　curve (irreducible), 4, 186.
　curve (reducible), 6, 218.
　dependence, 151, 333.
　element over a field, 147, 332.
　extension, 143 ff., 147.
　function, 49, 347.
　function field, 154, 180, 210.
　point-set of S_2, 32.
　series on a curve, 281.
　structure, 328.
　system of curves, 20, 221.
　variety, 209.
Algebraically closed field, 2, 333.
Allowable representation $\mathscr{R}$, 3.
　affine representation $\mathscr{R}_A$, 3.
Ambient space, 260.
Analytic curve at O, 99, 100, 314.
　invariant, 81, 303.
　theory of branches, 78, 101.
　transformation, 78, 81.
Analytically equivalent branches, 78, 319.
Apéry, R., 80.
Arf, C., 318.
Associated branches, 136.
Associated forms of a point-set, 35, 207.
　of a curve, 211.
Automorphism, 154, 329.

Base point of a linear system of curves, 21.
Basic form of a fractional power series, 295.
Basic Inequality (for multiplicity of intersection), 94.
Basis of a linear system of rational functions on C, 237.
Bertini, E., 248.
Bertini's Theorem, 176.
Berzolari, L., 350.
Bézout's Theorem, 37, 197, 220, 347.
Birational correspondence, 122, 152 ff., 188.

Birationally equivalent curves, 154, 187.
Branch, in S_2, 72 ff., 347.
　in S_3, 326.
　in S_r, 181 ff.
　algebraic or non-algebraic, 73, 181.
　characteristic numbers of, 76.
　dual, 136.
　formal equation of, 96.
　fractional equation of, 84.
　inflexional, 76.
　linear, 75, 183, 185.
　minimal representation of, 72.
　monomial, 77, 81.
　normal representation of, 75.
　of a curve, 73, 187.
　order of, 75, 181.
　primitive, 313.
　ramphoid cuspidal, 76, 77.
　reduced equations of, 77.
　redundant representation of, 72.
　simple cuspidal, 76.
　species of, 302.
　standard representation of, 73.
　tangent to, 75, 182.
　undulatory, 76.
Branch element, linear, 284.
　general, 285 ff.
Branch place of a correspondence, 165.
Brill, A., 349.

Canonical closure, 320.
Canonical curve, 279.
Canonical representation of a quasi-branch, 70.
Canonical series, 262, 267.
Canonical system of equivalence, 261, 267.
Castelnuovo, G., 349.
Cayley, A., 208, 348, 349.
Cayley coordinates of a curve, 218.
Cayley equations and forms, 212.
Cayley model, 220.
Cayley–Bacharach theorems, 276.
Centre of a formal transcendental point, 55.
　of a quasi-branch or branch, 69, 181.
Characteristic coefficients of a fractional power series, 296.
Characteristic exponents, 295.

PRINTED IN GREAT BRITAIN
AT THE UNIVERSITY PRESS, OXFORD
BY VIVIAN RIDLER
PRINTER TO THE UNIVERSITY